Experience Chemistry

in the Earth System

SAVVAS

LEARNING COMPANY

We are excited and proud to partner with Flinn Scientific in the development of this highly innovative program. Flinn Scientific supports science educators in opening young minds to the challenges and joys of scientific discovery.

The cover shows bismuth, a commonly used, naturally occurring metal that has some unique properties. The layered, hollowed-out shape of crystallized bismuth is typical of "hopper crystals." The multiple colors of a bismuth crystal are caused by differences in the oxide layer that forms on its surface. Sebastian Janicki/Shutterstock; Bkgd: Sylverarts Vectors/Shutterstock

ISBN-13: 978-1-4183-0698-4
ISBN-10: 1-4183-0698-3

Christopher Moore, Ph.D. is the Dr. George F. Haddix Community Chair in Physical Science at the University of Nebraska Omaha, where he directs programs for pre- and in-service secondary chemistry and physics teachers. Holding a M.S. in applied physics and a Ph.D. in chemistry from Virginia Commonwealth University, Dr. Moore has worked as a physical science teacher at several secondary schools in Virginia, as a professional materials scientist, and as a scholar of and consultant on science education. His education research focuses on the development of scientific reasoning and expert-like science practice abilities, and his materials science research focuses on electronic materials for devices. He is the author of the books *Teaching Science Thinking: Using Scientific Reasoning in the Classroom* and *Creating Scientists: Teaching and Assessing Science Practice for the NGSS.*

Michael Wysession, Ph.D. is a Professor of Earth and Planetary Sciences at Washington University in St. Louis and Executive Director of The Teaching Center. Author of more than 100 science and science education publications, Dr. Wysession was awarded the prestigious National Science Foundation Presidential Faculty Fellowship and Packard Foundation Fellowship for his research in geophysics, primarily focused on using seismic tomography to determine the forces driving plate tectonics. Dr. Wysession is also a leader in geoscience literacy and education; he is the chair of the Earth Science Literacy Initiative, author of several popular video lectures on geoscience in The Great Courses series, and a lead writer of the Next Generation Science Standards*.

Consulting Author

Bryn Lutes, Ph.D. is a chemist, technology translator, and educator. Holding a Ph.D. in Organometallic Chemistry, Dr. Lutes has worked both in and out of the classroom to help faculty incorporate active-learning techniques and technology to support student learning. She currently teaches General Chemistry for post-baccalaureate premedical students, Quantitative Reasoning, and Inorganic Chemistry Laboratory, where she continues to explore and incorporate active-learning and technology-assisted pedagogies.

Program Consultant

Tanya Katovich is a chemistry educator and consultant. In 2015, she received the Davidson Award, presented annually by the Chemical Industry Council of Illinois to the outstanding chemistry teacher in Illinois. In 2017, Tanya became an Illinois finalist for the Presidential Award for Excellence in Mathematics and Science Teaching (PAEMST). She currently serves as the Vice-President and a member of the board of directors for the nonprofit organization Northern Illinois Science Educators (NISE).

Academic Reviewers

Aida Awad
Adjunct Instructor
American InterContinental University
Buckeye, AZ

Nicole Bouvier-Brown, Ph.D.
Associate Professor of Chemistry & Biochemistry
Loyola Marymount University
Los Angeles, CA

Drew Budner, Ph.D.
Assistant Professor of Chemistry
Coastal Carolina University
Conway, SC

Thomas Bussey, Ph.D.
Assistant Teacher Professor
Department of Chemistry & Biochemistry
University of California, San Diego
La Jolla, CA

Stephen Contakes, Ph.D.
Associate Professor of Chemistry
Westmont College
Santa Barbara, CA

Michael Everest, Ph.D.
Professor of Chemistry
Westmont College
Santa Barbara, CA

Alison J. Frontier, Ph.D.
Professor of Chemistry
University of Rochester
Rochester, NY

Hasan Palandoken, Ph.D.
Associate Professor
Department of Chemistry & Biochemistry
California Polytechnic University
San Luis Obispo, CA

Robert Senter, Ph.D.
Instructor and Lab Coordinator
Department of Chemistry & Biochemistry
Loyola Marymount University
Los Angeles, CA

Amanda Silberstein, Ph.D.
Assistant Professor of Chemistry
Westmont College
Santa Barbara, CA

Shanju Zhang, Ph.D.
Associate Professor
Department of Chemistry & Biochemistry
California Polytechnic University
San Luis Obispo, CA

Teacher Reviewers

California

Gregory Aniol
Chemistry Teacher
Riverside Unified School District
Riverside, CA

Manny Colon
Science Department Chair/
  Science and Engineering
  Teacher
University Preparatory School
Victorville, CA

Stephanie Farmer
Chemistry Teacher
Dougherty Valley High School
San Ramon, CA

Rhonda Frohn
Chemistry Teacher
Conejo Valley Unified School
  District
Thousand Oaks, CA

Sean Gilbert
Chemistry Teacher
Leuzinger High School
Lawndale, CA

Rodger Golgart
Chemistry Teacher
Grand Terrace High School
Grand Terrace, CA

Ricardo Gutierrez
Biology/Earth Science Teacher
Temescal Canyon High School
Lake Elsinore, CA

Brittney Kang
Science Teacher
Portola High School
Irvine, CA

Katie Keeler
Chemistry Teacher
Newbury Park High School
Newbury Park, CA

Jeralyn Helnick Newton
Science Teacher
Portola High School
Irvine, CA

Ayanna Pantallion
Chemistry Teacher
Santa Monica-Malibu Unified
  School District
Santa Monica, CA

Michael Tang
Science Teacher
Portola High School
Irvine, CA

Dawn Toth
Chemistry Teacher
Redlands Unified School District
Redlands, CA

Amanda Waterfield
Chemistry Teacher
Victor Valley Unified School
  District
Victorville, CA

National

Jodi Fertoli
Chemistry Teacher
Staten Island Technical High
  School
Staten Island, NY

Martin Goldman
Chemistry Teacher
Edison High School
Edison, NJ

Jessica Johnson
Chemistry Teacher
Jackson Public Schools
Jackson, MS

Kurt Rogers
Chemistry Teacher
Northern Highlands High School
Allendale, NJ

Michelle Tindall
K-12 Curriculum Coordinator
Birmingham Public Schools
Birmingham, MI

Susan Todd
Chemistry Teacher
Claxton High School
Claxton, GA

Lab Review

All labs in the program
were developed and
tested by **FLINN**
SCIENTIFIC

PROGRAM CONTENTS

INSTRUCTIONAL SEGMENT 4

The Chemistry of Climate Change   2

ANCHORING PHENOMENON Why are we seeing more extreme weather?

GO ONLINE to find hands-on and virtual labs, CERs and Modeling activities, and other resources — authentic readings, videos and animations — that complete the Experiences.

INSTRUCTIONAL SEGMENT 5
The Dynamics of Chemical Reactions and Ocean Acidification 118

ANCHORING PHENOMENON How do our everyday activities impact Earth?

End-of-Book Resources

GO ONLINE to find hands-on and virtual labs, CERs and Modeling activities, and other resources — authentic readings, videos and animations — that complete the Experiences.

ASSESSMENTS

- Pre/Post-Test
- End-of-Course Test
- Experience Notebook Problem Bank

INSTRUCTIONAL SEGMENT 4

- Quizzes
- 3-D Assessments
- Online Problem Bank

INSTRUCTIONAL SEGMENT 5

- Quizzes
- 3-D Assessments
- Online Problem Bank
- Benchmark 3-D Assessment

FLINN
SCIENTIFIC
PERFORMANCE-BASED ASSESSMENTS

INSTRUCTIONAL SEGMENT 4

- Microhabitat in a Bottle
- Climate Change and the Carbon Cycle

INSTRUCTIONAL SEGMENT 5

- Rates of Reaction and Dissolution
- Quantitative Analysis of Acid Rain
- Calcium Carbonate and Shell Production

FLINN
SCIENTIFIC
INQUIRY LABS

INSTRUCTIONAL SEGMENT 4

- Feedback and Climate Change
- Energy in the Atmosphere
- Albedo and Composition of Earth's Surface
- How Melting Ice Affects Sea Level
- Observe Air Pollution
- Carbon Dioxide and Its Role in Climate
- How Nature Records Changes in Climate
- Human Activity and Carbon Emissions
- Model Climate Change with Melting Ice

- Climate Change and Keeping Cool
- Solar Cell Technology

INSTRUCTIONAL SEGMENT 5

- Reaction Rates: Iodine Clock
- Collision Theory
- Explore Chemical Equilibrium
- Measure Acid Strength
- Titrations—The Study of Acid-Base Chemistry
- Analysis of Buffer Solutions and Ranges
- The pH of Seawater
- Carbon Dioxide Levels in Water
- Ocean Currents
- The Fate of Carbonate in Acidifying Oceans

FLINN
SCIENTIFIC
ENGINEERING DESIGN CHALLENGES

INSTRUCTIONAL SEGMENT 4

- Design a Green Roof

INSTRUCTIONAL SEGMENT 5

- Use Equilibrium for a Commercial Application
- Design a Natural pH Indicator
- Design a Model of Ocean Acidification

ANIMATIONS

INSTRUCTIONAL SEGMENT 4

- The Carbon Cycle
- Energy to Earth
- Cold and White: A Reinforcing Feedback Loop
- Bad Vibes From Greenhouse Gases
- Can Volcanoes Change the Climate?
- Renewable Energy and Energy Storage

INSTRUCTIONAL SEGMENT 5

- Reaction Rate and Molecular Collisions
- Looking Closely at Collisions and Activation Energy

- Conductivity of Strong and Weak Acids
- Buffer Systems
- El Niño, La Niña, and Heat Storage
- Carbon Dioxide, Ocean Acidification, and Shell Formation

INTERACTIVITIES

INSTRUCTIONAL SEGMENT 4

- Wetlands and the Carbon Cycle
- Flow of Energy and Greenhouse Gases
- Climate Change and Fire

INSTRUCTIONAL SEGMENT 5

- Reaction Rates and Activation Energy
- Exploring Acid Strength and Concentration
- Ocean pH

VIRTUAL LABS

INSTRUCTIONAL SEGMENT 4

- Sampling the Past
- Glaciers on Rainier

INSTRUCTIONAL SEGMENT 5

- Equilibrium Shifting
- Explore Buffer Systems
- The Effect of Ocean Acidification on Shells

VIDEOS

- Anchoring Phenomenon
- Investigative Phenomenon
- Lab Demo
- Lab Summary
- Virtual Nerd Math Support

ADDITIONAL RESOURCES

- Authentic Reading
- Claim-Evidence-Reasoning
- Modeling
- Analyzing Data
- Discussion Rubric
- Peer Review Rubric
- Writing About Science
- Problem-Based Learning
- Virtual Reality
- Practice Problems
- PhET Simulations

The Chemistry of Climate Change

Why are we seeing more extreme weather?

Investigation 12
Weather and Climate

Investigation 13
Global Climate Change

ANCHORING PHENOMENON

Inquiry Launch Look at the image of pedestrian trying to make her way across a street during a blizzard. How do you think extreme weather events like this blizzard will be different in the future? Why?

A common misconception about climate change is that cold weather events will decrease in frequency or severity. Propose an explanation for why the frequency and severity of future extreme weather events are likely to only increase and become more extreme.

....

....

....

....

....

....

GO ONLINE to engage with real-world phenomena. Watch the anchoring phenomenon video and preview the optional **problem-based learning experience**.

INVESTIGATIVE PHENOMENON

 GO ONLINE to Engage with real-world phenomena by watching a video and to complete a CER interactive worksheet.

What is causing drought in California?

Weather and Climate

Some parts of California regularly experience droughts. However, these droughts have become more frequent and more severe in recent decades. Once you have viewed the Investigative Phenomenon video and used the Claim-Evidence-Reasoning worksheet to craft an explanation, answer the following reflection questions about things that might increase the chance of a drought.

1) **CCC Stability and Change** Feedbacks can stabilize or destabilize the climate, causing or preventing extreme weather events such as floods and droughts. List two factors that can affect the stability of California's climate. Identify if the factors stabilize or destabilize the climate. ✎

Factor	Effect

2) **SEP Develop and Use Models** Using a factor you identified in question 1, develop a simple model to explain how it stabilizes or destabilizes California's climate. ✎

....

....

....

....

Earth's Surface Systems

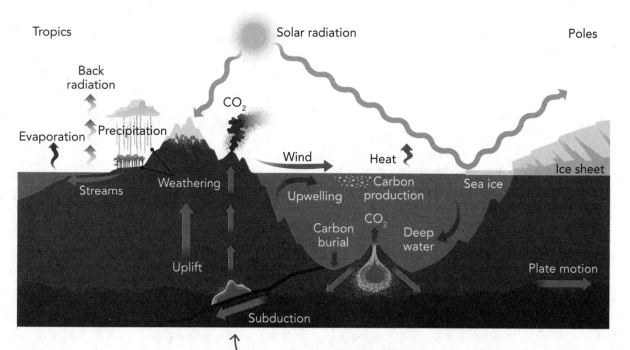

GO ONLINE to Explore and Explain activities to detect carbon dioxide and how carbon from familiar objects moves through the carbon cycle.

Flow of Energy in Earth Systems

Earth's surface geologic system processes are largely driven by the flow of electromagnetic radiation from the sun. Earth's interior geologic system processes are driven by something else: the flow of heat out of Earth. Earth's internal heat is primarily generated by the gradual radioactive decay of four isotopes: potassium-40, thorium-232, uranium-235, and uranium-238.

Over time, Earth's surface temperature goes up or down depending on whether the net energy flow at Earth's surface is positive or negative.

Solar Radiation The sun's energy powers the water cycle and the erosion of land, and it creates Earth's weather. It also moves the slow undersea currents that circle the planet.

Tropics

Back radiation

Evaporation Precipitation

Solar radiation

CO_2

Wind Heat

Streams Weathering

Upwelling Carbon production

Carbon burial CO_2 Deep water

Uplift

Subduction

Poles

Ice sheet

Sea ice

Plate motion

The flow of heat out of Earth moves the tectonic plates, causing earthquakes and creating volcanoes and other types of mountains.

Biogeochemical Cycles

Residence Time The energy arriving from the sun and escaping from Earth's interior drives the cycling of many types of matter through Earth's different systems (the geosphere, atmosphere, hydrosphere, and biosphere).

Those materials have different pathways and residence times in each system. Some, such as carbon, oxygen, nitrogen, phosphorus, sulfur, and water, are vital to life.

■ Biogeochemistry is an interdisciplinary field that studies the cycling of certain elements and compounds that are vital to life.

Water Reservoirs Fresh water is essential to human life, yet, as the table shows, it is only a small fraction of the water on Earth's surface, and most of it is frozen in glaciers and ice caps.

Water in the Hydrosphere		
Reservoir	**Volume (thousands of km³)**	**Residence Time**
Ocean	1,370,000	3100 years
Glaciers	29,000	16,000 years
Groundwater	4,000	300 years
Freshwater Lakes	125	1–100 years
Saline lakes	104	10–1000 years
Soil moisture	67	280 days
Atmosphere	14	9 days
Rivers	1.2	12–20 days

Residence time refers to the average amount of time a molecule spends in any of Earth's reservoirs. For instance, a raindrop that falls into a river might spend weeks in the river before it reaches a lake or the ocean.

(3) **CCC Systems and System Models** Explain how residence time is related to the relative size of a reservoir, and why. ✏️

....

....

....

The Sun-Driven Water Cycle Unlike geologic processes that occur deep inside Earth, processes that happen at Earth's surface are driven mostly by energy from the sun. The water cycle is a sun-driven system. As water on Earth's surface absorbs energy from sunlight, the water begins a series of changes that carry it into the atmosphere, back to Earth's surface, and back into the atmosphere again. Sunlight is also responsible for driving the large-scale atmospheric currents that carry water vapor all around the planet.

Although the cycling of matter within the hydrologic system is powered by energy from the sun, the force of gravity also plays a role in the cycle as it pulls water toward Earth's center, causing rain to fall and water to flow downhill across Earth's surface.

(4) **CCC Energy and Matter** Examine the diagram of the water cycle. Draw a circle around each process that requires energy input from the sun. Draw a square around each process where gravity plays a role. ✏️

As water vapor cools, it condenses to form water droplets or ice particles. These particles eventually fall back to Earth's surface as precipitation.

Energy from sunlight causes evaporation of water and warms the air near the surface, forming air currents that carry water vapor to higher altitudes.

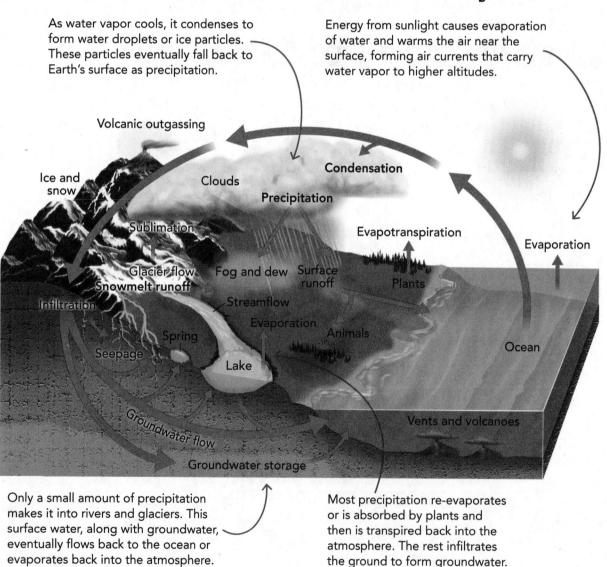

Only a small amount of precipitation makes it into rivers and glaciers. This surface water, along with groundwater, eventually flows back to the ocean or evaporates back into the atmosphere.

Most precipitation re-evaporates or is absorbed by plants and then is transpired back into the atmosphere. The rest infiltrates the ground to form groundwater.

Energy and Life Without photosynthesis, carbon dioxide would still dissolve in seawater, and weathering of rocks would still occur, but the carbon cycle would be very different.

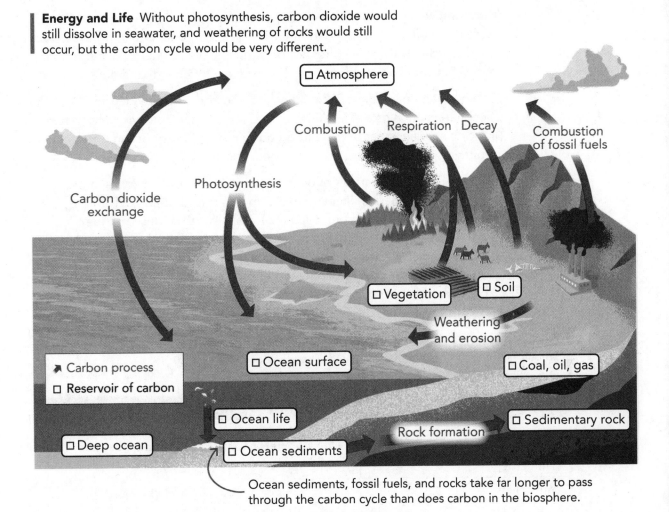

Ocean sediments, fossil fuels, and rocks take far longer to pass through the carbon cycle than does carbon in the biosphere.

Energy and the Carbon Cycle

Solar Energy to Carbon Photosynthesis is the vital process that plants use to create and store energy from the light of the sun. The energy needed for photosynthesis comes daily from the sun, but not the carbon used for storing it, which cycles continually through Earth's systems. About 550 billion tons of carbon is stored in the biosphere.

Photosynthesis is not very efficient; it typically captures and stores only 0.1–0.2% of the energy of sunlight. However, because fossil fuels such as coal and oil are the remains of millions of years of ancient organisms, they are, in a sense, millions of years of fossil sunbeams.

5 **SEP Obtain, Evaluate, and Communicate Information** Go online to investigate the range of ages of the coal that is used for generating electric power in the United States. Describe the differences between the residence time for carbon in coal and in other parts of the carbon cycle. ✏

....

....

Carbon Cycle One of the most important materials cycling through Earth's systems is carbon, the foundation for life on Earth. Understanding the carbon cycle involves studying not only the reservoirs where carbon resides, but its pathways among them and its residence times within them.

At any given time, about 550 billion tons of carbon is stored in the biosphere, with most (475 billion tons) as a result of photosynthesis. When living things die, most of the carbon goes into the soil or ocean bottom sediments and becomes part of the geosphere.

Nearly all of Earth's carbon is locked away in Earth's crustal rocks, most as calcium carbonate in limestone, a common rock that forms from the sedimentation of shells from millions of years' worth of dead marine organisms. Limestone returns to the surface very slowly, through geologic processes such as mountain building, uplift, and erosion. Vast amounts of carbon also exist in the geosphere in the soil and in fossil fuels such as coal, oil, and natural gas.

Carbon Reservoirs Earth's many carbon reservoirs differ vastly in the amount and form of carbon that they hold. The element also cycles at different rates through each reservoir.

Carbon in Earth's Systems		
Reservoir	**Mass (Billions of metric tons)**	**Estimated Residence Time**
Marine Life	6	20 days
Atmosphere	865	4 years
Surface Ocean	900	4 years
Land Vegetation	450	4–6 years
Dissolved Ocean Organic Carbon	700	350 years
Intermediate and Deep Ocean	37,300	370 years
Soil	1500–2400	1000s of years
Ocean Floor Surface Sediments	1750	10,000s of years
Ocean Methane Gas Hydrates	1500–6000	10,000s of years
Permafrost	1700	100,000s of years
Fossil Fuels	570–1500	Millions of years
Carbonate Rocks	48,000,000	10s of millions of years
Other Rocks in Earth's Crust	42,000,000	100s of millions of years

(6) **CCC Patterns** Use the table to compare surface carbon reservoirs, such as land vegetation and the atmosphere, with those in the rocks of Earth's crust. What pattern do you observe? 🖊

....

....

New Rock Igneous rock forms at Earth's surface during volcanic eruptions, such as this eruption of Volcán de Fuego in Guatemala in November of 2018. Other processes of erosion and deposition will alter this rock as it moves through the rock cycle.

Rock Cycle

Rock Cycle Forces The surface of Earth is constantly changing. Earth's systems interact in countless ways, and these interactions form the geologic processes that shape and reshape our planet's surface.

Geology occurs at time scales that range from milliseconds to millions of years and at spatial scales from atoms to tectonic plates. Nearly all geologic processes occur along a spectrum, from small-scale and continuous to large-scale and catastrophic. For example, volcanoes usually bubble out lava, creating new land, but the occasional supervolcano eruption can cover Earth's surface with ash and drive species to extinction.

Earth's surface is a battleground between two powerful dueling engines: the internal engine powered by heat from radioactive decay, which drives plate tectonics, and the external sun-powered water cycle, which drives precipitation, erosion, and sedimentation. These two combine to form the many pathways that Earth materials take, which is often summarized as the **rock cycle**. As fast as internal forces push up mountains or add surface rock through volcanism, the erosion from rain, ice, and wind tears them down. It is a constant battle, won sometimes by the internal engine when mountain ranges are thrust up into the sky, and other times by erosion, as those mountains are torn away, sometimes atom by atom, and carried to the sea.

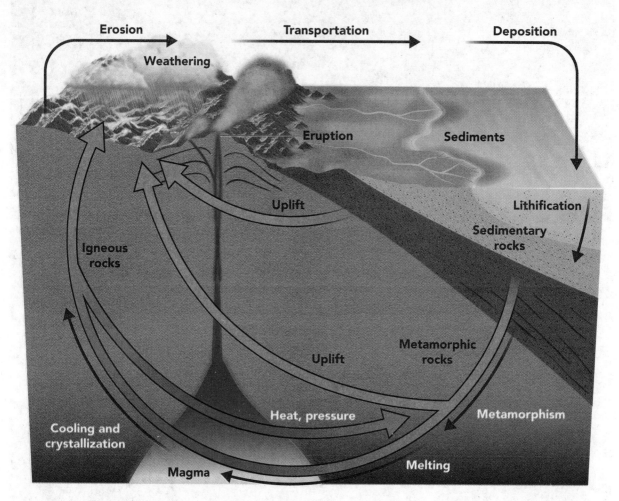

Erosion **Transportation** **Deposition**

Weathering

Eruption **Sediments**

Uplift

Lithification

Sedimentary rocks

Igneous rocks

Uplift

Metamorphic rocks

Heat, pressure

Metamorphism

Cooling and crystallization

Magma **Melting**

Constant Transformation Rock can be igneous, sedimentary, or metamorphic, but powerful processes, some driven by external energy from the sun and others by Earth's internal heat, constantly change one kind of rock into another.

The Cycling of Material An important part of the rock cycle is the melting of rock. Magma forms at Earth's surface for several reasons, including high temperatures, decreases in pressure, and the presence of water. Volcanoes form where magma reaches the surface and erupts, but magma can also cool and harden to form igneous rocks underground.

At the surface, rock is broken down into small pieces (sediments) through the processes of weathering, which can be both chemical and physical. Sediments are then removed and carried downhill by the processes of erosion, often as part of the water cycle through floods, streams, and glaciers. Sediments are primarily chemically dissolved ions, but also include solid pieces of gravel, sand, and silt, and they almost always end up in the ocean.

Sediments become rock again through the process of sedimentation, where sediments are compacted and squeezed and then cemented together by the chemical precipitation of new minerals out of aqueous solutions. If burial continues, with more rock piled on top, the increasing pressure and temperature will change existing minerals in a sedimentary rock into new minerals, forming a metamorphic rock. **Metamorphism** is primarily a chemical process where increasing temperature and pressure alter the shape and composition of minerals. If metamorphism goes too far, the rock will melt to form new magma and the rock cycle will begin again.

Reinforcing and Counterbalancing Feedbacks

Change to one Earth system almost always causes change to other systems. In certain cases, the affected system will respond and apply a change back on the first system. This process is called a **feedback**. Feedbacks that amplify a change are called **reinforcing feedbacks**, or "positive" feedbacks. Feedbacks that resist or reduce a change are called **counterbalancing feedbacks**, or "negative" feedbacks. Earth systems operate within set parameters that maintain a state of equilibrium. Therefore, most feedbacks are counterbalancing, which means they act in a way that keeps the system in balance.

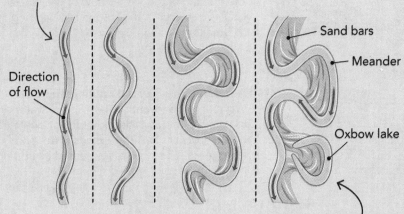

Reinforcing Feedback Water flows faster on the outside of a river curve, eroding the outside of the bend and making the meander grow.

Sand bars

Meander

Direction of flow

Oxbow lake

Counterbalancing Feedback Eventually, the meanders get so large that they cut themselves off and the system returns to the starting state of a straight river.

(7) **SEP Develop and Use Models** Use examples from your own experience to complete the diagrams by writing related processes that reinforce or counterbalance each other in the proper boxes. ✎

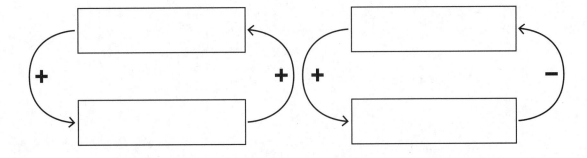

Feedback Tipping Points

When an old equilibrium cannot be restored by the usual feedback mechanisms, the system can reach a **tipping point.** These thresholds can cause sudden and irreversible changes to the system, which must then find a new equilibrium. These cycles are also called "non-linear" feedbacks, because the changes do not happen steadily, like the slope of a straight line.

Scientists worry that more natural systems will reach their tipping points as global temperatures rise. For example, following a century of gradual warming, some West Antarctic ice sheets that had existed for thousands of years recently disintegrated in a single day or a few weeks.

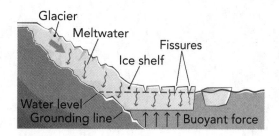

Warmer temperatures destabilize ice shelf
Meltwater from the glacier surface speeds up the melting and downhill flow of the glacier. It causes fractures in the ice shelf, which begins to break up.

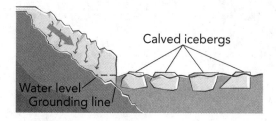

Acceleration of glacial melting and flow
Without the buoyant support of the water on the ice shelf, the glacier flows faster downhill due to gravity. Its surface melts faster and loses mass. The system has passed its tipping point and cannot rebuild the ice shelf.

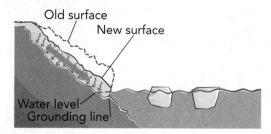

Unstable glacier after ice shelf collapses
Rapid fracturing and calving of sea ice breaks up the ice shelf. The glacier flows faster. The shelf reaches a tipping point when it retreats past the grounding line, because it has less support from seawater.

8 **SEP Constructing Explanations Based on Evidence** Explain why the complete disappearance of a glacier is an example of a non-linear tipping point. 🖊

....

....

....

....

Land Use in the United States

How do we **use our land** in the United States?

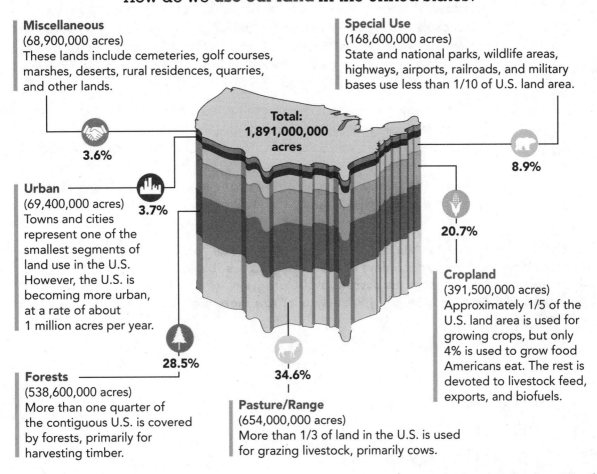

Miscellaneous
(68,900,000 acres)
These lands include cemeteries, golf courses, marshes, deserts, rural residences, quarries, and other lands.

3.6%

Special Use
(168,600,000 acres)
State and national parks, wildlife areas, highways, airports, railroads, and military bases use less than 1/10 of U.S. land area.

8.9%

Total:
1,891,000,000 acres

Urban
(69,400,000 acres)
Towns and cities represent one of the smallest segments of land use in the U.S. However, the U.S. is becoming more urban, at a rate of about 1 million acres per year.

3.7%

20.7%

Cropland
(391,500,000 acres)
Approximately 1/5 of the U.S. land area is used for growing crops, but only 4% is used to grow food Americans eat. The rest is devoted to livestock feed, exports, and biofuels.

28.5%

Forests
(538,600,000 acres)
More than one quarter of the contiguous U.S. is covered by forests, primarily for harvesting timber.

34.6%

Pasture/Range
(654,000,000 acres)
More than 1/3 of land in the U.S. is used for grazing livestock, primarily cows.

Human Impacts on the Earth System

Human Impacts on Earth's Surface Humans are now the main agent of geologic change at Earth's surface, controlling more than 50% of its land. We use 40% of land just to raise crops and graze animals to feed ourselves. Humans and the livestock we eat account for 96% of the total biomass of all land mammals—all wild mammals are now just 4%. In forty years, human activities have reduced the total number of Earth's vertebrates by more than half, and nearly all insects are gone in areas where people live. Human-released carbon dioxide has made the ocean 30% more acidic. In the U.S., the total area of developed land is now larger than the state of California, requiring the extraction of 8 billion tons of rock and minerals each year. Human activities such as mining, farming, and road-building now erode Earth's surface six times faster than all natural causes combined.

Human Impacts on the Atmosphere Many human activities put pollutants into the atmosphere. For example, the burning of fossil fuels releases greenhouse gases and large amounts of sulfur dioxide and nitrous oxides. These chemicals react with naturally occurring molecules in the atmosphere to become sulfuric and nitric acids, which acidify rainwater and damage organisms and property. These pollutants enter the hydrosphere and biosphere, where they harm living things. Greenhouse gases have led to a significant increase in atmospheric temperatures.

Fortunately, humans can monitor the release of these pollutants (especially using satellites), assess their impacts on Earth's systems, and take action to mitigate them. The U.S. Clean Air Acts have greatly reduced national air pollution levels. Global bans on chlorofluorocarbons have halted the destruction of the ozone layer. And international efforts are now underway to reduce the level of greenhouse gas emissions.

(9) **SEP Plan an Investigation** Do research to find out what an "ozone action day" is. How are ozone action days designed around feedbacks? Design an investigation to measure the success of the program. What data would you need to collect? How would you analyze it? Are there any tipping points? ✏️

....

....

Revisit

INVESTIGATIVE PHENOMENON

 GO ONLINE to Elaborate on and Evaluate your knowledge of the carbon cycle by completing the class discussion and writing activities.

In the CER worksheet, you drafted a scientific argument about the possible causes of droughts. With a partner, reevaluate the evidence cited in your arguments.

(10) **SEP Engage in Argument** Construct and defend an argument that the human use of lands in California has increased the severity of droughts. ✏️

....

....

....

....

Water and Energy in the Atmosphere

 GO ONLINE to Explore and Explain specific heat and its effects on climate.

Earth's Radiative Energy Budget

Energy Budget Earth's surface **energy budget** describes where energy comes from and where it goes. It is driven by incoming solar radiation, mostly in the form of visible light. This incoming sunlight is about 340 watts of power for each square meter (340 W/m^2), but nearly a third of the energy is immediately reflected back out into space by clouds and Earth's surface. The energy that is absorbed by Earth's surface is reradiated upward as infrared energy, some of which is absorbed by gases in the atmosphere and then reradiated back toward the surface, creating a cycle known as the **greenhouse effect.**

Earth's Surface Energy Budget Most pathways of energy to and from Earth's surface take the form of electromagnetic radiation, primarily in the form of incoming sunlight or outgoing infrared light.

Components of Earth's Energy Budget Earth's energy budget is a complex system fueled by energy incoming from the sun, and the transfer of energy back and forth between Earth's surface and its atmosphere.

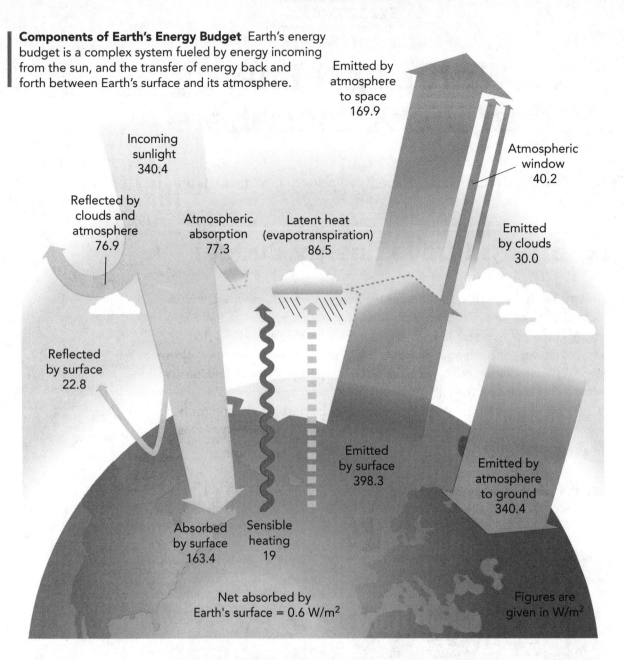

Emitted by atmosphere to space
169.9

Incoming sunlight
340.4

Atmospheric window
40.2

Reflected by clouds and atmosphere
76.9

Atmospheric absorption
77.3

Latent heat (evapotranspiration)
86.5

Emitted by clouds
30.0

Reflected by surface
22.8

Emitted by surface
398.3

Emitted by atmosphere to ground
340.4

Absorbed by surface
163.4

Sensible heating
19

Net absorbed by Earth's surface = 0.6 W/m²

Figures are given in W/m²

Unbalanced Budget The total amounts of incoming and outgoing energy are not the same. Due to human increases in greenhouse gases, more is entering than is currently leaving, causing Earth's surface to warm.

⑪ **SEP Develop and Use Models** Using this model of Earth's surface energy budget, explain why more than twice as much energy reaching Earth's surface is in the form of long-wave infrared radiation than short-wave visible radiation, despite the fact that sunlight is mostly visible radiation. ✎

....

....

....

Temperature and Pressure in the Atmosphere

Earth's atmosphere extends for hundreds of kilometers into space, but because its gases are compressible, most of the atmosphere can be found within 5.5 km of the surface. The atmosphere is divided into several layers based on composition and temperature. Clouds and weather exist in the dense troposphere. Temperatures increase through the stratosphere because ozone in this layer absorbs ultraviolet radiation from the sun. Aurorae (such as the northern lights) occur within the thermosphere and exosphere.

Earth's Atmosphere

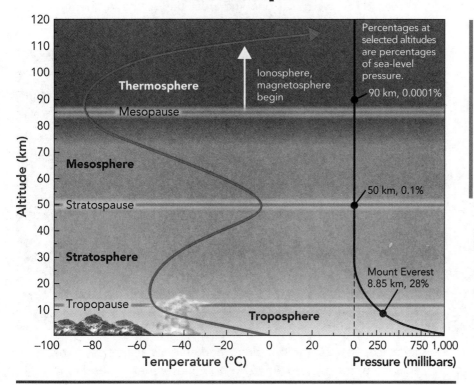

Layers and properties of Earth's Atmosphere
The temperatures at the stratopause and in the thermosphere are high, but this is misleading. Due to the near-vacuum conditions at these high altitudes, only a few gas molecules interact with sunlight, but they are very energetic.

(12) **CCC Cause and Effect** Most passenger airplanes fly at the top of the troposphere, about 10.5 km high, but don't go much higher than that. This height allows planes to combust the least amount of fuel. Construct an explanation for why passenger planes don't fly much below that and why they don't fly much above that. ✎

....

....

....

Evaporation and Transpiration

The water cycle starts with **evapotranspiration,** a combination of evaporation from bodies of water and transpiration from the leaves of plants. These are both driven by the energy of sunlight. The absorption of the sun's electromagnetic radiation by liquid water can change it into water vapor. Water vapor molecules are at a higher energy state than liquid water molecules, and sunlight provides this energy. Each year the equivalent of about 400,000 cubic kilometers of water evaporates from the ocean surface, and a lesser amount from lakes and soil on land.

Most evaporation occurs at the ocean's surface, and near the equator. Evaporation rates are higher near the equator because the angle of sunlight is more vertical in those regions. Right along the equator, however, evaporation is slightly decreased relative to surrounding areas due to the frequent formation of clouds.

Evaporation Feedback High levels of evaporation, such as those observed over the Gulf Stream, can increase air humidity and promote the formation of clouds, which in turn can slow down the evaporation process.

Through the process of respiration, plants and animals also release water vapor. In respiration, food is broken down to release energy needed by the organism, and six water molecules are produced for each molecule of glucose. In plants, this water, along with water absorbed through the roots, transpires into the atmosphere through leaf pores as water vapor.

13. **CCC Patterns** A narrow region of high evaporation in the Atlantic Ocean, east of North America, coincides with the Gulf Stream. A similar region exists in the Pacific Ocean, south of Japan. It corresponds to the Kuroshio Current. Explain why you think water is evaporating more rapidly from these currents.

....

....

....

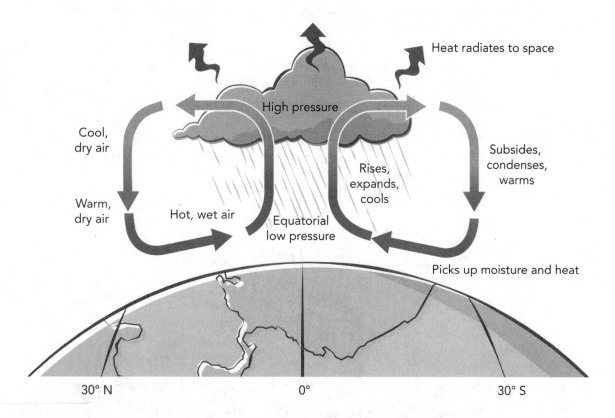

Heat radiates to space

High pressure

Cool, dry air

Subsides, condenses, warms

Warm, dry air

Rises, expands, cools

Hot, wet air

Equatorial low pressure

Picks up moisture and heat

30° N   0°   30° S

Convection in the Atmosphere

The air of the atmosphere is moved by convection. This convection is driven by the heating of air near Earth's surface from sunlight. The warm air expands, making it buoyant and causing it to rise. As the air rises and expands it cools, causing water vapor within it to condense and form tiny water droplets, creating clouds and eventually rain. The dryer air is pushed away from the equator by more rising air, which, now being cold and dense, falls back to Earth's surface. That air then flows across Earth's surface back towards the equator, as what are called the trade winds, warming over time until it is buoyant enough to rise again.

(14) **CCC Cause and Effect** All else being equal, air volume increases when pressure decreases. Use this relationship to explain why warm air at the equator rises up through the less dense air above it. 🖉

....

....

....

....

Atmospheric Pressure and Wind

Winds are a result of pressure differences in the atmosphere at Earth's surface, with air moving from regions of high pressure to regions of low pressure. These patterns are constantly shifting, day to day and season to season, causing our weather. Differences in pressure can occur for several reasons, but are usually the result of differences in heating rates. These differences can result from factors such as the changing locations of ocean currents and the movement of clouds.

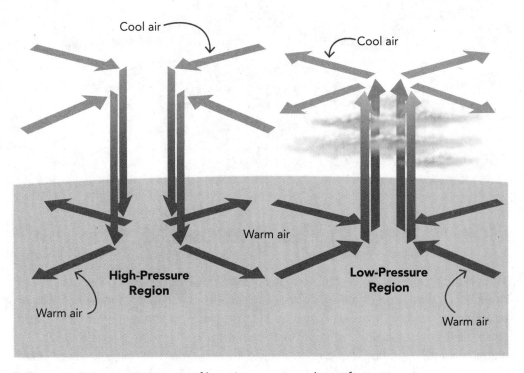

Cool air

Cool air

Warm air

High-Pressure Region

Low-Pressure Region

Warm air

Warm air

Pressure Systems At an area of low air pressure at the surface, moist warm air flows toward the center of the low pressure before rising, cooling, forming clouds, and then flowing away from the area. At areas of high pressure, dry cold air high in the atmosphere falls and warms as it approaches the surface. The air then flows away from the area.

(15) **CCC Cause and Effect** In the diagram, clouds form over the low-pressure region where air is rising, while at the high-pressure region, sunlight hits the ground as cold air is sinking. Explain why this pattern might change and reverse over time. ✎

....

....

....

....

Global Atmospheric Circulation

Due to Earth's size and rate of rotation, the general global pattern of air circulation is broken up into six cells. The locations and structures of these cells are always shifting, day-to-day and season-to-season. In the Northern Hemisphere, the bottom of the Hadley Cell forms winds that blow toward the west (trade winds), and the bottom of the Ferrel Cell forms winds that blow from the west (westerlies). This is why most of the weather in the United States goes from west to east.

Latitude Pressure Zones Places where air is rising are low-pressure zones. Places where the air is falling are high-pressure zones.

Some of the air that rises at about 60° north and south flows toward the poles, where it falls as very cold and dry air, producing **Polar cells**.

Ferrel cells form around 50–60° north and south. Air masses tend to rise, creating rainfall. Air then flows toward the equator at high altitudes, falling back at around 30° N and S.

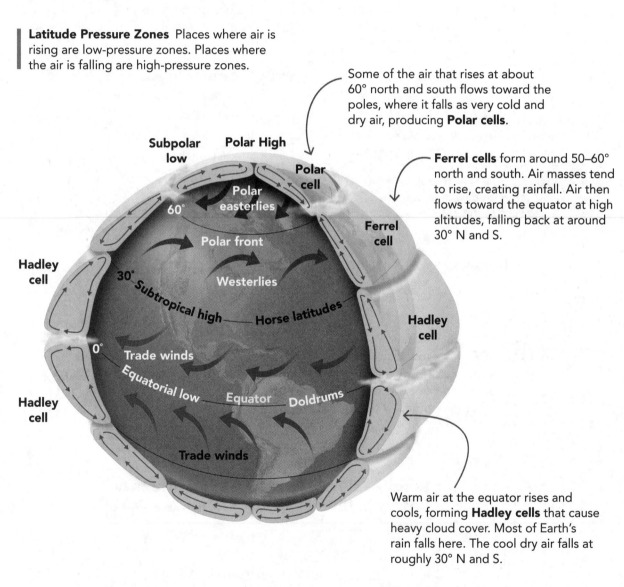

Warm air at the equator rises and cools, forming **Hadley cells** that cause heavy cloud cover. Most of Earth's rain falls here. The cool dry air falls at roughly 30° N and S.

16. **SEP Develop and Use Models** Use the model of atmospheric circulation to explain why most of the world's deserts are roughly 30° north, 30° south, or at the poles. 🖊

....

....

Humidity and Condensation

Humidity The amount of water vapor that can exist within air changes depending on temperature. Warmer air can contain a greater amount of water vapor than colder air. **Relative humidity** is a measure of the percentage of water vapor in the air compared to the maximum amount the air can hold at that particular temperature. If the humidity is high, the air feels damp and sticky. The dew point occurs when the relative humidity reaches 100%. At this point, no more water can be held in the air, and droplets of liquid water or crystals of ice will begin to form. Clouds are visible because they consist of tiny condensed ice crystals or water droplets.

Water Vapor and Temperature Dew and frost usually form late at night or early in the morning, when the air gets colder than the point of 100% humidity. As the temperature falls, the air can hold less water vapor, so dew or frost forms on surfaces such as the grass.

Water Content of Air at 50% and 100% Relative Humidity

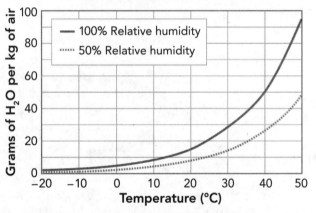

17 **CCC Patterns** Examine the graph of relative humidity compared to temperature for a city over a 3-day period. The temperature reaches a peak at about 3 pm on Day 3. Estimate how much water vapor is in the air at that time. 🖉

Relative Humidity and Temperatures in Chicago, Illinois for December 1–3, 2017

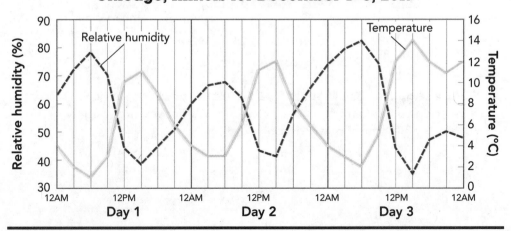

Types of Precipitation

How do different types of **precipitation form?**

Interacting Air Masses When warm air encounters a colder, denser air mass, the warm air is pushed up and over the colder air, forming clouds that may produce different types of precipitation.

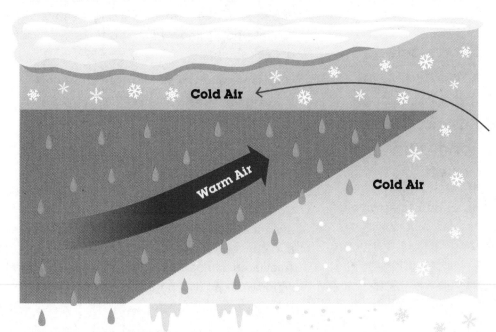

Cold Air

Warm Air

Cold Air

The temperature of the air high in the atmosphere is below the freezing point of water.

The type of precipitation that reaches the ground is dependent on the **temperature of the air** it falls through and the **temperature near the surface**.

Frozen precipitation melts as it falls, reaching the ground as **rain.**

Frozen precipitation melts as it falls but refreezes on cold surfaces becoming **frozen rain.**

Frozen precipitation melts in a shallow layer of warm air then refreezes into **sleet** before reaching the surface.

Snow falls through a continuous column of cold air, never melting before reaching the surface.

Precipitation When the humidity is 100% and air temperature continues to drop, water vapor will continue to condense and eventually fall to the ground as **precipitation.** Air temperature usually drops when one air mass is lifted during a collision with another, denser air mass. The form that the precipitation takes depends on the temperatures of the colliding air masses.

(18) **CCC Energy and Matter** In the diagram, notice that freezing rain and sleet fall as liquid rain through the cold air mass before freezing. Use what you know about the energy of changes of state to explain this phenomenon. ✏️

....

....

....

Severe Weather

Humans rely on precipitation for fresh water and for agriculture, but under certain conditions severe weather can pose a natural hazard and can be damaging and life-threatening.

▶ **When cold fronts collide with warm fronts, the warm air is quickly lifted and cools rapidly, and this can create storms with strong winds and lots of precipitation.**

Heavy precipitation can lead to catastrophic flooding. Snow blizzards can shut down towns and cities. Freezing rain can tear down trees and power lines. Hailstones the size of baseballs can damage houses and cars. In certain cases, tornadoes can spin off along these storm fronts, creating intense winds that can exceed 400 km/hr and tear up everything in their paths. Fortunately, real-time ground and satellite radar monitoring can identify places where severe weather is likely to occur, and provide the data for warning systems that can let people know when it is time to evacuate or seek shelter.

Hurricanes and typhoons are examples of **tropical cyclones**, which are large, rapidly rotating storm systems with high winds, a low-pressure center ("eye"), and spiraling arms of thunderstorms. Hurricanes tend to develop in tropical latitudes over warm water, which causes rising masses of humid air. Earth's Coriolis effect causes cyclones to rotate, taking evaporated water vapor from a very broad area and concentrating intense rainfall into a very small area. Human risks from hurricanes include wind damage, flooding, and coastal storm surges.

Paths of hurricanes near North and Central America The map shows the paths of hurricanes of varying intensities in the Atlantic and Pacific oceans. Note the large number of hurricanes that enter the Gulf of Mexico or come up the east coast of the United States.

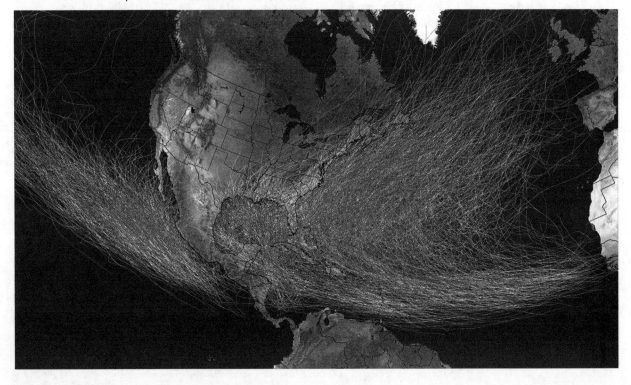

19 **SEP Develop and Use Models** On the weather map, draw where you might expect the warm and cold fronts to be a day later. Mark the part of the map that will see a drop in temperatures over the next day.

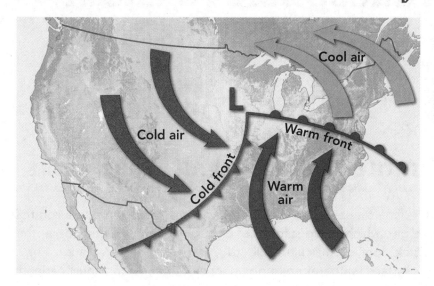

Colliding Air Masses
Moving air masses are often shown on weather maps with arrows. Severe storms are likely to occur where a cold air mass is colliding with a warm air mass.

Revisit

INVESTIGATIVE PHENOMENON

GO ONLINE to Elaborate and Evaluate your knowledge of Earth's energy budget by completing the class discussion and data analysis activities.

In the CER worksheet, you provided evidence and reasons to explain what causes droughts. With a partner, reevaluate the evidence cited in your arguments.

20 **SEP Engage in Argument** How do you think California's geographic location might limit the amount of precipitation it gets?

....

....

....

....

....

....

Atmospheric System Feedbacks

GO ONLINE to Explore and Explain climate forcing and atmospheric system feedbacks.

Climate Forcings and Feedbacks

Earth's climate system and therefore its surface temperature are controlled by sunlight, which includes forms of electromagnetic radiation other than just visible light, such as ultraviolet (UV) and infrared (IR) radiation. For Earth's surface temperature to go up, one of three factors must happen: (1) an increase in incoming sunlight (due to changes in the sun's activity), (2) a decrease in how much sunlight gets reflected from the surface back out into space, or (3) an increase in how much of that energy is kept by greenhouse gases. These factors driving the climate are called **climate forcings,** and there is a large number of Earth system impacts and feedbacks that result from them.

Tropical Deforestation Removing large portions of tropical rainforests generates both cooling and warming climate forcings. The bare ground reflects more sunlight back out into space than the highly absorbing forest, so this has a cooling effect. However, a larger effect is the warming due to the release of the forest's carbon dioxide into the atmosphere and the absence of those trees that otherwise would have continued absorbing carbon, so the net result of deforestation is warming.

Albedo of Various Surfaces

What are **the albedos** of different types of surfaces?

32–85%
Snow and Ice
Snow and ice have high albedos. Fresh snow reflects the most sunlight. Glacier ice is translucent, so it has a lower albedo because it absorbs more sunlight.

36–77%
Clouds
Clouds are generally more reflective than Earth's surface, so an increase in cloud cover has a cooling effect on Earth.

6–8%
Water
Liquid water is very transparent, so it absorbs nearly all incoming sunlight, reflecting only 6-8%.

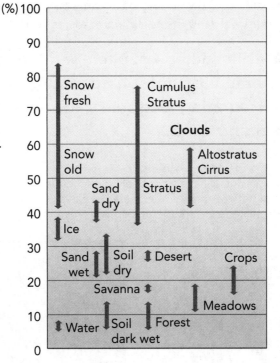

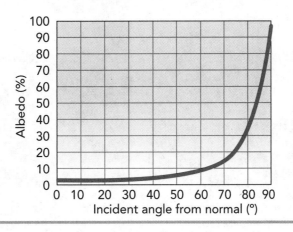

21–44%
Sand
The albedo of sand varies greatly; it is much higher for dry sand than for wet sand.

6–34%
Soil
Dark wet soil absorbs most sunlight, but dry soil is very reflective. with an albedo of 25-30%.

6–25%
Vegetation
Vegetated grounds have a low albedo, absorbing most sunlight. This varies for forest, meadows, and crops. Replacing forests with croplands has a cooling effect on the temperature.

Albedo is the proportion of incoming sunlight that reflects off of an object's surface. On Earth it is an important factor for retaining solar energy and therefore for climate. Albedo varies for different materials and also by incident angle; it increases as the angle of light relative to the surface increases, and so is naturally higher at Earth's poles.

(21) **SEP Analyze and Interpret Data** Construct an explanation for why croplands would have a higher albedo than forests. 🖉

....

....

Evaporation Feedbacks

An increase in Earth's temperatures causes an increase in evaporation and precipitation as the warming of ocean water increases evaporation from its surface and warming of the air increases its capacity to hold water vapor.

▶ **While increases in temperature and in water in the atmosphere produce both cooling and warming feedbacks, the net result is a warming effect.**

Cloud Forcing Though clouds have a net cooling effect during the day and a net warming effect at night, the overall effect is warming, providing a net reinforcing feedback for atmospheric warming.

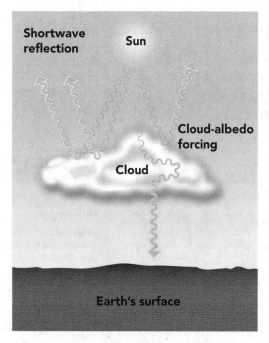

Shortwave reflection
Sun
Cloud-albedo forcing
Cloud
Earth's surface

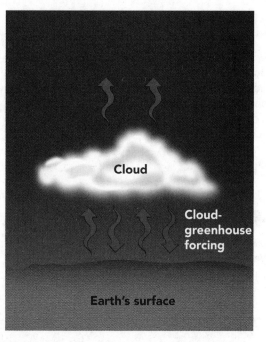

Cloud
Cloud-greenhouse forcing
Earth's surface

Cooling During the daytime, clouds have a cooling effect because cloud tops reflect some sunlight (mostly visible wavelengths) back into space. This is a counterbalancing feedback.

Warming Day and night, clouds absorb a portion of the long-wavelength infrared radiation emitted from Earth's surface. The clouds re-emit the infrared radiation, warming the atmosphere. This is a reinforcing feedback.

(22) **SEP Design Solutions** Jet airplanes create long, straight clouds called contrails. How could you change the schedules of airplane flights to reduce their warming impact?

....

....

....

North

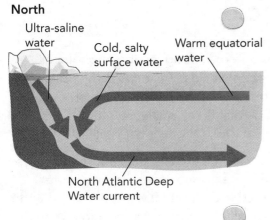

Ultra-saline water

Cold, salty surface water

Warm equatorial water

North Atlantic Deep Water current

How Currents Work Density differences between the cold and salty polar waters and the warmer equatorial waters drives the global convection cycle of deep ocean currents. In the Atlantic Ocean, ultra-saline water created when sea ice forms joins the cold and salty northward-flowing surface water to form the North Atlantic Deep Water current that drives Atlantic Ocean Circulation.

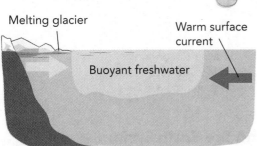

Melting glacier

Warm surface current

Buoyant freshwater

What Could Weaken Ocean Currents Buoyant freshwater from melted glaciers stays at the surface and blocks the northward surface currents, slowing down the deep convection cycle.

The Ocean and Carbon Dioxide

The ocean is involved in several feedbacks affecting carbon dioxide in the atmosphere. Ocean waters provide a strong counterbalancing feedback to global warming by absorbing CO_2 from the atmosphere, reducing the greenhouse effect. About 30% of the CO_2 that humans have released in the past century has been absorbed by the ocean.

However, reinforcing feedbacks also exist. When ocean water warms, it can hold less dissolved CO_2 than it otherwise would. This means more CO_2 in the atmosphere and more greenhouse warming. In addition, as water at the poles warms, the difference in temperature between equatorial waters and polar waters decreases, slowing the pattern of global ocean circulation, and reducing the ocean's ability to remove CO_2 from the atmosphere.

(23) **SEP Construct and Use Models** You have probably had the experience of leaving a cold bubbly soda out in the open and finding that it had gone flat when it warmed up. (The bubbles are CO_2.) Explain how this phenomenon can be used to model the ocean's ability to store CO_2. ✏

....

....

....

Biomass Feedbacks

The biosphere provides a strong counterbalancing feedback for global warming because plants absorb carbon dioxide. The more carbon dioxide in the atmosphere, the larger the biomass of the biosphere becomes, removing about a quarter of the CO_2 that humans release into the atmosphere each year. It is unclear how long this feedback will exist.

Only about 45% of the CO_2 that humans release into the atmosphere stays there. About 30% is absorbed by the ocean, and 25% by plants. Human release of CO_2 has more than doubled in the past 50 years, but plants and the ocean have removed more than half of it. Biomass absorption varies with climate fluctuations.

Biosphere Carbon The biosphere is estimated to contain about 550 billion tons of carbon, mostly in forest trees. Each year, plants produce new biomass containing over 100 billion tons of carbon.

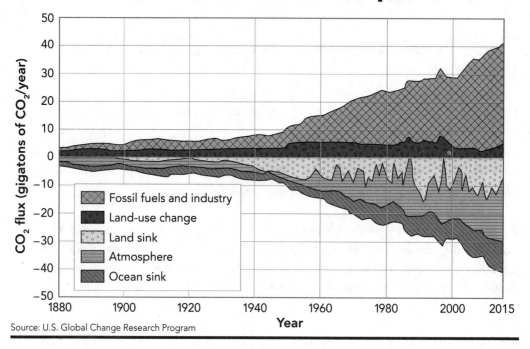

Carbon Dioxide and the Earth System

Legend:
- Fossil fuels and industry
- Land-use change
- Land sink
- Atmosphere
- Ocean sink

Source: U.S. Global Change Research Program

(24) **SEP Design Solutions** Describe what humans can do in the future using the biosphere to reduce CO_2 levels in the atmosphere. ✎

....

....

Methane Hydrate Feedbacks

Two significant reinforcing feedbacks, one in the frigid tundras and another in offshore ocean sediments, occur with the vast amounts of frozen methane gas hydrates called clathrates. Rapid warming in the Arctic is melting the permafrost of the tundras and releasing methane (a powerful greenhouse gas), driving more warming. Methane is also released when offshore waters warm, melting their frozen clathrates. The huge volume of offshore clathrates poses a serious threat for global warming.

Atmospheric Methane Global atmospheric methane levels have been rising due to many human factors, including agriculture, but the melting of clathrates is a significant one. Methane in the atmosphere converts into carbon dioxide in about a decade, but while it remains it is more than 20 times more powerful as a greenhouse gas.

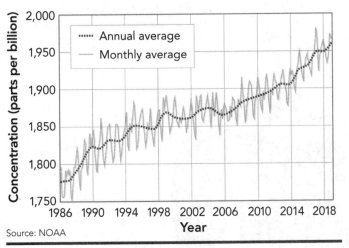

Methane (CH_4) in the Atmosphere at Barrow, Alaska

Source: NOAA

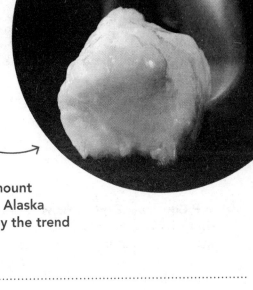

Burning Methane Clathrate It might be strange to see a piece of ice burn, but this isn't ordinary ice. This is a piece of methane clathrate—a combination of frozen methane and water.

(25) **SEP Analyze and Interpret Data** Notice how the amount of methane measured in the atmosphere at Barrow, Alaska changes over time. Construct an explanation for why the trend may continue upward in the future. ✏️

....

....

....

Surface Radiation Feedbacks

Feedbacks and Equilibrium One of the most important counterbalancing feedbacks is surface radiation feedback—the release of more and more energy as an object gets hotter. This means the more an object heats up, the faster it also cools off. Hotter objects release electromagnetic radiation at shorter wavelengths than cooler objects. The sun emits short-wavelength visible light because its photosphere is about 5800 K. In contrast, a person emits long-wavelength infrared radiation because the skin's surface is only 310 K (37°C). In addition, each square meter of the sun's visible surface emits a lot more energy than a person does. The energy emitted per square meter is proportional to T^4 – the fourth power of the temperature. The sun's surface temperature is 17 times hotter than that of a person, but it releases energy at a rate that is 80,000 times greater, for each square meter. So, as Earth's surface temperature increases, the amount it radiates back out into space also increases, until it approaches an equilibrium and stops getting hotter. However, it also means that if the greenhouse effect keeps increasing, Earth's surface will keep getting hotter as that equilibrium shifts over time.

Planetary Atmospheres The atmospheres of Venus, Earth, and Mars have very different temperatures and pressures, but Mars and Venus have runaway greenhouse feedbacks. Both planets have atmospheres of about 96% CO_2 (compared to only 0.04% for Earth).

Venus
Surface Temperature: 462°C
Atmospheric pressure: 91 Atm

Earth
Surface Temperature: 15°C
Atmospheric pressure: 1 Atm

Mars
Surface Temperature: −63°C
Atmospheric pressure: 0.003 Atm

 SEP Construct Explanations From what you know about differences between the surfaces of Venus, Earth, and Mars, construct an explanation for why Earth's atmosphere contains such a smaller percentage of CO_2 than both of its neighbors, Venus and Mars. ✏️

....

....

The Impact of Small Temperature Changes Earth's average surface temperature is about 15°C. If this temperature were to increase, the planet would emit more radiation. How significant would this change be? Suppose that the average temperature increases from 15°C to 20°C. The amount of radiation emitted at each temperature may be estimated by reading the peak spectral intensity of the corresponding black-body curve. On the graph, the 20°C curve has a peak spectral intensity of about 27.5. The graph does not include a 15°C curve, but we can estimate a value of 25.5 by interpolating between the 20°C and 30°C curves.

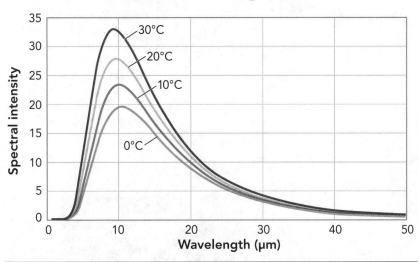

Black-Body Curves for Typical Terrestrial Temperatures

Ideal Curves Most objects do not radiate like perfect black bodies, but the curves reflect the general behavior of matter at different temperatures.

To calculate the percentage increase in temperature, we must use the Kelvin scale: 15°C = 288 K; 20°C = 293 K. The temperature increased by 1.7%, a factor of 1.017. But the spectral intensity increased by 7.8%, a factor of 1.078 (from 25.5 to 27.5). This is because spectral intensity increases with the fourth power of the temperature. We can verify this by raising the temperature change factor (1.017) to the fourth power: $(1.017)^4 = 1.07$, which is approximately the spectral intensity increase factor.

(27) SEP Develop and Use Models Use the information provided by the 30°C curve in the graph to estimate the percent increase in Earth's emitted radiation if the surface temperature of the planet increased from 15°C to 30°C. ✎

Arctic Sea Ice Feedbacks

A very significant reinforcing feedback occurs with ice in the Arctic Sea because ice is much more reflective (albedo between 35 and 80%) than ocean water (albedo = 6%). As the sea warms and more ice melts, the exposed ocean water absorbs more sunlight, accelerating the warming.

Arctic Sea Ice Melts The cycle begins with warm water and air melting the thin, floating arctic ice sheet. Global warming has significantly reduced its size over the past century.

Albedo Decreases As the reflective sea ice disappears, it leaves the darker ocean water exposed, which absorbs more of incoming sunlight during summer months, when the sun shines 24 hours a day in the Arctic Circle.

Temperatures Rise The added sunlight causes the Arctic water to warm, and it couples with the atmosphere to cause it to warm as well. The result is more melting of Arctic ice, and the cycle repeats.

(28) **SEP Analyze and Interpret Data** The graph shows the extent of sea ice over the past 1400 years. How much did the area of ice change prior to 1800? How much is the loss of sea ice area since 1800? ✏️

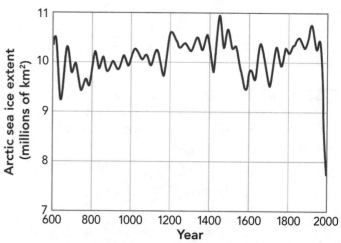

Changes in Arctic Sea Ice (Best Estimate)

Glacier Feedbacks

The melting of glaciers provides additional reinforcing feedbacks that lead to a decrease in ice. When glaciers melt, their fronts recede to higher elevations, exposing rock underneath. This rock absorbs more sunlight than the highly reflective ice and snow, and this warms the ground and leads to more melting. In addition, the loss of water due to the shrinking area of ice reduces the amount of regional water that evaporates and sublimates. This can reduce the snowfall that is needed to replenish the constantly flowing glaciers.

(29) CCC Stability and Change If the area exposed in the image of the glacier in the Purcell Mountains occurred over a period of 25 years, estimate the years until the rest of the glacier melts.

....

Receding Glacier Trees have yet to grow in the area left exposed from a receding glacier in the Purcell Mountains of British Columbia.

Revisit

INVESTIGATIVE PHENOMENON

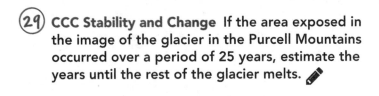

GO ONLINE to Elaborate on and Evaluate your knowledge of atmospheric feedback systems by completing the class discussion and engineering design activities.

In the CER worksheet, you drafted a scientific argument about the possible causes of droughts. With a partner, reevaluate the evidence cited in your arguments.

(30) SEP Engage in Argument Describe a reinforcing or counterbalancing factor you think can cause droughts in California. Explain your reasoning.

....

....

....

....

....

....

Long-Term Climate Factors

GO ONLINE to Explore and Explain the factors that cause climate to change over very long periods of time.

Climate Zones: Latitude and Altitude

Earth contains a great diversity of regional climates, which are critical in determining the biomes and communities of life that have evolved across the planet. Maps of Earth's climate zones have a limited usefulness because the zones constantly shift as regional and global climates change. However, these maps reveal that patterns of wet and dry zones are largely a result of latitude and altitude: temperatures decrease toward the poles, or as altitude increases.

Map of Climate Zones The Köppen climate map groups Earth's diverse climates into about a dozen types that allow for an analysis of patterns in climate variations.

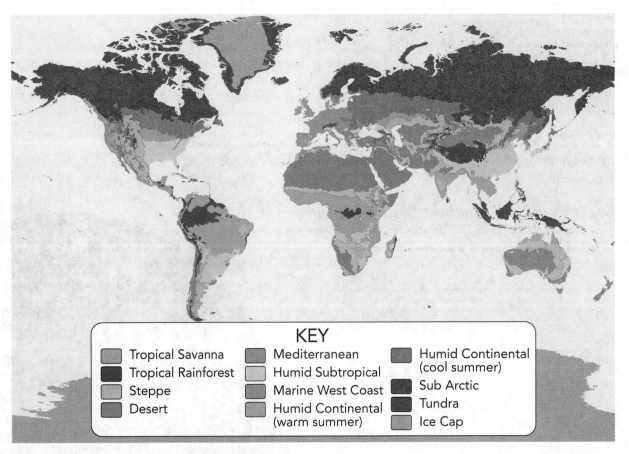

KEY

- Tropical Savanna
- Tropical Rainforest
- Steppe
- Desert
- Mediterranean
- Humid Subtropical
- Marine West Coast
- Humid Continental (warm summer)
- Humid Continental (cool summer)
- Sub Arctic
- Tundra
- Ice Cap

Long-Term Changes in Sunlight

The sun is the most important factor in Earth's weather and climate. Earth's surface would be nothing but ice if it were not for sunlight, but the amount of sunlight the planet receives is not constant. Like other stars, the sun changes over its lifetime. The energy of sunlight comes from the nuclear fusion of hydrogen atoms into helium within the sun's core. As the sun runs out of hydrogen, it will fuse helium to make larger elements, getting steadily hotter and more intense. The sun's output is 30% greater than when it formed, 4.6 billion years ago, and increases by 1% every hundred million years. The sun will likely remain a star for 4 to 5 billion years, but it will be hot enough to boil away Earth's ocean in less than a billion years.

Structure of the Sun The sun is primarily made of hydrogen and helium. Because of the extreme temperatures, atoms in the sun exist as a plasma, with electrons stripped off of the nuclei. That plasma forms several different layers.

Energy leaves the sun's **photosphere** primarily in the form of electromagnetic radiation (sunlight).

The sun's energy comes from the fusion of 620 million tons of hydrogen into helium each second in its **core.**

Energy radiates outward from the core through the **radiative zone** as high-frequency gamma rays, taking over 100,000 years to reach the convective zone.

In the **convective zone,** energy is primarily carried from the radiative zone to the sun's outer layers through plasma convection.

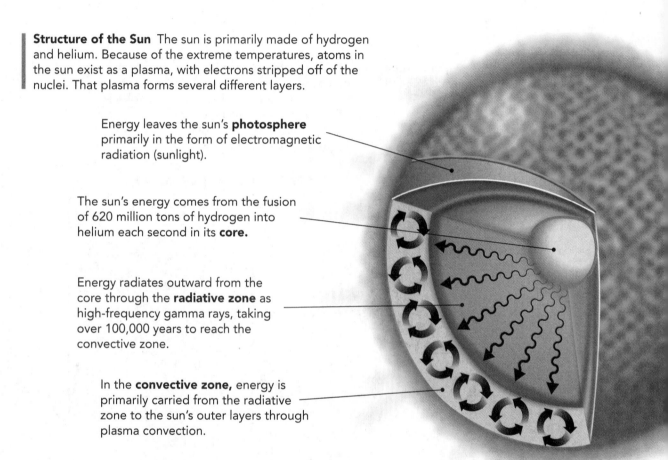

(31) **CCC Stability and Change** Liquid water has existed on Earth's surface for at least 4 billion years, even as the sun's energy output has continued to increase. The total area of continents (now 39% of Earth's surface) may have grown in size over Earth's history. Think about what you know about the albedos of land and water. Does an increase in land area explain why Earth's surface hasn't heated to a point that the ocean has boiled away? Why or why not? ✏

....

....

Past Climates

Determining a history of Earth's past temperature is challenging; scientists infer it from "proxy" data, which are other data sets that are a function of temperature. The most useful recent data set starts with the evolution of hard-shelled life forms at the start of the Cambrian Period, about 540 million years ago. This record shows periods of ice ages (when significant amounts of water were stored on land as glacial ice sheets) and warm periods (when there was little ice). Glacial periods have lasted for tens of millions of years. Earth has been in one such cold period for the past 50 million years. Not much is known about ancient climates for the first three-fourths of Earth's history because so few rocks remain from this time.

Oxygen Isotope Data Past temperatures can be inferred from the ratios of ^{16}O and ^{18}O isotopes in clam shells. Because ^{16}O is lighter than ^{18}O, the ^{16}O isotopes evaporate more easily. Rain, snow, and glaciers therefore contain very little ^{18}O, which stays in the ocean. Time periods that show an increase in ^{18}O in clam shells indicate that a great deal of ice (containing ^{16}O) was stored on land in glaciers.

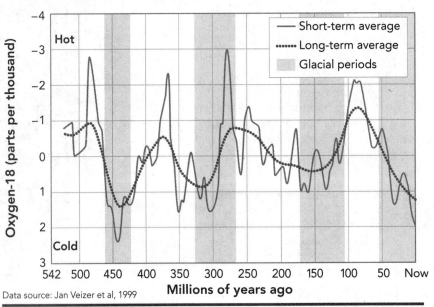

Phanerozoic Climate Change

Data source: Jan Veizer et al, 1999

(32) **SEP Analyze and Interpret Data** Calculate the mean time between the starts of cold glacial periods over the past 500 million years. ✎

Changing Composition of Earth's Atmosphere Earth's surface was blistering hot in its early years. It was almost completely molten, and greenhouse gases such as methane, water vapor, and carbon dioxide dominated the atmosphere. Life and the ocean gradually removed most of Earth's atmospheric CO_2.

Composition of Earth's Atmosphere

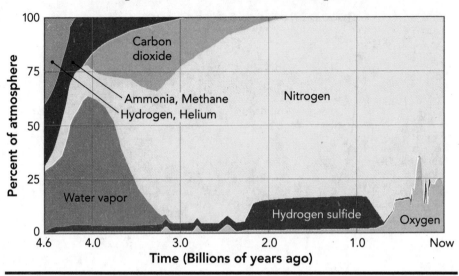

Life and Carbon Dioxide

Life has had a dramatic effect on all of Earth's surface systems, especially the atmosphere. If not for plant life and the ocean, the atmosphere would be mostly carbon dioxide. The ocean began removing carbon dioxide from the atmosphere more than 4 billion years ago. The later expansion of photosynthetic plant life brought atmospheric CO_2 levels nearly to zero (0.04%), keeping Earth's surface from becoming too hot and uninhabitable. The atmospheric carbon removed by life was stored away in the ground as rocks such as limestone and fossil fuels such as coal, oil, and natural gas.

33 **SEP Construct Explanations** Explain why it would make sense that the amount of water vapor in Earth's atmosphere would decrease as Earth's surface cooled. Where did that water go? ✐

....

....

....

....

....

Atmospheric Carbon Dioxide and the Diversity of Life The levels of atmospheric CO_2 have fluctuated over Earth's history, as have the number of genera, which are groups of similar species. Scientists do not have a good way to measure the volumes of past biomass, but the diversity of life can be used as a rough indicator of the degree to which life had expanded.

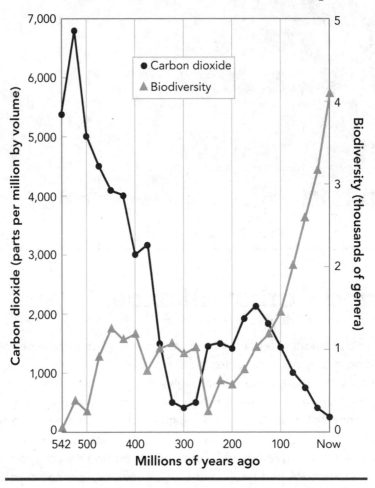

Carbon Dioxide and Biodiversity

CO_2 and Biodiversity Over the past 542 million years, the amount of carbon dioxide in the atmosphere has decreased while the diversity (and number) of living things has increased.

(34) SEP Analyze and Interpret Data Observe the correlation between the patterns of the two curves. Land plants evolved about 470 million years ago and expanded across the continents, developing into forests. Explain the carbon dioxide curve during this time. ✏️

....

....

....

Volcanic Activity and CO$_2$

While not occurring now, there have been times in Earth's history, usually associated with the initial arrival of mantle plumes of hot rock at the surface, when vast amounts of lava have erupted for millions of years. This volcanic activity has triggered extended warm periods.

◼️ **Extended periods of volcanic activity add large amounts of CO$_2$ to the atmosphere.**

> **Areas of Large Flood Basalts** Basalt rock forms from cooling lava. Due to mid-ocean ridge volcanism, the ocean seafloor is mostly basalt. However, there are times when large volcanoes have erupted for millions of years, sometimes in the middle of plates. These regions are called **flood basalts.**

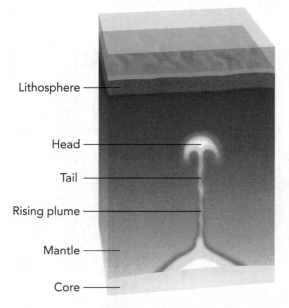

Lithosphere

Head

Tail

Rising plume

Mantle

Core

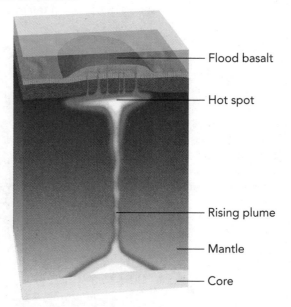

Flood basalt

Hot spot

Rising plume

Mantle

Core

Step 1 Heat conducted into the mantle from Earth's core can cause a plume of hot mantle rock to rise a few centimeters per year toward the surface.

Step 2 When the mantle plume nears the surface, it spreads out along the underside of the lithosphere. Heat from the plume melts part of the lithosphere above it, causing eruptions of magma that then cool to form flood basalts.

(35) **SEP Construct Explanations** The "Deccan Traps," large flood basalts covering much of western India, formed around 66 million years ago. What effects did their formation likely have on Earth's atmosphere? Explain. ✎

....

....

Erosion and Carbon Dioxide

The chemical weathering of rocks removes CO_2 from the atmosphere, reducing the greenhouse effect. Carbon dioxide in the atmosphere reacts with water vapor to form carbonic acid (H_2CO_3), which makes rain water slightly acidic and accelerates the weathering of minerals. The carbon, often in the form of bicarbonate ions (HCO_3^-), enters the ocean. It becomes part of the shells of marine organisms, and when they die, is stored away under the seafloor as sedimentary limestone. Periods of increased erosion, such as when large mountain ranges are uplifted, can contribute to global cooling through the removal of CO_2 from Earth's surface systems.

Erosion of the Himalayan Plateau The high erosion rates of the Himalayan Plateau over the past 50 million years have removed significant amounts of CO_2 from the atmosphere.

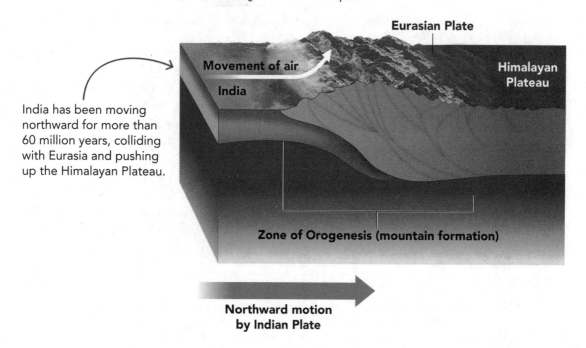

India has been moving northward for more than 60 million years, colliding with Eurasia and pushing up the Himalayan Plateau.

36 **CCC Cause and Effect** If the velocities of tectonic plates were to significantly decrease, would it have a cooling or warming effect on Earth's climate? Explain. ✏

....

....

....

....

Climates During Pangaea (350–250 Million Years Ago) India and Australia show evidence of large glaciers 300 million years ago because at that time they were adjacent to Antarctica, near the South Pole. Patterns of past regional climates on continents only make sense when the locations of the continents in the past are considered.

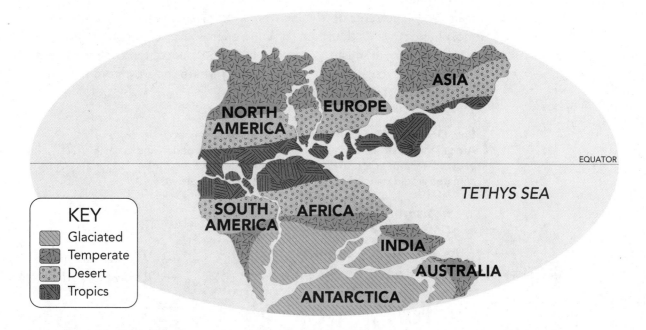

KEY
- Glaciated
- Temperate
- Desert
- Tropics

NORTH AMERICA, EUROPE, ASIA, SOUTH AMERICA, AFRICA, INDIA, AUSTRALIA, ANTARCTICA, EQUATOR, TETHYS SEA

Continent Distributions and Ocean Currents

Continental Distribution Due to plate tectonics, the sizes and locations of continents have continually changed over the past 4 billion years. Regional climates are affected by the locations of the continents in relation to atmospheric circulation cells and air currents. Fragmented continents experience steadier climates due to the moderating effect of the surrounding ocean water. Large supercontinents tend to have monsoon climates, with alternating wet and dry seasons.

The amount of continent surface that is above sealevel is also an important climate factor. Though continents occupy 39% of Earth's surface, about 8% of this surface is now underwater in the form of continental shelves. Due to differences in albedo of land and water, a reinforcing feedback occurs during ice ages when glaciers accumulate on land: sea level drops, shorelines recede, and less ocean surface results in less sunlight absorbed by the low-albedo ocean.

37) **CCC Cause and Effect** The United States has the largest deposits of coal in the world. Coal forms from fossilized swamp vegetation. Use the map to explain why most of these coal deposits likely formed between 350 and 250 million years ago.

....

....

....

Ocean Circulation Patterns Ocean currents are a major climate factor because ocean water stores an enormous amount of energy and ocean currents move this energy around the planet in the form of heat. Not only does ocean water cover most of Earth, but it absorbs 94% of the sunlight that hits it. Therefore, most of the sun's energy ends up in the ocean. Ocean currents determine where this energy ends up, warming atmospheric currents that then carry the energy over continents. During the course of Earth's history, changes in the outlines of the continents have altered ocean circulation patterns, affecting where the heat from sunlight ultimately ended up.

> **Past Ocean Surface Currents** Only 50 million years ago, South America, Africa, and Australia were separated from North America and Eurasia. This allowed a warm equatorial current to travel around the globe. Regional climates would have been very different than they are now.

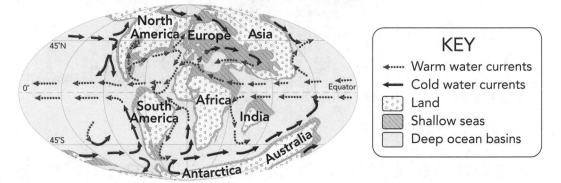

KEY
◀┄┄┄ Warm water currents
◀─── Cold water currents
Land
Shallow seas
Deep ocean basins

Revisit

INVESTIGATIVE PHENOMENON

GO ONLINE to Elaborate on and Evaluate your knowledge of long-term climate factors by completing the peer review and writing activities.

In the CER worksheet, you drafted a scientific argument about the possible causes of droughts. With a partner, reevaluate the evidence cited in your arguments.

38 **SEP Engage in Argument** How does the vicinity of the Pacific Ocean affect California's climate? Explain.

....

....

....

....

....

Short-Term Climate Factors

 GO ONLINE to Explore and Explain the short-term and intermediate-term factors that affect Earth's climate.

Cycles within Cycles

Climate Cycles Earth's climate at any given time is a function of long-, intermediate-, and short-term factors. As a result, there are climate cycles within cycles within cycles. At the moment, Earth has been cooling over the long term for the past 60 million years, cooling over the intermediate term since the peak of the present interglacial period (7500 years ago), and warming over the short term from human contributions. Importantly, scientists are beginning to understand how all of these different factors combine to affect global climates.

Solar Fluctuations A graph of annual average global temperatures shows the contributions from different factors. Part of the wobble results from an 11-year cycle of fluctuating solar output.

The overall upward trend is a result of the increase in greenhouse gases such as carbon dioxide from the human combustion of coal, oil, and natural gas.

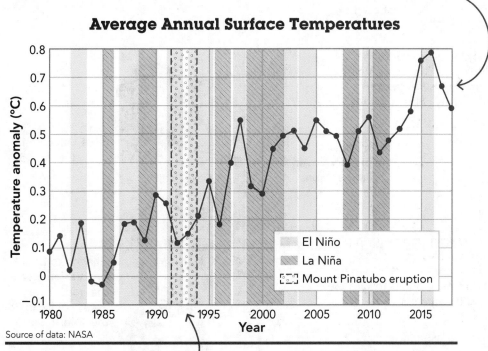

Average Annual Surface Temperatures

Source of data: NASA

The eruption of Pinatubo caused global cooling, even though this occurred during an El Niño period, when global climates would otherwise have been warmer than usual.

El Niño / La Niña The shaded bars show times of El Niño and La Niña currents in the Pacific Ocean. Heat is borrowed from the Pacific Ocean during El Niño episodes, so mean surface temperatures increase.

Milankovitch Cycles

How do Earth's orbital cycles affect its **long-term climate variations?**

Orbital Parameters Earth's long-term climate variations are dominated by forces outside of our planet: the gravitational tugs of other planets, primarily Jupiter and Saturn. The variations in **three orbital parameters, called the Milankovitch cycles,** control the timing of ice ages and other intermediate-term climate changes.

Eccentricity The longest of the Milankovitch cycles is the change to the shape of Earth's orbit around the sun that occurs on a scale of **100,000 to 413,000 years.**

Changes to **eccentricity** alter the amount of sunlight reaching Earth's surface.

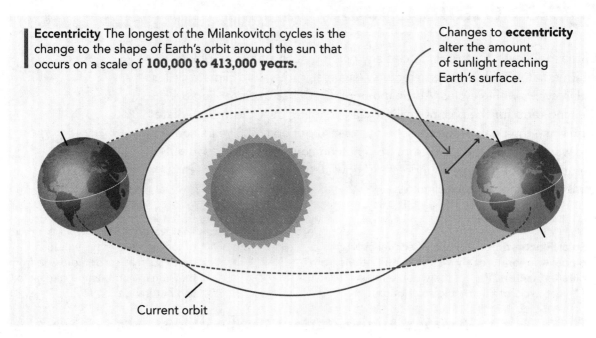

Current orbit

Tilt Gradual changes occur to the tilt, or obliquity, of Earth's rotation axis about every **41,000 years.** The moon's gravity helps stabilize Earth's tilt.

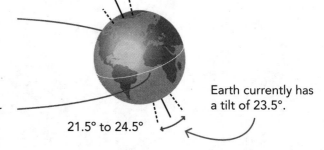

Earth's tilt is the primary driver of yearly seasons.

21.5° to 24.5°

Earth currently has a tilt of 23.5°.

Precession Like a wobbly toy top, Earth also wobbles on its axis every **19,000 to 24,000 years**, changing which hemisphere points toward the sun during the summer and winter.

Polaris

Change to Earth's **precession** means the north pole won't always point to Polaris, the "North Star."

Precession can be modeled by a spinning top.

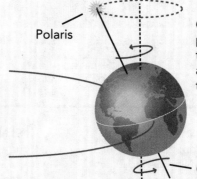

Current pole

Solar Variations The variation in Earth's eccentricity is the only one of the three Milankovitch cycles that actually changes the total amount of sunlight Earth receives in a year. However, the three cycles work together in important ways. A planet moves faster in its orbit when it swings by closer to the sun, and more slowly when it is farthest from the sun. Continents are more reflective than ocean water, and most continents are in the Northern Hemisphere. Therefore, whether the Northern or Southern Hemisphere points toward the sun when Earth swings closest to the sun affects how much total sunlight Earth absorbs in a year. The tilt of Earth's axis as it passes close to the sun also impacts how much sunlight is reflected or absorbed.

Orbital Cycles and Global Climate The graph shows the calculated Milankovitch cycles over the past million years, as well as how they would sum up ("Solar Forcing") at a location 65°N. The bottom curve shows Earth's actual global temperature record, based on the ice core record.

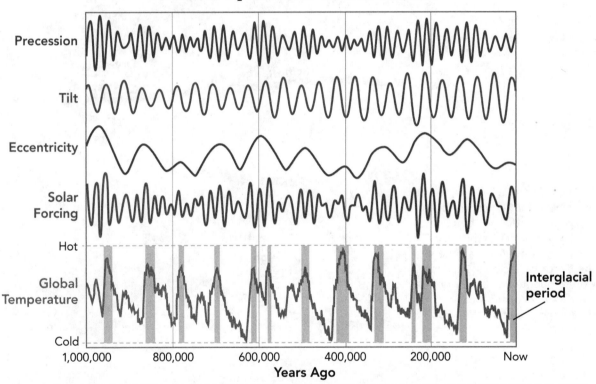

Orbital Cycles and Global Climate

39) **SEP Develop and Use Models** Study the curve for stages of glaciation and then study the curve showing eccentricity. Describe how well the two curves correspond to one another. Explain what this suggests about the possible cause of the recent cycle of ice ages. 🖉

....

....

....

Ocean/Atmosphere Circulation Changes

Ocean currents are constantly shifting in many different ways. Because of the ocean's important role in moving heat around the planet, these shifting ocean currents are responsible for much of the regional climate variations that occur over the time scale of decades. Sometimes, these variations repeat with enough regularity that they are given names. The most important of these is the

El Niño Southern Oscillation (ENSO). During average times, there is a steady westward current along the equatorial regions of the Pacific Ocean that brings warm water to the western Pacific. However, this current is altered during El Niño and La Niña phases. The results are changes in global atmospheric currents and the distribution of heat around the planet.

El Niño During an El Niño, warm waters in the western Pacific start flowing towards the east. The polar atmospheric jet stream carries warm and dry air to central North America. The Pacific jet stream is strong and brings cooler air and lots of rain to southern North America.

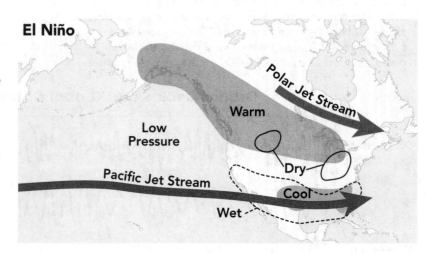

La Niña During a La Niña, the warm westward equatorial ocean current gets stronger, bringing more warm water to the west Pacific. A high-pressure zone in the North Pacific brings cold air with frequent rains to central North America, and warmer drier air to the south.

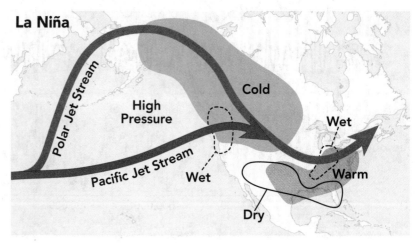

(40) **SEP Analyze and Interpret Data** Suppose that you are a farmer living in Texas. Would you prefer an El Niño or La Niña phase of Pacific Ocean oscillation? Use the maps to construct an explanation to support your response. ✏️

....

....

Variations in Solar Output

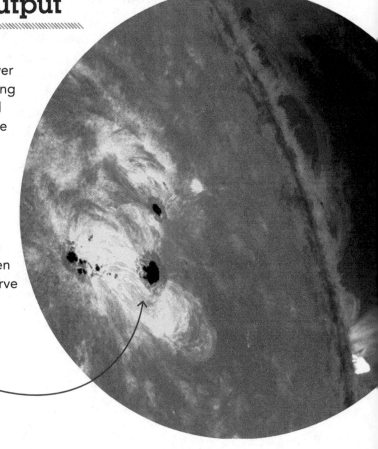

Shorter-Term Fluctuations The amount of light Earth receives from the sun fluctuates over the time scale of decades to centuries, affecting global temperatures. The sun's magnetic field flips polarity approximately every 11 years (the full cycle lasts about 22 years), and the total amount of radiation Earth receives varies by about 0.25 W/m^2 over this cycle.

The number of sunspots also varies over an 11-year cycle, correlated with the irradiance. This is useful because we have records of the number of sunspots going back to 1610, when Galileo first started using telescopes to observe the sun. This extends our record of the solar cycle back 400 years.

Sunspots Sunspots are not physical objects, but slightly cooler regions of the sun's photosphere. The arcing solar prominences leave and return to the sun at the locations of the sunspots. When the sun's surface is hotter and energetic, there are more prominences and sunspots.

Solar Irradiance

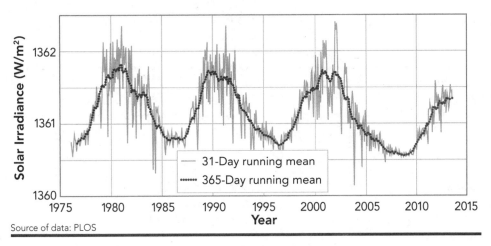

Source of data: PLOS

Solar Irradiance Due to the reversals of the sun's magnetic field, the amount of sunlight reaching Earth's orbit fluctuates by about 1 W/m^2, approximately between 1360.7 and 1361.7 W/m^2. However, because this sunlight gets distributed across the sphere of Earth's surface, averaging about 340 W/m^2 at any point on Earth's surface, the climate forcing from these sunlight fluctuations is about 0.25 W/m^2.

Longer-Term Fluctuations The amount of sunlight Earth receives also fluctuates over centuries. A useful proxy for this is the record of carbon-14 (^{14}C) production in the atmosphere. Carbon-14 decays over time, but it is replenished when cosmic rays from distant supernovae interact with nitrogen-14 (^{14}N) in the air. When the sun is more active, its stronger solar wind interferes with the cosmic rays, slowing ^{14}C production. The ^{14}C record for the past thousand years shows several pronounced dips that correspond to four distinct episodes of cold temperatures during the Little Ice Age, which extended from about 1300 to 1850. These periods of low solar activity—the Wolf, Spörer, Maunder, and Dalton minima—were times of extreme cold, frequent crop failures, famines, and human conflict. The impacts of the Little Ice Age on human cultures were large, even though the global decrease in temperature was only about 0.5°C.

| **Solar Activity from ^{14}C Production** The record of changes in ^{14}C production serves as a proxy for solar activity. The production of ^{14}C decreases (negative values) when solar activity increases.

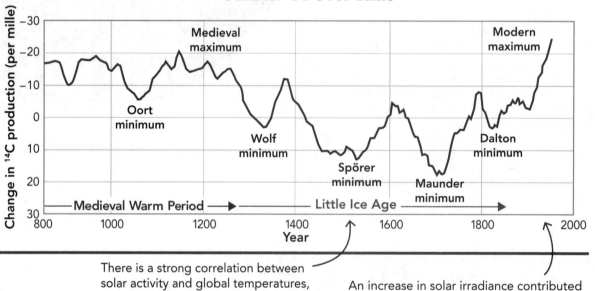

Carbon–14 Over Time

There is a strong correlation between solar activity and global temperatures, especially during the Little Ice Age.

An increase in solar irradiance contributed to rising global temperatures in the first half of the 20th century. However, sunlight has been weakening for the past 60 years.

(41) **SEP Use Mathematics** Use the equations for the area of a circle ($A = \pi r^2$) and a sphere ($SA = 4\pi r^2$) to explain why the insolation, or exposure to the sun's rays, is 1361.2 ± 0.5 at Earth's orbit but is about 340.3 ± 0.125 for any point on Earth's surface. 🖊

....

....

....

....

Volcanic Eruptions

Cooling Effects Volcanic eruptions can increase global warming through the release of CO_2, but they have more significant short-term cooling effects. Erupted sulfur dioxide (SO_2) reacts with water vapor in the atmosphere to form tiny droplets (aerosols) of liquid sulfuric acid (H_2SO_4). These aerosols and volcanic ash block out sunlight and cause a cooling period that can last for years or much longer for large eruptions. Several historical periods of cold temperatures, agricultural failure, and famines correlate with large volcanic eruptions.

Average Surface Temperature Changes

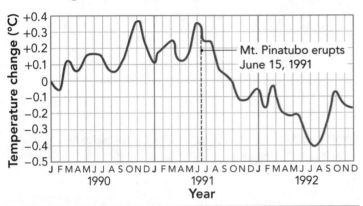

Mt. Pinatubo erupts
June 15, 1991

Pinatubo Temperature Impact Global temperatures dropped by more than a half-degree over the year following the eruption of Mt. Pinatubo.

Mt. Redoubt (Alaska) The eruption of Mt. Redoubt in 2009 ejected vast volumes of volcanic rock, ash, and millions of tons of sulfur dioxide (SO_2) into the atmosphere.

Erupted ash and sulfuric acid (H_2SO_4) aerosols block out a portion of sunlight (yellow arrows), reflecting it back into space, causing a net cooling effect.

Historic Impacts There have been many climate-altering volcanic eruptions over the past 1000 years. The effects of these eruptions have been quantified in records of ice cores and tree-ring growth, as well as documented in historical records. The release of millions of tons of sulfate aerosols affects climates by altering atmospheric patterns, causing extreme weather events such as snow in the summer, flooding, or droughts, as well as crop failures, famines, epidemics, and large-scale human migration.

Large Eruptions Most of the volcanic eruptions that altered global climates have occurred within the Ring of Fire, the belt of subduction zones that borders much of the Pacific Ocean.

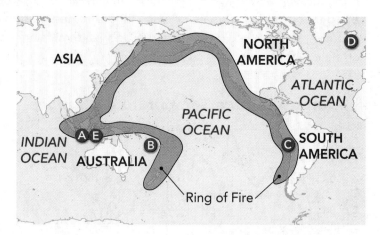

Large Volcanic Eruptions			
Year	Volcano, Location	H_2SO_4*	Impact
A 1257	Rinjani/ Samalas, Lombok (Indonesia)	~158	global cold temperatures, crop failures, and famines; helped trigger the start of the Little Ice Age
B 1452	Kuwae, Vanuatu	~250–400	tree growth stunted globally; severe famines in China; Yellow River frozen for 20 km out to sea; contributed to the 2nd phase of the Little Ice Age
C 1600	Huaynaputina, Peru	55	severe cold and famines in Northern Hemisphere, particularly Russia; agricultural collapses in South America and Europe
D 1783	Laki, Iceland	120	global freezing; droughts and famines in Africa and Southern Asia; severe weather and crop failures in Europe; contributed to the French Revolution
E 1815	Tambora Sumbawa (Indonesia)	90–120	extreme cold and flooding in Europe; extreme cold and famines in Eastern North America, driving the settling of western US territories; extreme flooding in south Asia, triggering a global cholera pandemic

*Volume of sulfate aerosols (million tonnes)

42 **SEP Construct Explanations** Examine the map of the Ring of Fire. Construct an explanation for why most large-scale volcanic eruptions occur in and around the area highlighted on the map. ✏️

....

....

....

Climate and Humans

Prehistoric Impacts Climate has impacted human history in many more ways than just volcanic eruptions. When climates were favorable, humans flourished and populations expanded. When climates shifted and became unfavorable, crops failed, populations diminished, civilizations collapsed, and conflicts between cultures increased.

▪ Trends in climate change have historically determined where agriculture could and could not be practiced, shaping the course of human civilizations.

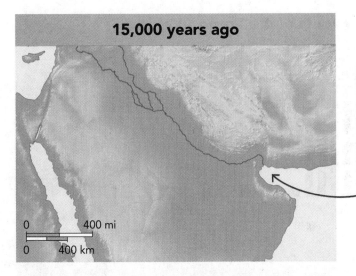

15,000 years ago

0   400 mi
0   400 km

Persian Gulf, 15,000 Years Ago Sea-level rise and changes in coastlines are significant impacts of climate change on humans. Melting glaciers at the end of the last ice age caused sea levels to rise almost 130 meters (400 feet). About 15,000 years ago, there was no Persian Gulf.

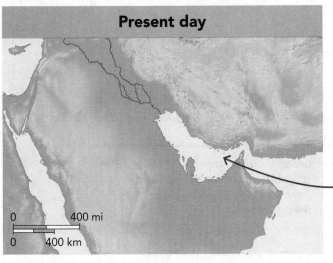

Present day

0   400 mi
0   400 km

Persian Gulf, Today As the sea-level rose, the fertile deltas of the Tigris and Euphrates Rivers were flooded, and shorelines rapidly advanced inland. Early settlements had to be abandoned and are now under the Persian Gulf. Many early cultures share stories of expulsion from their homelands, as a result of rising sea levels.

(43) SEP Use Mathematics and Computational Thinking Examine the two maps. The current shape of the Persian Gulf has changed little in the past 6000 years. Calculate how fast the Persian Gulf coastline moved landward between 15,000 and 6,000 years ago. ✏️

Historic Climate Events A good example of the impact of past climate changes on human history can be seen in the rise and fall of the Roman and Byzantine empires. An important natural cycle for people in the Mediterranean region was the annual flooding of the Nile river, which peaked around October of each year. The monsoon flooding carried water and rich sediments onto the lands, which allowed for crops to be grown. During about 50 BCE to 250 CE, frequent flooding of the Nile allowed for plentiful harvests that helped the Roman empire grow to a large size. After that time, regional climates changed. The annual Nile floods got smaller and harvests decreased. At the same time, periods of extreme severe weather and resulting famines increased. The Roman and Byzantine empires weakened under the increasing famines, and were eventually overrun by Eurasian tribes such as the Huns, Goths, Visigoths, and Vandals.

Extreme Climate Events of the Roman Empire

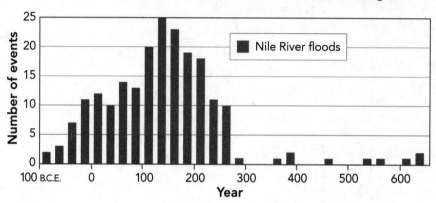

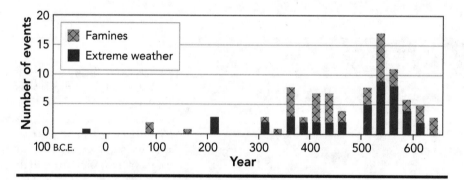

Climatic Changes Historical evidence shows a strong inverse correlation between crop-supporting Nile River floods (top) and periods of both famines and extreme weather, which includes extreme heat, cold, drought, or precipitation (bottom).

(44) **SEP Analyze and Interpret Data** In the years 536 and 540 there were very large volcanic eruptions (in Iceland and Central America). What evidence do you see of this in the graph? ✏️

....

....

....

Humans and Present-day Climate For 4.6 billion years, many natural factors have changed climate in different ways. Some changes have been gradual; others, immediate and catastrophic. Currently, however, humans are driving climate change faster than any of these natural causes. The most significant impacts are due to rising levels of atmospheric greenhouse gases from the burning of fossil fuels and agricultural land practices.

Climate Forcing Factors Human impacts to the climate system can be quantified in terms of how they affect Earth's surface energy budget, which starts with 340 W/m² of incoming sunlight. The graph shows changes between the years 1750 (pre-industrial) and 2011. Different human activities cause either warming or cooling, but the net effect is now over 2 W/m² of warming, which is driving up Earth's temperature. The contribution from changes in sunlight (solar irradiance) is shown for comparison.

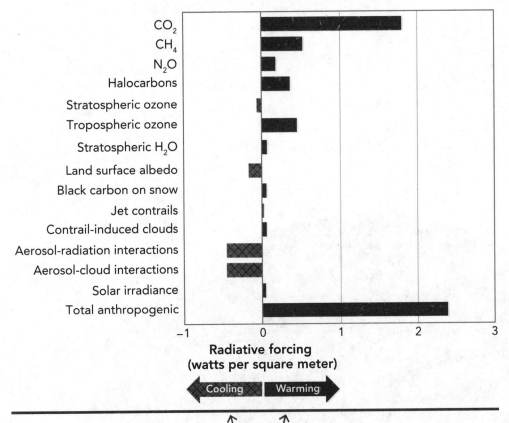

Near-Term Climate Forcing Factors

Radiative forcing
(watts per square meter)

Cooling Warming

Cooling factors include deforestation and aerosols in air pollution. Both increase Earth's albedo, which reflects more sunlight back into space.

The greatest warming factors are the release of greenhouse gases (carbon dioxide, methane, nitrous oxides, and halocarbons), but also tropospheric ozone, soot on snow, and airplane contrails.

INVESTIGATIVE PHENOMENON

GO ONLINE to Elaborate on and Evaluate your knowledge of short-term climate factors by completing the peer review and data analysis activities.

In the CER worksheet, you drafted a scientific argument to explain what is causing droughts in California. With a partner, reevaluate the evidence cited in your arguments.

(45) **SEP Engage in Argument** Based on what you've learned in this investigation, revisit and answer the question "What is causing drought in California?" Explain.

....

....

....

....

....

GO ONLINE to Evaluate what you learned about the factors and feedbacks that affect Earth's climate by using the available assessment resources.

In the Performance-Based Assessment, you modeled the feedbacks among different Earth systems by growing plants in a closed container. Wrap up your analysis by answering the following question.

46 **SEP Use Models** Suppose there is a small variation in the amount of energy flowing into Earth's surface system. Under what conditions is it possible for that small variation to cause significant changes in the system? ✏

....

....

....

....

....

47 **Revisit the Anchoring Phenomenon** How does what you learned in this investigation help you understand why we are seeing more extreme weather? ✏

....

....

....

....

....

INVESTIGATIVE PHENOMENON

GO ONLINE to engage with real-world phenomena by watching a video and to complete a CER interactive worksheet.

What is causing an increase in floods?

Global Climate Change

Local weather is strongly influenced by global climate factors. Changes to the global climate can result in changes to local weather, increasing the chances of extreme weather events, such as droughts and floods. Once you have viewed the Investigative Phenomenon video and used the Claim-Evidence-Reasoning worksheet to craft an explanation, answer the following questions about things that might cause an increase in floods.

(1) **CCC Energy and Matter** Where does the water that causes a flood come from? Why is the flooded area not inundated by water all the time? 🖊

....

....

....

....

....

(2) **CCC Patterns** What type of information would you look for in meteorological records to identify patterns in the locations, frequency, or intensity of flooding around the world? How long a period of time would you need records for in order to identify global patterns in flooding? 🖊

....

....

....

....

....

The Chemistry of Earth's Atmosphere

 GO ONLINE to Explore and Explain the chemistry of Earth's atmosphere and how it affects climate.

The Greenhouse Effect

Climate change is one of the most interesting topics of geoscience because it combines the sun's fluctuations, planetary orbits, atmospheric chemistry, radiation physics, ocean circulation changes, and biomass and land feedbacks. It is also a highly relevant topic because of its impacts on human society—past, present, and future. Currently, the biggest changes to climate involve increasing greenhouse gas concentrations, so to understand climate change, we first need to understand the greenhouse effect.

Earth's Energy Budget The greenhouse effect is part of Earth's surface energy budget, which begins with incoming radiation from the sun, mostly as visible light.

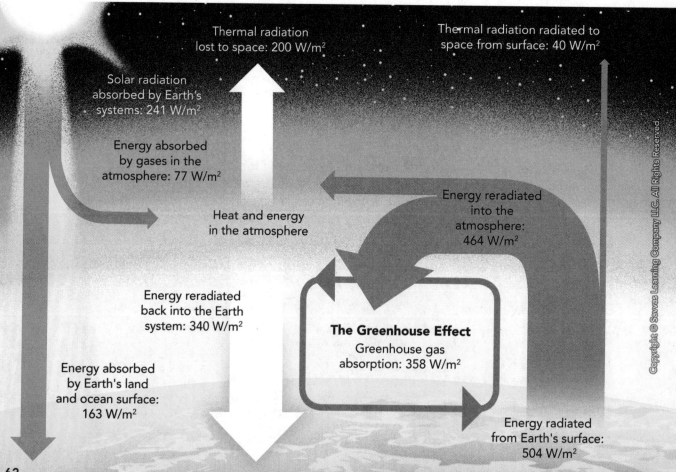

Thermal radiation lost to space: 200 W/m²

Thermal radiation radiated to space from surface: 40 W/m²

Solar radiation absorbed by Earth's systems: 241 W/m²

Energy absorbed by gases in the atmosphere: 77 W/m²

Heat and energy in the atmosphere

Energy reradiated into the atmosphere: 464 W/m²

Energy reradiated back into the Earth system: 340 W/m²

The Greenhouse Effect
Greenhouse gas absorption: 358 W/m²

Energy absorbed by Earth's land and ocean surface: 163 W/m²

Energy radiated from Earth's surface: 504 W/m²

Greenhouse Gases

All gases absorb electromagnetic radiation, but each gas absorbs radiation only of specific wavelengths. **Greenhouse gases** are particularly effective at absorbing wavelengths that correspond to infrared radiation, the kind of energy that Earth's surface emits. Most of Earth's atmosphere is nitrogen and oxygen, which absorb very little infrared radiation.

Greenhouse gases exist only in small amounts, but they absorb enough heat to keep Earth's surface about 35°C warmer than it otherwise would be. The **global warming potential (GWP)** is a measure of the heat-trapping capacity of a greenhouse gas over a given period of time, compared to that of a similar amount of CO_2. Except for the chlorofluorocarbons, which have been banned because they destroy the protecting ozone layer, the amounts of all greenhouse gases are increasing due to human activities.

Effects of Greenhouse Gases Different gases warm the atmosphere to different degrees, and they remain in the atmosphere for different amounts of time, so they have very different long-term warming effects.

Human-Released Greenhouse Gases						
Gas	Carbon dioxide (CO_2)	Methane (CH_4)	Nitrous Oxide (N_2O)	CFC-11	CFC-12	HCFC-22
Atmospheric Lifetime (years)	multiple	~12	~114	45	100	12
GWP for 20 years	1	86	268	7,020	11,000	5,160
GWP for 100 years	1	34	298	5,350	10,900	1,810
Concentration in 2019	415 ppm	1,866 ppb	332 ppb	228 ppt	504 ppt	233 ppt
Annual % increase	0.5	0.3	0.3	−0.9	−0.4	4.3
Total Greenhouse forcing (W/m²)	1.82	0.48	0.17	0.26 (all CFCs)	N/A	0.05 (all HFCs)

(3) CCC Address Questions About the Natural World The GWP of N_2O is higher than that of methane and changes less when calculated for 20 and for 100 years. Why does the GWP of nitrous oxide change less, and why does methane have a large total greenhouse forcing contribution? 🖊

....

....

....

....

Oscillations of a Water Molecule

How do individual **atoms vibrate** within the H$_2$O structure?

Water Vibration Modes Molecules vibrate at frequencies that depend on their mass, their size, and the types of vibrations allowed by their structure. The different kinds of vibrations can all occur at the same time.

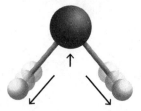 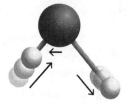 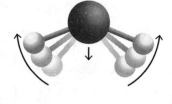

The distances between atoms of the water (H$_2$O) molecule can **stretch in and out** like a spring. This can occur **symmetrically**, with both hydrogen atoms going in and out together, or **asymmetrically**, with one going in when the other goes out.

The water molecule can oscillate by **bending the arms** of the hydrogen atoms out and in, with the angle between them alternately increasing and then decreasing.

The water molecule can **rotate back and forth** around an axis of rotation, a process called **libration**. This twisting can occur around the x-axis, y-axis, or z-axis, and each mode has a different frequency of oscillation.

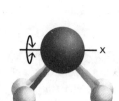 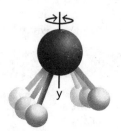 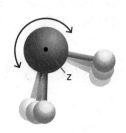

Radiation: Absorption and Reradiation

When gas molecules absorb electromagnetic radiation, the radiant energy transforms into kinetic energy of the molecule. The motions of the molecule become more energetic. Eventually, the molecule reemits that energy as radiation, but until it does, the molecule moves with more kinetic energy. These motions take three general forms: stretching, bending, and twisting. Because different molecules have different sizes and shapes, they stretch, bend, and twist at different frequencies. It is similar to the way that bells of different sizes and shapes make different sound pitches and tones. This is why different gases absorb and reradiate radiation at different wavelengths.

(4) **SEP Engage in Argument from Evidence** Water vapor has more distinct ways to absorb radiation than oxygen gas does. Make a claim, based on the diagrams, as to why this might be. ✏

....

....

....

Water and Ozone

Water and Water Vapor The most powerful greenhouse gas is water vapor (H_2O), which accounts for about 50% of the total absorption of infrared radiation in the atmosphere. Clouds (liquid and solid water) account for another 20%, and carbon dioxide, methane, and everything else absorb the remaining 30%. However, water vapor also absorbs some wavelengths of incoming sunlight, so it has both warming and cooling effects.

◗ Water vapor abundance in the atmosphere is impacted indirectly, not directly, by human activities.

Oxygen and Ozone Ozone (O_3) is a powerful absorber of the sun's ultraviolet radiation, which is dangerous to living tissues. This is why the ozone layer in the stratosphere is so important. International action was taken to stop the release of chlorofluorocarbons when it was discovered that those gases were destroying stratospheric ozone.

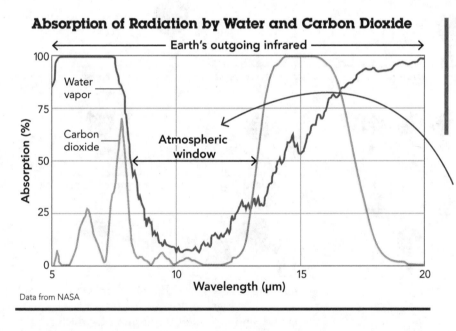

Absorption of Radiation by Water and Carbon Dioxide

Earth's outgoing infrared

Water vapor

Carbon dioxide

Atmospheric window

Absorption (%)

Wavelength (μm)

Data from NASA

Atmospheric Window Most of Earth's outgoing infrared radiation occurs in the range of about 5 to 20 micrometers (μm), which corresponds to a gap in the absorbance spectrum of both carbon dioxide and water vapor.

Although carbon dioxide has almost no absorbance in the 8–13 μm range, water vapor does. An increase in atmospheric water vapor would close this window (the water vapor curve will move upward, and greenhouse warming would increase).

⑤ **CCC Matter and Energy** Construct an explanation for why an increase in atmospheric carbon dioxide would lead to an increase in atmospheric water vapor. 🖊

....

....

....

....

Carbon Dioxide and Methane

In general, a molecule will have more absorption modes if it has more atoms and if the molecule is asymmetrical. For example, oxygen gas (O_2) has fewer absorption modes than water (H_2O) or carbon dioxide (CO_2) because there are fewer ways to arrange the smaller number of atoms. However, CO_2 has fewer absorption modes than H_2O because its molecule is linear and therefore is more symmetrical than water vapor's.

The atomic isotopes involved also affect the oscillation. For common carbon dioxide molecules, the carbon atoms can be ^{12}C or ^{13}C and the oxygen atoms can be ^{16}O, ^{17}O, or ^{18}O. Each of the possible combinations will have a different mass distribution and therefore absorb radiation at different wavelengths.

Oscillation and Radiation Absorption Symmetric molecules such as carbon dioxide and methane don't have a molecular dipole in the ground state. Asymmetrical vibrations, librations, and bending produce a structure with a molecular dipole.

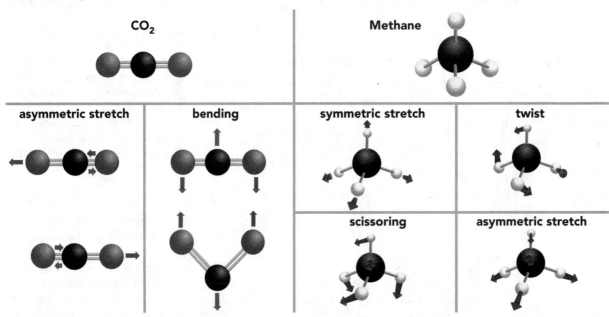

Carbon dioxide has two main modes of oscillation that will absorb infrared radiation: **bending** and **asymmetric stretching**.

Of methane's four oscillating modes, only the scissoring and asymmetric stretch modes have both the carbon and hydrogen atoms moving, which causes a change in the dipole moment of the bonds and absorbs infrared radiation.

6. **SEP Develop and Use Models** Both CO_2 and H_2O have one atom surrounded by two atoms of a different element. Explain why you wouldn't expect CO_2 and H_2O to have modes of oscillation at the same frequencies. ✏️

....

....

....

Incoming and Outgoing Radiation

Incoming Radiation Most (55%) of the incoming solar radiation passes through Earth's atmosphere and reaches the surface. Of the sun's energy that reaches Earth's solid surface, about 12% gets immediately reflected back out to space, and the rest is absorbed by Earth's surface.

Of the 45% that doesn't reach the surface, about half gets reflected back out to space by Earth's atmosphere and half is absorbed by Earth's atmosphere. The absorbed radiation is largely ultraviolet radiation absorbed by oxygen and ozone molecules and short-wavelength infrared radiation.

1 **CCC Matter and Energy** The dashed curve shows the average amount of radiation emitted by each square meter of Earth's surface. On its way up, some of that energy is absorbed or scattered by the atmosphere. The solid curve shows the amount that would be observed looking down from the "top of the atmosphere" (TOA). Explain why there are "dips" in that curve. ✏️

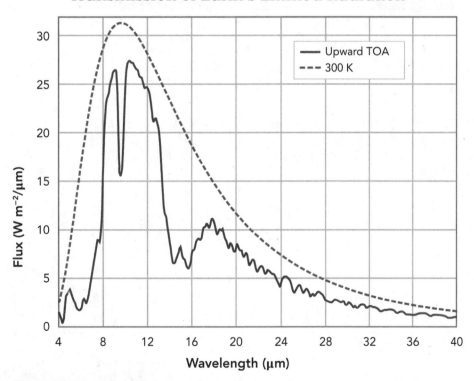

Transmission of Earth's Emitted Radiation

MODTRAN® is a registered trademark owned by the United States Government as represented by the Secretary of the Air Force. Chart provided courtesy of Spectral Sciences, Inc.

....

....

....

Outgoing Radiation Earth's surface warms as it absorbs incoming sunlight, but not indefinitely. It reradiates roughly the same amount of energy it receives, but in the long-wavelength infrared spectrum. The infrared radiation is absorbed by greenhouse gases at the wavelengths corresponding to their different modes of molecular oscillation.

Only about 10% of Earth's outgoing infrared radiation passes directly out into space, mostly through an atmospheric "window," such as the broad notch seen in the total absorption curve at wavelengths of about 8 to 12 μm. About half of the radiation absorbed and reemitted by greenhouse gases goes back to Earth's surface. This energy warms Earth's surface and is reradiated again, with most being absorbed once again by the greenhouse gases. If the amount of greenhouse gases increases, the amount of energy stuck in this loop increases.

Revisit

INVESTIGATIVE PHENOMENON

GO ONLINE to Elaborate and Evaluate your knowledge of greenhouse gases by completing the class discussion and data analysis activities.

In the CER worksheet assigned at the beginning of this investigation, you drafted a scientific argument about floods. With a partner, reevaluate the evidence cited in your arguments.

8 **SEP Engage in Argument** Water covers about 71% of Earth's surface, and it absorbs and releases energy more slowly than rock does. How might water at Earth's surface contribute to the greenhouse effect?

....

....

....

....

....

....

....

....

Evidence of Climate Change

 GO ONLINE to Explore and Explain past changes to Earth's climate.

In some cases, ice cores have been shaved into slices about 120 micrometers thick so that monthly temperature, pollen, and volcanic ash changes can be observed.

Ice Cores and Ice Ages

Glacier ice forms from the compaction of snow year after year, building up a record of climate that extends back millions of years. The isotopes in the ice provide clues about temperature—the heavy isotopes ^{18}O and ^{2}H (deuterium) are less abundant when temperatures are cold. Ice core analysis reveals a repeating pattern of long, cold "ice ages" separated by brief, warm periods called interglacials. This roughly 100,000-year-long cycle is largely a result of oscillations in the elliptical shape of Earth's orbit around the sun.

Paleoclimate Reconstructions Scientists use data from ice cores, including analysis of gases from bubbles trapped in the ice and other inclusions, to reconstruct past temperature changes.

The amount of carbon dioxide stored in the ocean changes as a function of temperature. As temperatures have changed, atmospheric CO_2 levels have also changed.

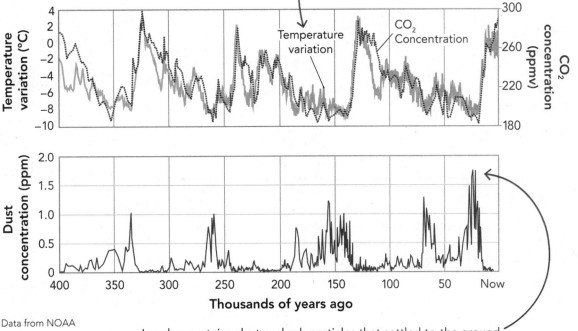

Data from NOAA

Ice also contains dust and ash particles that settled to the ground as the ice formed. These particles can be used to reconstruct the extent of deserts and the timing of volcanic eruptions.

Sea Level Change and Civilization

At the peak of the last Ice Age, about 26,000 years ago, there was so much ice on land in the form of continental glaciers that the level of the ocean was almost 125 m (about 400 ft) lower than it is today. So much continental shelf area, now offshore, was exposed that the world had almost 25% more land. When the Ice Age ended about 15,000 years ago, temperatures rose, glaciers melted, and the sea level started rising.

▶ Permanent human civilizations began just 11,000 years ago, partly because global temperatures warmed and stabilized, allowing for the beginnings of agriculture.

Rapid Sea-Level Rise A sea level rise of 125 m can cause shorelines to advance inland hundreds or thousands of kilometers.

Global sea levels and shorelines have stayed remarkably stable over the past 6,000 years, allowing the establishment of large permanent coastal communities.

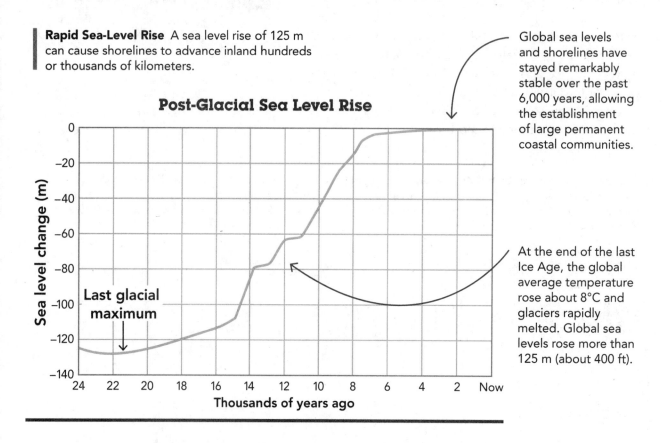

Post-Glacial Sea Level Rise

At the end of the last Ice Age, the global average temperature rose about 8°C and glaciers rapidly melted. Global sea levels rose more than 125 m (about 400 ft).

(9) **SEP Analyze and Interpret Data** Sea levels rose most rapidly between 15,000 and 8,000 years ago. Use the graph to calculate the rate of sea level rise during this time, both in meters per century and mm per year. ✏️

Melting Ice and Rising Sea Levels

Sea levels started to rise again about 200 years ago, when the burning of fossil fuels released carbon dioxide into the atmosphere during the Industrial Revolution. The rate of current sea level rise, more than 3 mm/yr, is equally due to the melting of alpine and tidewater glaciers, the melting of Antarctic and Greenland ice, and thermal expansion of ocean water as it warms. As water warms, its rate of expansion also increases. Because of the long circulation time of deep ocean currents, the warming today will cause elevated sea levels for thousands of years.

Melting Ice Together, Greenland and Antarctica are now losing more than a half-trillion tons of ice each year. If all glaciers melted, sea levels would rise approximately 68 m (around 220 ft).

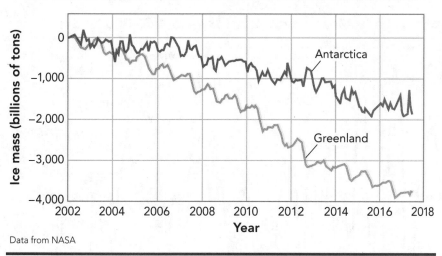

Ice Sheet Mass Loss in Greenland and Antarctica

Data from NASA

10) **SEP Analyze and Interpret Data** On the graph of sea level change, draw two separate straight lines through the curve, one for 1993–2011, and the other from 2011–2018. Use a star to identify the time frame during which the rate of sea-level change was higher. ✏

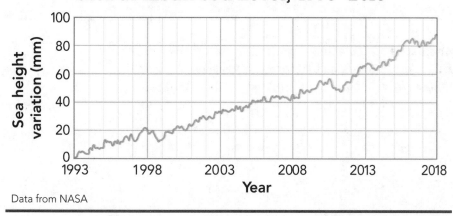

Global Mean Sea Level, 1993–2018

Data from NASA

Ice Cores and Human History

Ice cores have revealed climate variations not only over the past 800,000 years, but also within the last 10,000 years. Within this period, average regional temperatures have fluctuated by a few degrees. Some of the temperature swings for the past 4,000 years correlate with human mass migrations, human population changes, and the rise and fall of civilizations.

For example, ice cores contain a layer of ash from a large volcanic eruption in Iceland during the year 536. The ice also recorded a severe drop in temperatures that followed over the next decades. Widespread famines resulted around the world and allowed the first recorded global plague pandemic to spread, killing up to 100 million people.

11) **CCC Stability and Change** Fit a straight line through this curve of the temperatures in Greenland over the past 8,000 years. ✏️

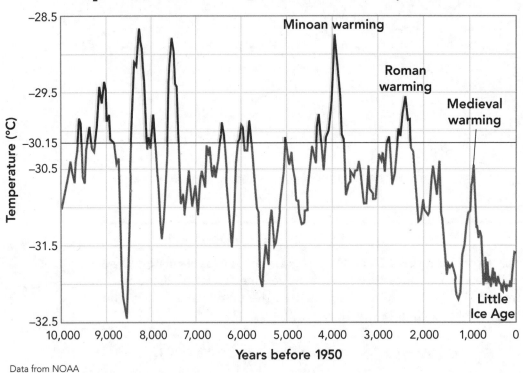

Temperature in Greenland Over the Last 10,000 Years

Data from NOAA

12) **SEP Use Mathematics** Calculate the general trend of the curve. (Note: This graph ends just before the year 1950. Global temperatures have increased since then.) ✏️

Varves, Corals, and Tree Rings

Varves Some lakes contain a record of annual sediment layers called **varves**, which are characterized by larger particles deposited by spring storms separated by finer particles that accumulate the rest of the year. Varves are very useful for studying regional climates over the past few thousand years. They also contain pollen, which shows the kinds and amounts of plants that grew nearby.

Fossil Corals Corals grow by making calcium carbonate layers from ions in seawater. These layers change in density as water temperature and availability of

nutrients change. The composition, thickness, and color of these annual layers provide a record of ocean temperature, ocean pH, and regional rainfall amounts.

Tree Rings The widths of annual tree rings vary depending on seasonal light and water availability. By comparing living trees with dead trees and with boards used for ancient ships and houses, scientists have established a continuous tree-ring record extending back more than 10,000 years in places.

(13) **SEP Analyze and Interpret Data** PDSI, or Palmer Drought Severity Index, is a measure of ground dryness and is positive for wet times and negative for dry times. A severe drought that occurred in the New York City region in the 1960s is pointed out on the graph. Circle other times of significant drought suggested by the data. 🖊

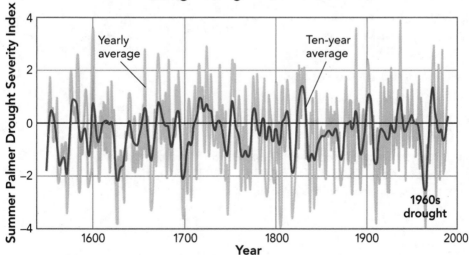

Tree-Ring Drought Reconstruction

Data from NIH (National Institute of Environmental Health Sciences)

Analyzing Graphs to Find Ancient Ocean Temperatures

Recent correlations between sea surface temperature (SST) and coral oxygen isotope anomalies can be used as a proxy for ancient temperatures. For the past 85 million years, Earth has been in a gradual cooling phase. The average $\delta^{18}O$ anomaly has increased by about 4.0 units. Use the correlation between the graphs to calculate the amount of SST cooling over this period. (Assume that the correlation is linear.)

ANALYZE List the knowns and unknown.

Knowns	Unknown
$\delta^{18}O$ and SST values for 1945–1995	change in average SST (ΔSST) over 85 million years = ?
change in average $\delta^{18}O$ anomaly over 85 million years = 4.0 units	

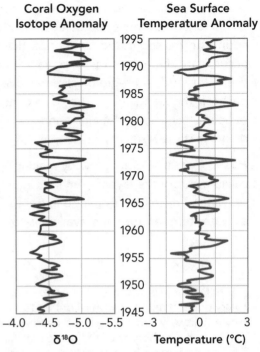

Coral Oxygen Isotope Anomaly — Sea Surface Temperature Anomaly

Data from: Urban, F.E. J. Cole, and J.T. Overpeck, 2000, Influence of mean climate change on climate variability from a 155-year tropical Pacific coral record. Nature 407, 989-993.

CALCULATE Solve for the unknown.

Use the data from the graphs to find the difference between the minimum and maximum values for $\delta^{18}O$ and SST between 1985 and 1990.

Total variation in $\delta^{18}O$ = $-4.5 - (-5.3) = 0.8 \, \delta^{18}O$ units

Total variation in SST = $-1.5°C - 2.0°C = -3.5°C$

Correlate the variations by dividing the total variation in SST by the total variation in $\delta^{18}O$.

$$\frac{-3.5°C}{0.8 \, \delta^{18}O \text{ units}} = -4.4°C/\delta^{18}O \text{ unit}$$

Multiply $\Delta\delta^{18}O$ by the calibration value to determine the average SST change.

$$\Delta\text{SST} = 4.0 \, \delta^{18}O \text{ units} \times \frac{-4.4°C}{\delta^{18}O \text{ unit}} = -18°C$$

EVALUATE Does the result make sense?

The result suggests SST were, on average, about 18°C warmer 85 million years ago.

(14) **SEP Analyze and Interpret Data** For coral $\delta^{18}O$ and for SST find the curves that best fit the overall trend in the data from 1945 to 1995. Take the ratio of the two amounts and compare it to the ratio you found above.

GO ONLINE for more practice problems.

Medieval Climate Anomaly and Little Ice Age

Climate changes have been connected to large changes in past human populations. One example is the global plague pandemic known as the Black Death that occurred during the 1300s, during which 70% of the human population of Western Europe died.

Black Death In the mid-1300s, the bubonic plague may have caused as many as 100 million human deaths, killing a large percentage of Western Europeans.

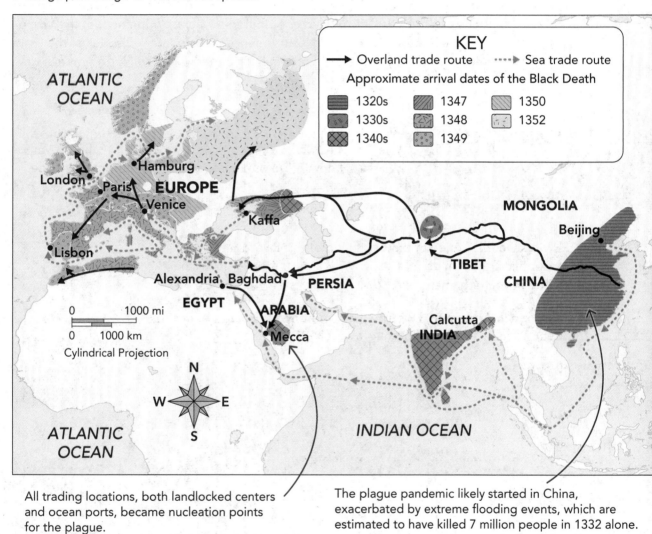

KEY

→ Overland trade route   ⋯▶ Sea trade route

Approximate arrival dates of the Black Death

1320s	1347	1350
1330s	1348	1352
1340s	1349	

All trading locations, both landlocked centers and ocean ports, became nucleation points for the plague.

The plague pandemic likely started in China, exacerbated by extreme flooding events, which are estimated to have killed 7 million people in 1332 alone.

(15) **SEP Analyzing and Interpreting Data** The plague began to spread within China around 1330; it reached England and Ireland in 1349. Using distances on the map, calculate the average rate of spread of the pandemic (in km/yr). 🖊

The Little Ice Age and Its Consequences The Black Death illustrates the link between historical events and climate changes. Following several centuries of relatively stable and warm climates, Mt. Rinjani in Indonesia erupted, ejecting over 250 million metric tons of sulfate aerosols into the atmosphere. This reduced sunlight for decades and caused cold rains, crop failures, and famines. This was the start of the **Little Ice Age,** which lasted about 500 years and had several periods of colder temperatures that correlate with periods of decreased solar activity and sunlight.

The Little Ice Age also affected the European exploration of North America. During the warm Medieval times, the North Atlantic was relatively free of ice, and Vikings settled in Iceland, Greenland, and Canada. But as the Little Ice Age progressed, increasing levels of North Atlantic sea ice made fishing and ocean trade difficult and contributed to the abandonment of the Viking colonies in Greenland and North America. During later episodes of the Little Ice Age, large numbers of European fur traders came to North America to capture beavers for fur hats and coats.

Revisit

INVESTIGATIVE PHENOMENON

GO ONLINE to Elaborate on and Evaluate your knowledge of climate change by completing the class discussion and data analysis activities.

In the CER worksheet assigned at the beginning of this investigation you drafted a scientific argument about floods. With a partner, reevaluate the evidence cited in your arguments.

16 **SEP Engage in Argument** Describe how melting ice could affect the frequency and intensity of flooding events.

....

....

....

....

....

....

Anthropogenic Carbon Emissions

 GO ONLINE to Explore and Explain anthropogenic carbon emissions and their effects on Earth's atmospheric chemistry and climate.

Carbon Dioxide and Temperature

Whether over hundreds of millions of years, hundreds of thousands of years, or just the past hundred years, global temperature and atmospheric carbon dioxide concentrations are highly correlated with each other. If some other factor changes the temperature, such as when Earth's orbital parameters drive the Ice Age cycle, carbon dioxide levels change in response.

When atmospheric carbon dioxide levels change, temperature responds in parallel. This is what has been happening since the start of the Industrial Revolution, first with the burning of coal and then with the burning of oil and natural gas. Global temperatures had generally been falling for the past 7,500 years, but are now rising quickly.

Global Average Temperature Globally averaged temperatures have increased steadily over the past 120 years. Temperatures fluctuate from year to year due to several factors, but the overall upward trend correlates with the concentration of carbon dioxide.

Atmospheric CO_2 levels fluctuated between 170 and 280 ppm for the past million years, but are now more than 415 ppm and rising. Temperatures are following suit.

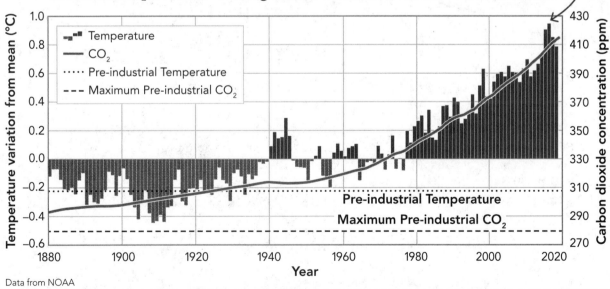

Global Temperature Change and Carbon Dioxide Concentration

Data from NOAA

Greenhouse Gas Release

Atmospheric concentrations of most major greenhouse gases—including carbon dioxide, nitrous oxide, and methane—are increasing due to human activities. However, the concentrations of most chlorofluorocarbons, or CFCs, are slowly declining. CFCs are refrigerants released by human industry that destroy ozone. A nearly global ban on them was enacted in 1989. However, these molecules have very long atmospheric lifetimes and will continue to damage the ozone layer for centuries.

Greenhouse Gas Concentrations Carbon dioxide concentrations show seasonal fluctuations due to summer/winter vegetation cycles, and nitrous oxide and methane exhibit annual cycles due to agricultural practices.

Atmospheric Carbon Dioxide (CO_2)

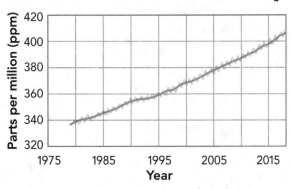

Atmospheric Methane (CH_4)

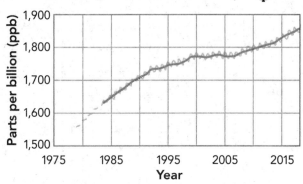

Atmospheric Nitrous Oxide (N_2O)

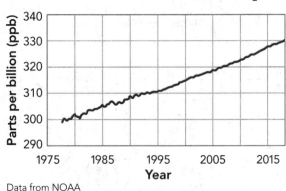

Other Important Gases

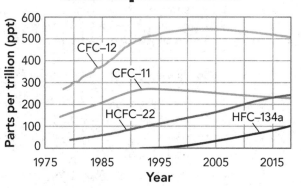

Data from NOAA

(17) **SEP Develop and Use Models** The horizontal axes are the same for these curves; the vertical axes are not. Calculate the percentage increase from 1980 to 2018 for the CO_2, N_2O, CH_4, and HCFC-22 curves. Which of these had the largest percentage increase during this time? ✏

Global Temperature Anomalies Over 100 Years These maps compare the surface temperatures in 1917 and 2017 to the average temperature over the time period of 1951–1980.

In the early 1900s most places on Earth were colder than the 1951–1980 average.

Land areas generally warm faster than the ocean, but Arctic regions have warmed at twice the rate of the rest of Earth's surface.

Most places on Earth are now warmer than the 1951–1980 average.

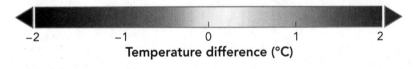

Temperature difference (°C)

Regional Temperature Changes

Earth's average global surface temperature is increasing, but temperatures everywhere aren't getting hotter. Some places are colder now, on average, than they were 100 years ago. Annual variations in weather are much greater than gradual climate shifts. In the central U.S., temperatures may change more than 30°C in a single day, which is much larger than the 1°C increase in average global temperature. However, it is significant that there are now more than twice as many record high temperatures, at any given place and time, than there are record low temperatures.

(18) **SEP Constructing Explanations** Some of the few geographic regions in the 2017 map that are colder than the 1951–1980 average are off the coasts of Greenland and Antarctica. Construct an explanation for this observation. ✏️

....

....

Human Population and Consumption

The impact of global warming is amplified by Earth's large human population, which exceeds 7.5 billion people and grows by another billion every 15 years. In addition, the standard of living is improving for more people. Every day, on average, another 300,000 people get access to electricity and clean water, which requires increased burning of fossil fuels. This releases more carbon dioxide into the atmosphere.

Trends in Population Growth and GDP Gross domestic product, or GDP, and population growth provide insight into rates of consumption of material and energy resources. Any plans for dealing with future climate change must take into account the growth rates of human population and per-capita production and consumption.

Populations have increased so fast that more than 7% of all humans who have ever lived are alive today.

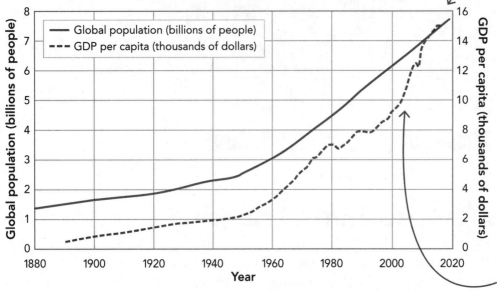

Global Population and Gross Domestic Product

— Global population (billions of people)
- - - GDP per capita (thousands of dollars)

Global GDP is a measure of the value of all goods and services produced by humans in the world. GDP has steadily increased as population increased.

Data from: Broadberry, S., Campbell, B. M., Klein, A., Overton, M., & Van Leeuwen, B. (2015). British economic growth, 1270–1870. Cambridge University Press and The United Nations.

⑲ **CCC Energy and Matter** The number of people living on Earth cannot increase indefinitely. Explain what you think the limiting factor will be, and how many people Earth will hold at its maximum. ✎

....

....

....

Carbon Isotopes and Fossil Fuels

In light of the correlations between human activities and the increases of greenhouse gases in the atmosphere, it may seem logical to conclude that human activities play a major role in recent global warming. However, it is important to demonstrate whether human-released CO_2 is primarily responsible for the atmospheric CO_2 rise, or if the CO_2 could be coming from some other reservoir, such as the ocean, soil, or volcanoes.

Of stable carbon isotopes, 98.9% is ^{12}C and 1.1% is ^{13}C. However, the $^{13}C/^{12}C$ ratio is even lower for plants. It is much easier for plants, on land and in the ocean, to use ^{12}C than ^{13}C to convert sunlight and carbon dioxide into food during photosynthesis. Therefore, biomass is very low in ^{13}C, and, as a result, so are fossil fuels, which form from ancient biomass. Thus, the relative concentrations of these two isotopes of carbon in atmospheric CO_2 can help scientists determine the source of the recent CO_2 emissions.

Carbon Isotopes and Carbon Source For the atmosphere, the $\delta^{13}C$ is naturally about −6.5. The $\delta^{13}C$ differs for different carbon sources. This value is around −4 for volcanic emissions, −7 for weathered rock, and −25 for biomass and fossil fuels.

The strong correlation between the increase in CO_2 and decrease in $\delta^{13}C$ is evidence that human-burned fossil fuels are driving the $\delta^{13}C$ value down.

The $\delta^{13}C$ value shows how much of the C in CO_2 is in the form of ^{13}C.

Atmospheric $\delta^{13}C$ is now −8.5 and not −25 because most atmospheric CO_2 is still from other sources, but the amount from fossil fuels is rapidly increasing.

Relative Concentration of ^{13}C in the Atmosphere

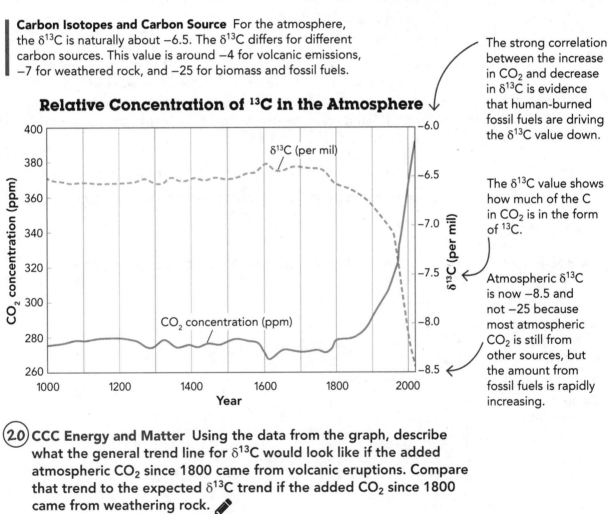

20. **CCC Energy and Matter** Using the data from the graph, describe what the general trend line for $\delta^{13}C$ would look like if the added atmospheric CO_2 since 1800 came from volcanic eruptions. Compare that trend to the expected $\delta^{13}C$ trend if the added CO_2 since 1800 came from weathering rock.

....

....

....

....

Sources of Anthropogenic Carbon

The term **anthropogenic** is used to describe anything caused or produced by humans. As of 2019, humans released about 10 billion tons of carbon into the atmosphere per year (10 Gigatons/yr). Most of this carbon comes from the burning of fossil fuels to get energy for electricity, transportation, industry, agriculture, and heat. Fossil fuels are concentrated and compacted remains of millions of years' worth of photosynthesis, so they are very energy-dense. In a sense, they contain the stored energy from millions of years of sunbeams.

Coal, Oil, and Natural Gas Humans have been burning coal and oil for more than 2,000 years, but mostly just what could be found at the surface, at relatively low levels. Coal mining increased rapidly in the eighteenth and nineteenth centuries. Coal burning was the major source of anthropogenic carbon well into the 20th century.

The use of petroleum, particularly as fuel for cars, trucks, boats, and planes, surged after WWII, and oil surpassed coal as the major source of human-released carbon until coal-fired power plants had a resurgence at the start of this century. Natural gas, mostly methane, is increasingly being used for electricity, transportation, and home heating.

◾ The main sources of human-released non-fossil carbon are agriculture, biomass burning, and changes in land use.

Fossil Sources of Human-Released Carbon Fossil sources of carbon account for most anthropogenic carbon release (for example, concrete is made from the fossilized carbon in limestone).

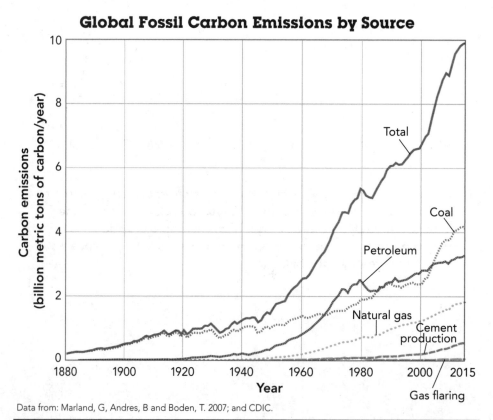

Global Fossil Carbon Emissions by Source

Data from: Marland, G, Andres, B and Boden, T. 2007; and CDIC.

Human Greenhouse Gas Emissions
How do **humans** produce **greenhouse gases?**

Greenhouse gases are generated by many different sources. The bar graph shows how different human activities contribute to the overall production of greenhouse gases. The pie charts show how these contributions vary depending on the particular greenhouse gas under consideration.

25.6%
Electrical energy production

15.9%
Industrial processes

13.2%
Transportation fuel

12.1%
Land use, biomass burning

11.6%
Agricultural production

10.5%
Fossil fuel retrieval

7.5%
Residential, commercial

3.6%
Waste disposal and treatment

Carbon dioxide

Most human activities release **carbon dioxide,** especially **electrical power generation,** industrial processes, and transportation.

Methane

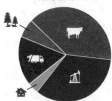

Most **methane** is produced by **agricultural production** (40.8%) and by **fossil fuel retrieval,** processing, and distribution.

Nitrous oxide

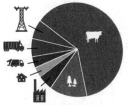

The largest source of **nitrous oxide** is **agricultural production,** which makes 62.5% of the nitrous oxide released by humans.

Greenhouse Gas Emissions by Sector Look around you right now. Everything you see that was human-made involved fossil fuels, including shipping and transportation that brought products to you and any electric lights you are using to see them. But it also takes energy to make energy— about 11% of all human-released greenhouse gases comes from mining, processing, and distributing fossil fuels. Different human practices involve the release of different gases. This makes the reduction of greenhouse gas emissions very challenging.

21) **SEP Use Mathematics and Computational Thinking** The amount of carbon humans release is 10 Gt/yr. If this were all in the form of carbon dioxide, how many tons of CO_2 would humans release each year? ✏️

GO ONLINE to Elaborate and Evaluate your knowledge of carbon emissions by completing the class discussion and data analysis activities.

In the CER worksheet assigned at the beginning of this investigation, you drafted a scientific argument about floods. With a partner, reevaluate the evidence cited in your arguments.

22 **SEP Engage in Argument** How could anthropogenic greenhouse gas emissions affect the frequency and intensity of flood events? ✏️

....

....

....

....

....

....

....

Climate Models

 GO ONLINE to Explore and Explain different models of weather and climate.

Physical Models of Weather and Climate

Weather and climate are different, but they both result from interactions among components of the Earth system: the atmosphere, hydrosphere, geosphere, and biosphere. These interactions can be modeled using computer programs. In computer models, the different component systems are joined together by a framework called a *coupler*. By running these programs multiple times using different input parameters, predictions can be made about future weather and climate conditions.

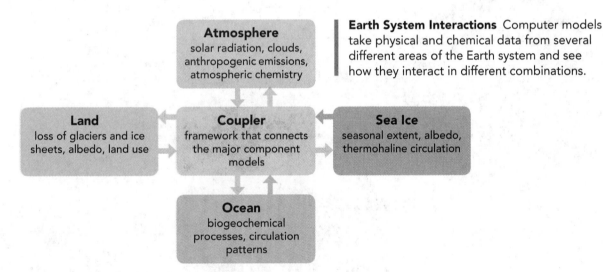

Earth System Interactions Computer models take physical and chemical data from several different areas of the Earth system and see how they interact in different combinations.

Modeling Weather and Climate Data collected by satellites are used to predict atmospheric conditions in both the short-term and long-term future.

Weather models determine what is likely to happen in the next hours or days.

Comparing Weather and Climate Models		
	Weather Model	**Climate Model**
Timescale	Hours to days	Decades to centuries
Time step	Seconds to 10s of seconds	~30 min
Grid size	~1 km	~100 km
Sensitivity	Very sensitive to complete initial conditions	Highly sensitive to boundary values
Interaction	Continuously nudged with new observations	Free-running

Climate models determine what is likely to happen in the next decades or centuries.

Earth System Models

A climate **Earth System Model (ESM)** is a computer model that uses a set of equations to calculate interactions between various parameters in specific geographic locations. The five basic parameters are pressure, temperature, mass, water vapor amount, and momentum. Data are largely collected by satellites.

The model divides Earth into individual 3D grid cells, and the equations are solved for every side of every cell at every time step. Using an ESM to make climate predictions involves starting with current parameters and adding input forcings—such as sunlight, volcanism, and human activities—to predict future conditions (outputs). Accurate input data about all of Earth's systems is needed in order to get reliable outputs.

Model Parameterization Earth's atmosphere, ocean, and land are broken up into small 3D grid cells. The horizontal grid is based on latitude and longitude. The vertical grid is based on altitude, depth, or pressure.

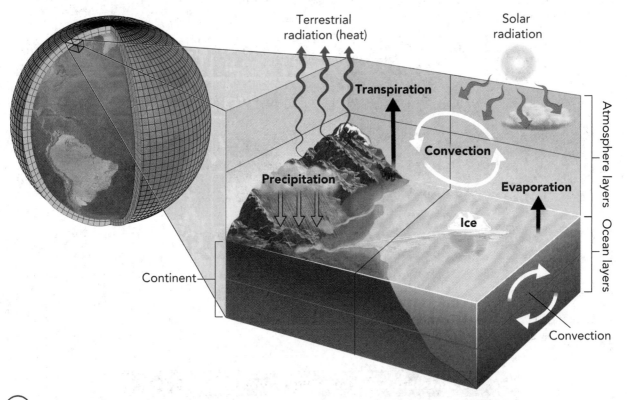

23 CCC Systems and System Models Explain why the creation of accurate weather and climate models was not possible until high-resolution weather and climate data were available from satellites. ✏️

....

....

....

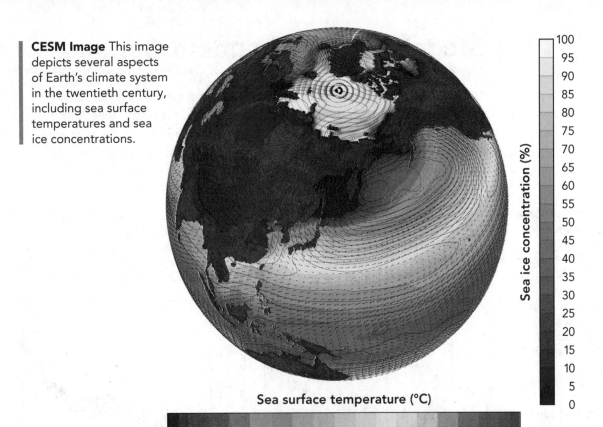

CESM Image This image depicts several aspects of Earth's climate system in the twentieth century, including sea surface temperatures and sea ice concentrations.

Sea ice concentration (%)

100
95
90
85
80
75
70
65
60
55
50
45
40
35
30
25
20
15
10
5
0

Sea surface temperature (°C)

-2 0 2 4 6 8 10 12 14 16 18 20 22 24 26 28 30 32

IPCC Models

The most powerful ESM is the **Community Earth System Model (CESM).** Climate scientists from around the world contribute data to this model, and predictions from the CESM are used in official reports issued by the **Intergovernmental Panel on Climate Change (IPCC).** Climate scientists developed the CESM to make predictions about future climate conditions based on current and projected inputs and conditions.

The 2014 IPCC report used a CESM that divided Earth's surface into 32 atmospheric layers, 60 ocean layers, 25 land layers, and latitude and longitude divisions that were smaller than 1° × 1°. Computations were done for all grid cells at 30-minute time steps, thousands of years into the future.

(24) CCC Systems and System Models Climate scientists also use the CESM to create paleoclimate models, or models of past climate conditions. These models use larger map grid cells than future climate models. Why do you think that is? ✏

....

....

....

Models of the Twentieth Century

Scientists are also able to use the CESM to determine which past inputs have contributed to conditions seen in Earth's recent past. They do this by inputting hypothetical initial conditions at some point in the past and then running the program up to the present. If the data projections are inaccurate, then the scientists know that the inputs were wrong.

Modeling Global Temperature History

The CESM was used to identify which inputs (human or natural forcings) were responsible for the pattern seen in Earth's mean global temperature from 1860 to 2010. Note that complex systems, such as climate models, cannot be predicted with total certainty. The shaded areas around the curves represent this uncertainty.

When the model was run using only natural forcings—such as sunlight and volcanism—as inputs, the results showed similar variability but did not match the recent upward trend.

When the model was run using only human forcings—such as greenhouse gas emissions and land use—as inputs, the upward trend was modeled but not the variability.

When the model combined the effects of both human forcings and natural forcings, the computed temperatures matched the actual data temperatures very closely.

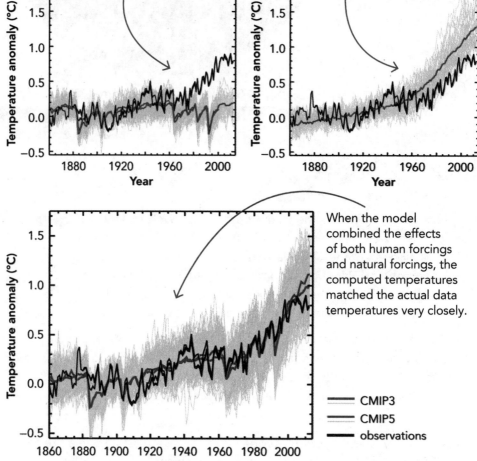

CMIP3
CMIP5
observations

(25) **SEP Analyze and Interpret Data** Analyze the climate model runs with only human and then only natural climate forcings. Then describe how each contributes to actual recorded temperature data when they are combined. ✏️

....

....

....

Scenarios for the Twenty-First Century

To develop future climate projections, the IPCC has to make some assumptions about global greenhouse gas output in the coming decades. Countries can take an infinite number of pathways, ranging from stopping all fossil fuel use immediately to burning it all as quickly as possible. Not every scenario can be tested, so the IPCC's fifth assessment report (or AR5, published in 2014) picked four different possible Representative Concentration Pathway (RCP) scenarios for the release of greenhouse gases between now and the year 2100. Full climate model runs were then made for each of these four RCPs.

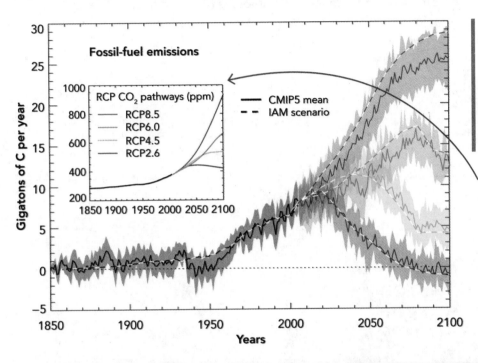

Carbon Emission Pathways The main graph shows the amount of carbon emissions required between now and 2100 in order to produce the CO_2 pathways shown in the inset.

The four RCP scenarios show human-induced radiative forcing, in W/m^2, in the year 2100. The colored lines show Earth's mean atmospheric CO_2 levels between now and 2100, for each scenario.

IPCC Scenarios of Representative Concentration Pathways (RCPs)	
Model	**Description**
RCP8.5	Radiative forcing pathway to 8.5 W/m^2 in 2100 and still rising. "Business as usual" scenario, with greenhouse gas use still increasing in 2100. Least optimistic.
RCP6.0	Radiative forcing pathway to 6 W/m^2 in 2100 and still rising. Carbon emissions peak around 2080, then decline.
RCP4.5	Radiative forcing pathway to stable 4.5 W/m^2 level in 2100. Carbon emissions peak around 2040, then decline.
RCP2.6	Radiative forcing pathway to 2.6 W/m^2 in 2100, already declining. Carbon emissions peak around 2020 and drop to zero around 2080. Most optimistic.

26) **CCC Stability and Change** Describe which of the four RCP scenarios you see as being the most likely, and why. ✏️

Projected Temperatures

In all of the scenarios of the IPCC AR5 report, temperatures will be warmer in the year 2100 than they are now. This is not surprising for the RCP8.5 scenario, with continued aggressive fossil fuel burning. However, this also occurs for the other three scenarios, where greenhouse gas emissions start to decline before the end of the century. There are several reasons for this. Some greenhouse gases remain in the atmosphere for a long time and continue to trap Earth's infrared radiation long after they are released. The ocean also has a long circulation time, so the large amounts of heat that are currently being pumped into the deep ocean will come back up centuries later to rewarm the atmosphere.

Projected Radiative Forcings These curves show predicted radiative forcings from the release of greenhouse gases, reduction of light reflected from Earth's surface due to sea ice melting, human-released aerosols, and soot.

Projected Temperatures These curves show predicted global temperature changes in response to the four RCP scenarios shown at left. Note that for RCPs 4.5, 6.0, and 8.5, temperatures continue to rise for centuries.

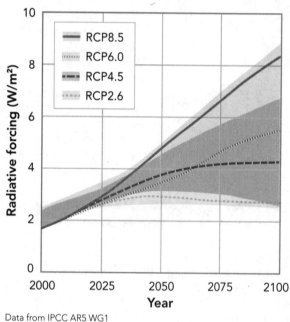

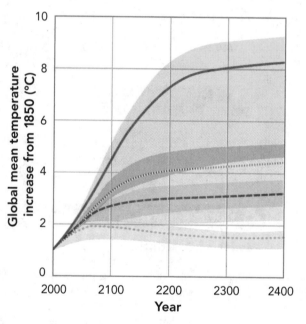

Data from IPCC AR5 WG1

(27) **SEP Analyze and Interpret Data** Continents warm faster than the ocean, so assume that land temperatures increase 20% faster than the global average. For scenario RCP8.5, how much warmer are average land temperatures expected to be in the year 2300 (with respect to 1850), converted to °F? What temperature would that make your town right now? ✏

....

....

....

Regional Temperature and Precipitation Projections

Computations made by the CESM allow scientists to predict the likely climate conditions for all regions of the globe. It is instructive to use the most optimistic (RCP2.6) and the least optimistic (RCP8.5) scenarios to provide a bracket for predicting future conditions. What will likely occur is probably somewhere in between these two scenarios. While the RCP2.6 and RCP8.5 models differ in the magnitudes of their predicted changes, their patterns are generally similar.

Future Regional Temperatures We can expect continents to warm about 50% faster than ocean basins. The Arctic region will experience the accelerating melting of permafrost, sea ice, and the Greenland glacier.

RCP2.6   RCP8.5

Change in Average Surface Temperature (1986–2005 to 2081–2100)

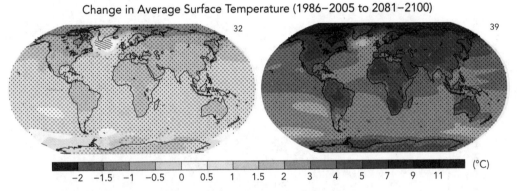

Future Regional Precipitation In general, the dry desert regions about 30° north and south of the equator will get drier. The moist tropical regions will get wetter, and the poles will also see an increase in precipitation.

Change in Average Precipitation (1986–2005 to 2081–2100)

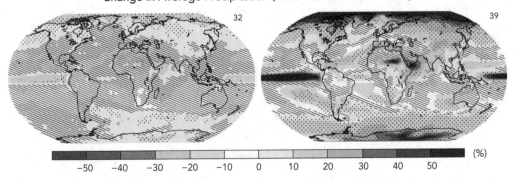

28 **SEP Analyze and Interpret Data** One of your classmates wants to move to Italy when she retires because she likes a cool and moist climate. Using the maps, explain whether you think her decision is good or not, and why. ✏

....

....

Projected Sea Level Rise

As global temperatures increase, ice will melt and sea water will warm and expand. The last time there were more than 415 ppm CO_2 in the atmosphere (the level in the year 2019) was 3.6 million years ago, when sea levels were 15–25 meters higher. At that level, nearly every coastal town or city around the world would be flooded. In all climate models, sea levels, which have been stable for 6,000 years, will keep rising, but it is uncertain how quickly.

Rate of Sea Level Rise Most ecosystems and human systems cannot adapt to sea level rise greater than 1 m. Even a rise of less than 0.5 m can endanger coastal areas around the globe. How much sea levels will rise in the future depends on how much atmospheric CO_2 levels are increased by human activities.

According to the RCP8.5 model, sea level will rise 0.8 m by 2100, flooding many coastal cities and towns.

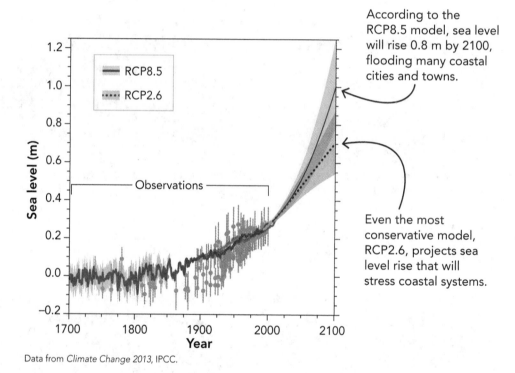

Even the most conservative model, RCP2.6, projects sea level rise that will stress coastal systems.

Data from *Climate Change 2013*, IPCC.

(29) **CCC Stability and Change** Explain the role that water's latent heat of melting plays in controlling the rate of sea level rise. ✐

....

....

....

....

Projected Changes in Extreme Weather

One result of global warming is an increase in regional temperature differences. Models show that these differences can lead to increased episodes of extreme weather—such as more intense tornadoes and hurricanes—more frequent short-term precipitation events, and more intense droughts and floods. One climate model prediction that is perhaps surprising is that nearly all of the world will experience more extended five-day precipitation events. Even in places that are predicted to get less total rainfall, the rainfall will occur in a small number of more intense precipitation events. This will result in more flooding worldwide.

30) **SEP Analyze and Interpret Data** Climate models predict an increase in the intensity of both heavy precipitation events and droughts. On the map of consecutive dry days, circle the regions that are projected to have more frequent consecutive dry days but also increased maximum five-day precipitation events. ✎

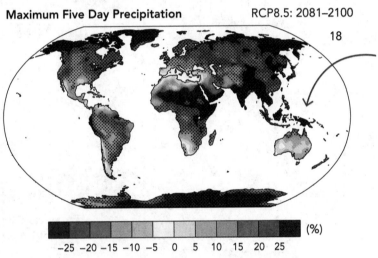

Maximum Five Day Precipitation   RCP8.5: 2081–2100

18

Intense precipitation events are projected to increase for nearly every land region, even those regions that are expected to receive less annual water.

(%)
−25 −20 −15 −10 −5 0 5 10 15 20 25

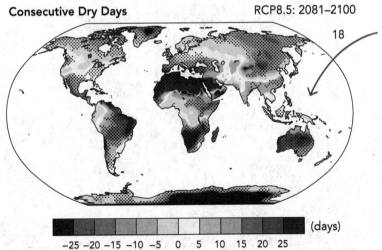

Consecutive Dry Days   RCP8.5: 2081–2100

18

Regions that are already dry and suffer frequent droughts will experience even more frequent dry periods.

(days)
−25 −20 −15 −10 −5 0 5 10 15 20 25

INVESTIGATIVE PHENOMENON

GO ONLINE to Elaborate on and Evaluate your knowledge of climate models by completing the peer review and data analysis activities.

In the CER worksheet assigned at the beginning of this investigation, you drafted a scientific argument about floods. With a partner, reevaluate the evidence cited in your arguments.

(31) **SEP Engage in Argument** What do CESM projections say about the likelihood of flooding in the future? ✏️

....

....

....

....

....

....

Consequences of Climate Change

 GO ONLINE to Explore and Explain the effects to Earth's systems of continued climate change.

Droughts

Climate change has an impact on numerous Earth systems. Many of these impacts directly affect people. For example, humans depend on food produced by agriculture for survival. Currently, 40% of global land area is used to grow crops and raise livestock. But in 15 years, there will be an additional billion people on Earth to feed. Climate models suggest that parts of the world are expected to receive less rainfall and experience more frequent extended droughts in the near future, negatively impacting the ability of their societies to grow food crops.

IPCC climate models predict increased droughts in the Southwest U.S. and in Central America. Similar droughts occurred in those regions during the warm Medieval Climate Anomaly. One tree-ring data set in the Southwest U.S. shows that almost no rain fell for a period of 40 years, around 1160–1200. It is likely that these droughts contributed to the collapse of some of the native American Ancestral Puebloan cultures, as well as the Mayan cultures in Central America.

Drying Up Cachuma Lake in California's Santa Ynez Valley is in danger of disappearing. Recent droughts in many southwestern U.S. states seem to be repeating the climate pattern seen during the Medieval Climate Anomaly.

Extreme Precipitation

Over the past 50 years, there has been a significant increase in the number of extreme one-day precipitation events worldwide. Climate models suggest that the trend of extreme precipitation will continue as global temperatures increase. Even regions that are predicted to receive less overall rainfall will likely find that rain will fall in a smaller number of more intense downfalls.

A similar pattern of correlation can be observed in other weather-related phenomena, such as hurricanes, tornadoes, and droughts. One example of record-breaking flooding occurred in 2018, when up to 3 feet of water rained in parts of North Carolina due to Hurricane Florence.

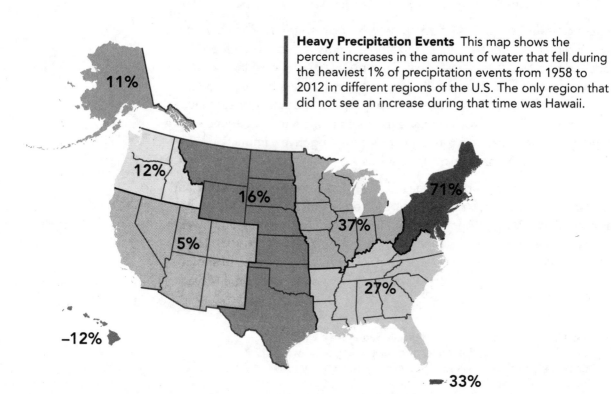

Heavy Precipitation Events This map shows the percent increases in the amount of water that fell during the heaviest 1% of precipitation events from 1958 to 2012 in different regions of the U.S. The only region that did not see an increase during that time was Hawaii.

(32) **CCC Patterns** Examine the map. What geographic patterns do you observe? Explain. 🖊

....

....

....

....

As more rain falls in shorter amounts of time, the frequency and intensity of flooding increase. Floods pose many hazards to communities, including physical injury or loss of life, destruction of homes and infrastructure, and pollution of drinking water.

Computational weather models can now reliably forecast dangerous flooding up to three days in advance, allowing for planned evacuations and greatly reducing loss of life. However, floods still have many negative longer-term impacts, including financial loss, destruction of food crops, and the forced relocation of residents.

▶ **Patterns in the magnitude and frequency of extreme weather events, such as droughts or heavy precipitation events, may be observable on one time scale and not exist at other scales. That is why scientists observe daily changes, annual changes, and decadal averages.**

(33) **SEP Analyze and Interpret Data** The bars in the graph show annual data for extreme one-day precipitation events in the contiguous United States as a percentage of land area. The line shows the trend in annual data using a nine-year weighted average. This line averages data over a nine-year period, but gives more weight to the middle year. There are other ways to represent trends within a data set on a graph. Try the following:

a. For each 10-year period (1960s, 1970s, etc.), circle the top of the highest year's bar. Then draw a set of lines, left to right, connecting your circles.

b. Draw a single straight line that best fits all of the years (the tops of the bars).

c. Draw two straight lines, one between 1910–1960, the other between 1960–2015, that best fit the data in two parts.

Extreme One-day Precipitation Events 1910–2015, Contiguous United States

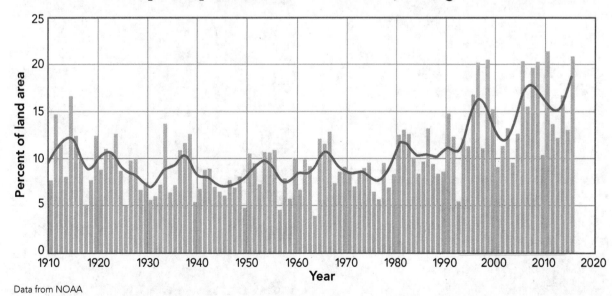

Data from NOAA

Disappearing Glaciers

One of the most important impacts of climate change is the loss of glaciers. In many parts of the world, glaciers store water throughout the year and slowly feed rivers, keeping them flowing. Many rivers originate in alpine glaciers, so the loss of this ice threatens human water supplies. The slow release of glacial water is also important for recharging depleted groundwater reservoirs.

Global Glacial Mass Loss Data show an overall decrease in glacial mass over the past 40 years. Glaciers are becoming both shorter and thinner.

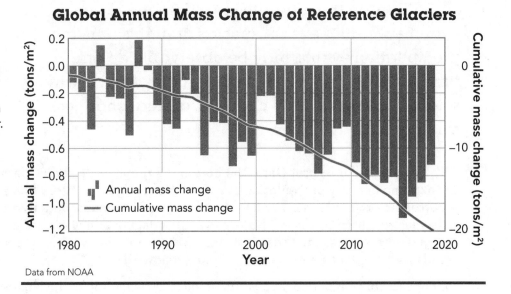

Global Annual Mass Change of Reference Glaciers

Legend:
▮ Annual mass change
— Cumulative mass change

Data from NOAA

(34) **Stability and Change** These two photos of Grinnell Glacier in Glacier National Park, Montana, were taken 43 years apart. Trace the outline of the glacier in each photo using one color. Then, using a second color in the right-hand photo, trace where you think the glacier is today.

1938

1981

Glaciers and Sea Level Melting glaciers contribute to a rise in sea levels. Nearly 3 billion people live within 100 miles of a coastline, where rising sea levels increase the risk of flooding. The risks are worse in flat areas such as river deltas, which often have high populations. In some areas, the risk is exacerbated by sea surges during large storms, such as hurricanes. However, the hazards are not limited to storms. Already, many coastal areas experience so-called *sunny-day flooding*, where the streets of coastal towns now regularly flood during peak monthly high tides.

Coastal Flooding Relatively small increases in sea level can affect large areas of land, depending on the topography. Many coastal areas, such as this portion of the California coast, are relatively flat, allowing the sea to encroach well inland from the current shoreline.

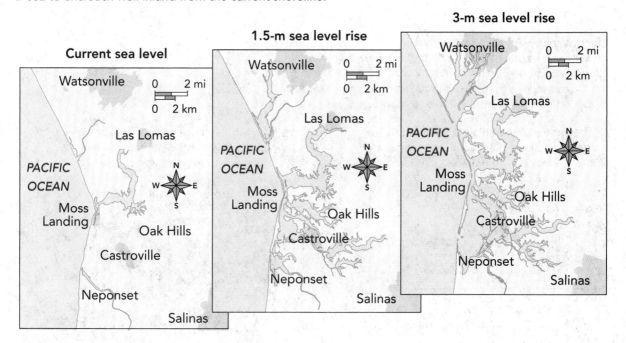

35 **CCC System and System Models** Use the scale on the map to determine how far inland Castroville is currently. Explain how a 1.5 m sea-level rise could flood parts of Castroville. 🖉

....

....

....

....

....

Impact on the Biosphere

Human activities are changing Earth's biomes at rates not seen in millions of years, to the extent that humans now have their own geologic time period, the **Anthropocene**. Climate change is a significant part of this impact. Plant and animal species evolve to thrive in areas with particular patterns of temperature and precipitation, and if these patterns change faster than species can adapt, they may be decimated, or even go extinct. Climate change can also encourage the spread of invasive species—such as the kudzu vine or pine beetle—into new areas, competing with local species that are struggling under the new conditions. Changing climate patterns affect human food crops as well. Many crop plants that once grew well in certain areas are struggling with rising temperatures and no longer thrive in the same zones.

Northward Shift Plant hardiness zones define geographic areas where certain plants thrive under a particular set of climate conditions. These conditions are largely a function of average annual extreme low temperatures. Zone 4 has the coldest temperatures while Zone 10 has the warmest.

The widths of the colored bands show the locations of the plant zone boundaries over the 10-year period between 2000 and 2010.

The widths of the colored bands show how the plant zone boundaries are projected to expand and shift by 2040.

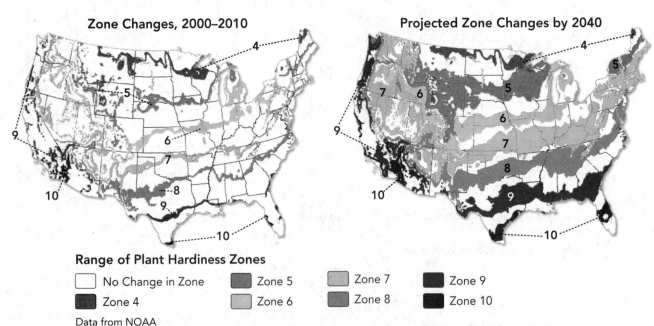

Zone Changes, 2000–2010

Projected Zone Changes by 2040

Range of Plant Hardiness Zones

- ☐ No Change in Zone
- ■ Zone 4
- ■ Zone 5
- ■ Zone 6
- ■ Zone 7
- ■ Zone 8
- ■ Zone 9
- ■ Zone 10

Data from NOAA

36 SEP Use Mathematics and Computational Thinking Obtain a map of Missouri and use the information in the future map to compute the rate at which the southern border of Plant Zone 7 will be moving northward. ✎

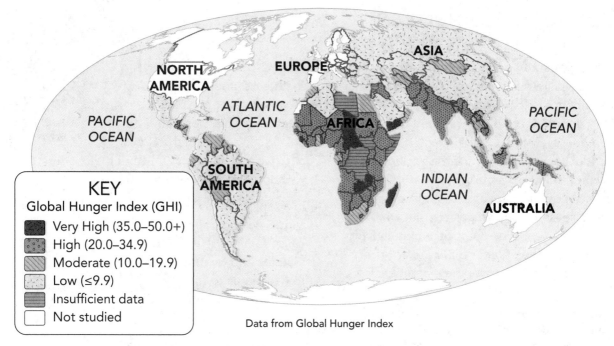

KEY

Global Hunger Index (GHI)

- Very High (35.0–50.0+)
- High (20.0–34.9)
- Moderate (10.0–19.9)
- Low (≤9.9)
- Insufficient data
- Not studied

Data from Global Hunger Index

Famine Susceptibility Global Hunger Index (GHI) values are calculated using data about child undernourishment and mortality. High GHI values indicate countries where climate change and other local factors have caused food shortages.

Famines and Wildfires

Climate and Hunger The correlation between climate change and famine is strong. Famines triggered by volcanic eruptions or decreases in sunlight have had an impact on the rise and fall of past civilizations, and famines will become more frequent as the impacts of global warming are felt. Unfortunately, some of the areas most at risk of famine due to climate change are also areas where hunger is already widespread and where population growth rates are high—such as Africa, India, and Southeast Asia.

Wildfire Incidence Wildfires in California are connected to the El Niño / La Niña Southern Oscillation cycle, and this connection extends to other forms of climate change as well. Areas of increased dryness will become susceptible to more wildfires, especially if climates shift to alternating periods of extreme precipitation followed by drought.

(31) **CCC Cause and Effect** Construct an explanation to explain why alternating periods of extreme precipitation and drought might lead to an increase in the number of wildfires. 🖊

....

....

....

Spread of Diseases

Rising global temperatures have also been implicated in the spread of infectious diseases. Many bacteria thrive at warmer temperatures. The number of cases of infection from *Salmonella, E. coli, Campylobacter,* and other harmful bacteria greatly increases during summer months. As global temperatures increase, the number of cases will continue to rise. Disease-carrying parasites that were once found only near the equator are now thriving farther from the equator thanks to warming conditions. For example, the Asian tiger mosquito carries viruses that cause diseases such as yellow fever and West Nile fever. This mosquito arrived in the U.S. in the 1960s and has spread across much of the southeast, west into Texas, and north into New York.

In addition, many global pandemics have been triggered by sudden changes in climate, which cause famines that weaken human immune systems and lead to the migration of humans to new areas to find food.

Spread of Deer Tick Habitats These maps show projected changes in the distribution probabilities of tick populations that carry Lyme disease in the eastern U.S.

Lyme-infected ticks have spread through most of the Southern U.S. and New England.

Tick populations are expected to expand northward and inland in the coming decades.

Probability of Established Tick Habitat (%) ☐ 0–39 ▨ 40–99

(38) **SEP Analyze and Interpret Data** Based on these maps, which U.S. states are expected to see the biggest increase in the distribution of ticks bearing Lyme disease between now and 2080? Which states could see the biggest decrease? 🖊

....

....

Climate Change, Migration, and Conflict

How might **climate change** affect **human social interactions?**

Shifting Climate Average **global temperatures rise** as a result of human carbon emissions.

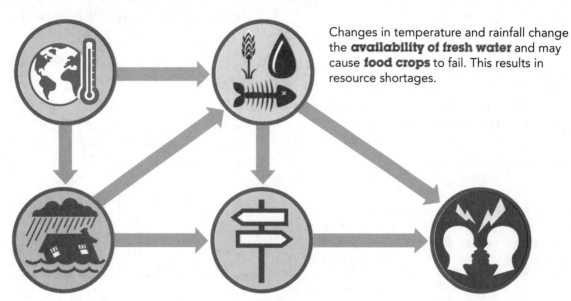

Changes in temperature and rainfall change the **availability of fresh water** and may cause **food crops** to fail. This results in resource shortages.

Climate changes cause **more severe and frequent weather** events, such as floods, storms, and droughts.

Lack of resources and damage caused by disasters **force humans to move** to areas with better or more stable resources.

Humans compete for resources such as food, water, energy, and space to live. **Competition leads to conflict** and violence.

(39) **CCC Cause and Effect** Studies have shown a correlation between increasing temperatures and decreasing school math test scores. Construct a hypothesis to explain why this might occur. 🖊

....

....

....

....

....

....

....

Impact on Human Societies

Displacement of Populations A changing climate can have many negative impacts on human populations, including flooding, drought, disease, and famine. These events often result in the mass migration of large numbers of people to new areas, creating potential for conflict with local inhabitants.

Increased Conflict and Civil Unrest
Historically, times of rapid climate change have correlated with increased incidences of war and conflict. Even today, many regions experiencing severe political conflicts are places where climate change has negatively impacted agriculture and caused hunger and famine.

Global Conflict Risk in Tropical Regions This graph shows the percent change in conflict risk in tropical regions (between 30°N and 30°S) as a function of the change in average Pacific Ocean temperatures, which have a strong effect on tropical climates.

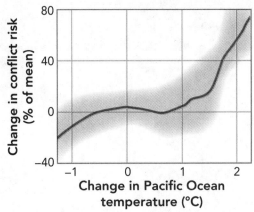

Conflict Risk and Temperature

Data from Hsiang et al., Quantifying the Influence of Climate on Human Conflict. Science, Vol. 341, Issue 6151, September 13, 2013.

Revisit

INVESTIGATIVE PHENOMENON

GO ONLINE to Elaborate on and Evaluate your knowledge of climate change impacts by completing the class discussion and data analysis activities.

In the CER worksheet assigned at the beginning of this investigation, you drafted a scientific argument about floods. With a partner, reevaluate the evidence cited in your arguments.

40 **SEP Engage in Argument** What further evidence for increasing floods could you offer, having completed this learning experience? ✏

....

....

....

....

....

....

Responses to Climate Change

GO ONLINE to Explore and Explain responses and proposed solutions to climate change.

Solving Global Warming

Halting further ecological damage by climate change will require a combination of technological innovation, political will, and a shift in cultural practices. People need to either reduce the emissions of greenhouse gases or remove them from the atmosphere. Preventing gases from being emitted in the first place is much easier than trying to remove them, and that's where low-carbon communities come in.

Reducing Emissions Governments can provide tax incentives to help individuals make low-carbon investments, such as electric cars and solar panels. Increased use of energy-efficient public transportation and sustainable agricultural practices also help to reduce a community's carbon output.

Low-Carbon Communities Cities that employ "green" technologies and urban planning strategies can significantly reduce their carbon footprints. Such cities are the key to sustainable development.

Drivers of Climate Change There are five principal drivers of climate change at work in society today. Implementing changes that will combat these drivers will require international cooperation at an unprecedented level. Economic legislation may be required to encourage efficient practices and deter the release of greenhouse gases. In all areas, education will be needed in order to develop intelligent uses of resources.

Five Ways to Reduce the Drivers of Climate Change

Carbon Economics		**Reveal "true costs" of fossil fuels** Fossil fuels have maintained their dominance in the marketplace in part because their "true costs"—costs associated with damage from carbon emissions—have been passed on to taxpayers. Imposing a carbon tax would allow renewable energy sources to compete fairly in the energy marketplace.
Carbon Subsidies		**Remove fossil fuel subsidies** An estimated $5 trillion in global subsidies are provided to the fossil fuel industries each year—more than a half-trillion in financial aid and the rest in the form of exemptions for "true costs." If not for these subsidies, fossil fuels might have been abandoned long ago for financial reasons.
Renewable Energy		**Implement clean energy sources** The use of electricity from sources such as wind, solar, and hydroelectric power releases little or no greenhouse gases. In many regions, wind and solar are already cheaper than fossil fuels.
Modern Agriculture		**Adopt "green" farming practices** Sustainable agricultural practices can help combat climate change and also be more profitable. These practices involve the intelligent use of water, fertilizers, and pesticides. They also include appropriate crop selection, crop timing, and crop rotation.
Efficient Cities		**Design low-carbon communities** Designing systems of transportation, architecture, urban design, and industry with energy efficiency in mind will greatly reduce energy demands and greenhouse gas emissions. Changing business practices, such as using teleconferencing instead of airplane travel, will also reduce climate impacts.

(41) **SEP Engage in Argument from Evidence** Which of these five drivers will be the hardest to reduce? Explain your reasoning. 🖉

....

....

....

....

....

Energy Sources

Humans use energy at an enormous rate—about 20 TW (terawatts), or 20 trillion joules per second. This is equivalent to the work that would be done if every person on the planet bench-pressed a set of 580-lb weights one meter every second. Fossil fuels have been doing most of this work for us, but fortunately there is a cleaner, cheaper, and inexhaustible source of energy: the sun.

Global Energy Sources Most of the energy used by humans comes from fossil fuels, including oil, coal, and natural gas. A smaller percentage comes from renewable sources.

For many years, the largest low-carbon sources of energy have been hydroelectric and nuclear fission.

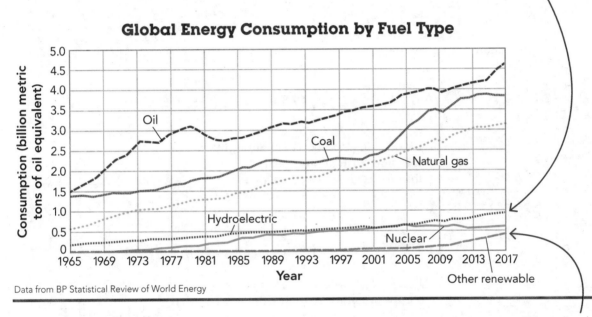

Global Energy Consumption by Fuel Type

Data from BP Statistical Review of World Energy

Although solar and wind still provide a small percentage of the global energy supply, they are now the fastest-growing energy sources.

Solar Energy About 125,000 TW of sunlight reaches Earth continuously—that's more than 6,000 times what humans use. We need only a tiny fraction of this to meet all our energy needs. Commercial solar panels are approaching 20% efficiency, and large solar farms yield almost 10 W/m^2.

Other Renewable Sources of Energy Research in materials has allowed wind turbines to continue to get lighter, larger, and cheaper. There are many designs of wind turbines. The largest has three blades spanning >150 m and yields 8 MW, enough to power over 6,500 houses. There are other low-carbon sources of energy, but they are not growing as rapidly as wind and solar.

One of these other low-carbon sources of energy is geothermal energy. In some places, it is possible to use Earth's internal heat as a clean, renewable source of energy. Geothermal energy is produced from the decay of radioactive materials below Earth's surface and the loss of heat originally produced during Earth's formation. Where easily accessible, near hot spot volcanoes, for example, this energy can be used to produce electricity for homes and industries.

Global Growth of Renewable Energies
How fast are **low-carbon energy** sources **growing globally?**

2018 electricity in GW: **178**
2018 electricity as a % of total electricity: **5.8%**
2013–2018 average annual growth in capacity: **13.5%**

Wind Farms of **wind turbines** can yield about 2.5 W/m² while the land is used for other purposes. This combination is ideal for the windy **agricultural plains** of the central U.S.

Water Hydroelectric power requires large areas and is only cost-effective in a few parts of the world. Nevertheless, it is the **largest renewable energy source** in current use.

2018 electricity in GW: **492**
2018 electricity as a % of total electricity: **16.2%**
2013–2018 average annual growth in capacity: **2.7%**

2018 electricity in GW: **71**
2018 electricity as a % of total electricity: **2.3%**
2013–2018 average annual growth in capacity: **28%**

Solar About 125,000 TW of **sunlight reaches Earth continuously**—more than 6,000 times what humans use. Large solar farms yield almost 10 W/m².

Nuclear Nuclear fission **does not release greenhouse gases,** but it raises a variety of environmental concerns and is very expensive.

2018 electricity in GW: **296**
2018 electricity as a % of total electricity: **9.8%**
2013–2018 average annual growth in capacity: **1.3%**

(42) **CCC Influence of Engineering and Technology on Society** Humans use electricity at a rate of approximately 3 TW (3000 GW). If this and the growth rate of solar power stayed the same, in how many years would solar energy be able to supply all of the world's electricity needs?

Transptation

Motorized vehicles are major contributors to carbon emissions. In fact, about one-fifth of global human-released CO_2 comes from transportation. Fortunately, advances in battery technology are driving the transition from combustion-engine to electric vehicles. The greatest challenges remain for ocean shipping and air travel. Ocean freighters could use nuclear power. Planes will likely continue to run on the combustion of liquid fuels, but can greatly reduce CO_2 output by using lightweight materials and flying with full passenger loads.

Electric Vehicles Cars and trains that run on electricity generated by renewable energy sources provide transport without the release of greenhouse gases.

Energy Use per Mode of Transportation			
Mode of Travel	**Efficiency (J/m per person)***	**Mode of Travel**	**Efficiency (J/m per person)***
Bicycle	~100	Combustion-engine Car	600–1000
Walking	~200 (depending on diet)	Ferry Boat	~750
Electric Train	50–300	Airplane	~1500
Electric Car	120–180	Ocean Liner	3400–6600
Bus	200–700	Helicopter / Private Jet	~5400
Hybrid Car	350–500	Jet Ski	~18,000

* Assumes that large passenger vehicles are full (and cars have four people)

43 **SEP Engage in Argument from Evidence** Suppose a group of people are planning to drive between cities in combustion engine cars. Use data from the table to outline the conditions under which they would or would not use less energy than flying. 🖉

....

....

....

....

....

....

Home Heat Loss
In this enhanced infrared image of a house on a cold day, heat loss is indicated by color.

Areas of high heat loss are shown in red. Areas of the highest rates of heat loss are shown in white.

The lowest rates of heat loss are occurring in places shown in blue.

Infrastructure

Older homes, schools, and other buildings are not very energy-efficient. Much of the energy used to heat and cool them is lost to the environment. In fact, more than 10% of total human greenhouse gas emissions come from heating and cooling older buildings. Newer structures built with modern "green" architecture require much less energy to heat in the winters and air condition in the summers. Rooftop solar panels and heat pumps also greatly reduce energy needs.

◀ A sustainable city functions as a system made up of smaller subsystems, including public transportation, embedded green spaces, and recycling programs.

44) **CCC Influence of Engineering, Technology, and Science on Society and the Natural World** In the infrared photo of the house, which areas are experiencing the highest rates of heat loss? Propose an engineering solution to reduce loss in these areas. 🖉

....

....

....

....

Carbon Capture and Sequestration

If humans continue to burn fossil fuels, we will need to find ways to prevent the resulting carbon dioxide from entering the atmosphere. The removal and containment of excess carbon dioxide is known as carbon capture and sequestration (CCS). Carbon dioxide can be captured by stripping it out before the fuel is combusted, or by using chemicals to separate it from exhaust gases. The carbon dioxide can then be used for industrial processes or sequestered away in reservoirs.

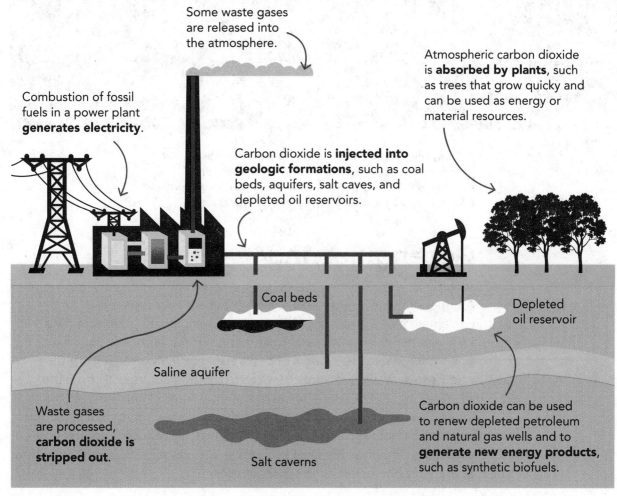

Some waste gases are released into the atmosphere.

Atmospheric carbon dioxide is **absorbed by plants**, such as trees that grow quicky and can be used as energy or material resources.

Combustion of fossil fuels in a power plant **generates electricity**.

Carbon dioxide is **injected into geologic formations**, such as coal beds, aquifers, salt caves, and depleted oil reservoirs.

Coal beds

Depleted oil reservoir

Saline aquifer

Waste gases are processed, **carbon dioxide is stripped out**.

Salt caverns

Carbon dioxide can be used to renew depleted petroleum and natural gas wells and to **generate new energy products**, such as synthetic biofuels.

45 **CCC Science Addresses Question About the Natural and Material World**
Carbon dioxide can also be sequestered by combining it with quicklime (CaO) to produce limestone (CaO + CO$_2$ → CaCO$_3$). Unfortunately, this process requires a lot of energy. Provide a proposal for where this energy might come from that does not further contribute to global warming.

....

....

....

Capturing CO$_2$ Fans pull exhaust from this waste incineration plant into the collectors, where a filter removes the carbon dioxide and converts it to a pure form that can be used industrially or sequestered.

Geoengineering

Another possible approach to reversing climate change is the implementation of massive, planet-wide geoengineering projects. One idea is to dump large amounts of iron or other nutrients into the ocean to encourage massive blooms of phytoplankton that would absorb CO$_2$. Another is to build large-scale devices to remove CO$_2$ directly from the air. Yet another involves pumping massive amounts of aerosols into the atmosphere to partially block out sunlight. However, some climate models suggest that artificial aerosols might inadvertently reduce precipitation, worsening droughts. We must proceed with caution in any large-scale effort, as there may be unintended consequences.

46 **CCC Influence of Engineering, Technology, and Science on Society and the Natural World** Describe a situation where an engineering solution to one problem could inadvertently create a new problem of a different sort. ✏

....

....

....

....

Sustainability

The path to global sustainability will need to be not only scientifically possible, but also economically viable and socially equitable. Governments play an important role in this effort by offering financial incentives and passing laws that cost relatively little to implement but reap enormous savings in money and health over time. However, governments must ensure that these regulations can be implemented equitably and do not put unfair burdens on any one community.

Sustainable Development For a plan of sustainable development to be successful, it must be environmentally sound, socially just, and economically realistic.

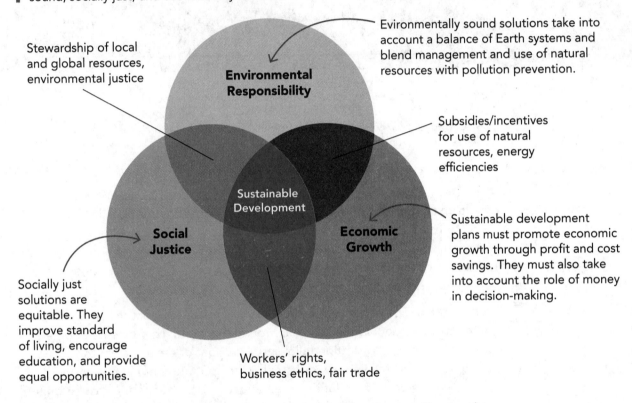

Stewardship of local and global resources, environmental justice

Evironmentally sound solutions take into account a balance of Earth systems and blend management and use of natural resources with pollution prevention.

Subsidies/incentives for use of natural resources, energy efficiencies

Socially just solutions are equitable. They improve standard of living, encourage education, and provide equal opportunities.

Sustainable development plans must promote economic growth through profit and cost savings. They must also take into account the role of money in decision-making.

Workers' rights, business ethics, fair trade

Economics Switching from fossil fuels to wind and solar power will not only reduce greenhouse gases, but save money by reducing health care costs and environmental damage associated with pollution.

Industry The efficiency of industrial practices can be improved to reduce their impact on climate and save money. Factories can use cogeneration, where leftover heat from a factory or power plant is used for other commercial purposes. Advances in materials science can allow machines to run at higher temperatures that make them thermodynamically more efficient.

Forests Tropical rain forests are the lungs of our planet, absorbing much of the CO_2 we produce and releasing the oxygen we breathe. It is tempting for tropical countries to cut down their forests to grow crops or raise cattle, but ironically these are some of the least fertile soils in the world, so tropical-climate agricultural efforts typically fail. International cooperation is needed to provide tropical countries with financial incentives to protect their forests.

Low-carbon Agriculture These soybeans were planted between rows of wheat stubble just after the wheat was harvested, eliminating the need to till the soil. Double cropping increases soil moisture, reduces erosion, and increases profits.

Agriculture Currently, more than 12% of human-released greenhouse gases come from agricultural practices. But research efforts are continually leading to more efficient uses of land, water, and fertilizers. Some agricultural crops have been used to make biofuels for cars, but these fuels are also producers of greenhouse gases. Given increasing global populations, these croplands may be needed instead for growing food.

Social Justice The negative impacts of climate change affect the poor more than the wealthy, both in the U.S. and around the world. Low-income people are more vulnerable to malnutrition following a drought or devastating storm. They are also more likely to live near industrial plants, putting them at greater risk for diseases associated with pollution. International organizations such as the United Nations Framework Convention on Climate Change are needed to ensure that climate decisions that affect people are made as fairly and justly as possible.

(47) SEP Design Solutions Propose an improvement to a practice at your school that will reduce climate impacts. Be sure to consider economic and social effects of the change alongside environmental consequences.

....

....

....

Calculations Involving Land Area and Wind Power

Wind farms are developing rapidly across the Plains states thanks to their compatibility with farms and pasturelands. Wind farms have an efficiency of about 2.5 W/m^2. The total area of the U.S. is 9,147,593 km^2. If the entire energy needs of the U.S. (3.4 TW) were supplied by these wind farms, what percentage of U.S. land would the farms have to occupy?

ANALYZE List the knowns and unknown.

Knowns	Unknown
Wind farm efficiency = 2.5 W/m^2	Total area of U.S. land devoted to wind farms = ? %
Total area of the U.S. = 9,147,593 km^2	
Total U.S. rate of energy consumption = 3.4 TW	

CALCULATE Solve for the unknown.

Find the area of wind farms needed to supply U.S. energy needs, in m^2.

$$\frac{3.4 \; \cancel{TW}}{2.5 \; \cancel{W}/m^2} = 1,360,000,000,000 \; m^2$$

Convert area to km^2.

$$1,360,000,000,000 \; m^2 = 1,360,000 \; km^2$$

Calculate what % of U.S. land that value is.

$$\frac{1,360,000 \; \cancel{km^2}}{9,147,593 \; \cancel{km^2}} = 15\%$$

EVALUATE Does the result make sense?

The calculated percentage of 15% makes sense because the U.S. consumes a very large amount of energy, and wind farms occupy relatively large areas. Therefore, a significant percentage of the country's surface area would have to be covered with wind farms in order to meet all our energy needs.

(48) SEP Calculate Solar panel farms have an efficiency of about 10 W/m^2. What percentage of U.S. lands would solar panels need to occupy in order to meet U.S. energy demands?

GO ONLINE for more practice problems.

GO ONLINE to Elaborate on and Evaluate your knowledge of tools to fight climate change by completing the class discussion and writing activities.

In the CER worksheet assigned at the beginning of this investigation, you drafted a scientific argument about floods. With a partner, reevaluate the evidence cited in your arguments.

(49) SEP Engage in Argument What engineering solutions to flooding could you offer having completed this learning experience? ✏️

....

....

....

....

....

....

GO ONLINE to Evaluate what you learned about the causes and effects of global climate change by using the available assessment resources.

In the Performance-Based Assessment, you modeled two mechanisms that can remove CO_2 from the atmosphere. Wrap up your analysis by answering the following questions.

50 **SEP Define Problems** To be effective, any method to remove CO_2 from the atmosphere would have to be applied on a very large scale. Choose one of the methods you modeled and use what you learned in this investigation to describe the criteria and constraints of scaling it up. ✎

Criteria	Constraints

Revisit

ANCHORING PHENOMENON

51 **Connect to Society** Think about the blizzard image presented at the beginning of Instructional Segment 4. Use what you have learned to answer the question "Why are we seeing more extreme weather?"

....

....

....

 GO ONLINE for a problem-based learning activity that you can tackle after completing Instructional Segment 4.

The Dynamics of Chemical Reactions and Ocean Acidification

How do our **everyday** activities impact **Earth?**

Investigation 14
Reaction Rates and Equilibrium

Investigation 15
Acid-Base Equilibria

Investigation 16
Ocean Acidification

ANCHORING PHENOMENON

Inquiry Launch The image shows people driving during rush hour, an everyday activity that contributes to climate change. Which other everyday activities can you think of that may also influence Earth's climate?

While not intentional, many of the everyday activities we perform, when added all together, have large-scale effects on Earth and its systems. Write a short list of activities besides driving that you or your family do regularly, and describe how each of the activities likely helps mitigate or contributes to climate change by affecting Earth's atmosphere or ocean. ✏️

....

....

....

....

....

....

....

GO ONLINE to engage with real-world phenomena. Watch the anchoring phenomenon video and preview the optional **problem-based learning experience**.

INVESTIGATIVE PHENOMENON

 GO ONLINE to Engage with real-world phenomena by watching a video and to complete a CER interactive worksheet.

How do limestone caves form?

Reaction Rates and Equilibrium

Limestone caves are underground cavities formed in limestone rock. They often have icicle-like structures hanging from their ceilings and jutting upward from their floors. Once you have viewed the Investigative Phenomenon video and worked on a first draft of a Claim-Evidence-Reasoning exercise to help explain the phenomenon you observed, answer these reflection questions about limestone caves.

1. **CCC Cause and Effect** Some of the structures in the photo appear almost to be flowing. What does that observation indicate about the physical or chemical processes that might be acting in the cave? ✎

....

....

2. **CCC Stability and Change** How would you describe the rate of change in this system? Which observations from the photo or video are evidence that support your conclusion? Fill in the graphic organizer with your answer. ✎

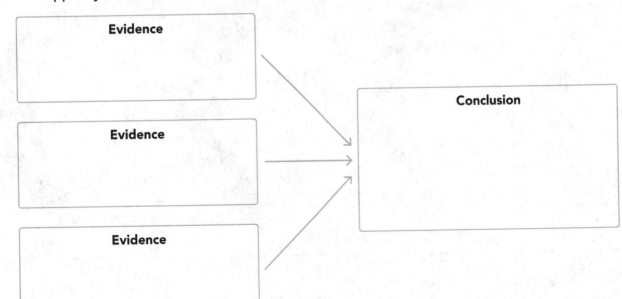

Rates of Reaction

🖥 **GO ONLINE** to Explore and Explain the relationships among particle collisions, temperature, concentration, and reaction rates.

Expressing Rates of Change

A **rate** is the ratio between two related quantities expressed in different units. Many rates describe how much something changes within a specified amount of time. Such rates can have time intervals ranging from less than a second to centuries or even longer. Average speed is an example of a rate. It is a change in distance over a given interval of time, or Δt.

$$\text{Average speed} = \frac{\text{change in distance}}{\text{change in time}} = \frac{\Delta d}{\Delta t}$$

For example, you can measure the average speed of a car in meters per second or in miles per hour. The measured speed is the same, just expressed in different units. The rates of chemical changes are usually described in terms of changes in concentration over time, although changes in mass, volume, and pressure over time are also used.

Changes Over Time You could measure the area of a banana's skin that turns from yellow to brown as it ripens over several days. That information would allow you to calculate a rate. By weighing it, you might also find that the mass of the banana changes, giving you another rate. As the banana begins to spoil, the change in color tells you that chemical changes are taking place.

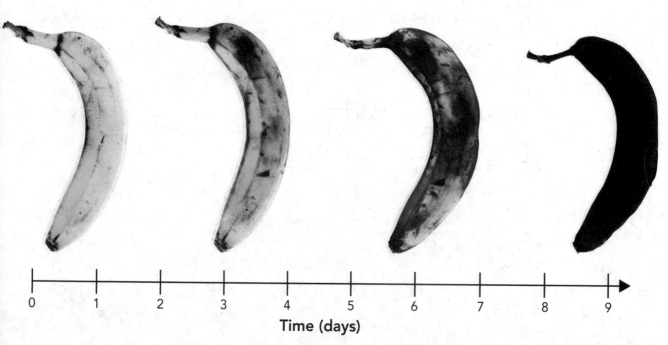

Time (days)

Calculating Reaction Rates

The **reaction rate** is the rate at which the reactants of a chemical reaction form the products. Reactions are commonly described in terms of concentration, written as [X] for a reactant or product X. Over a time interval from t_1 to t_2, the average rate of change of concentration of X can be determined from this relationship:

$$\text{Rate} = \frac{\Delta[X]}{\Delta t} = \frac{[X]_2 - [X]_1}{t_2 - t_1}$$

The calculated average rate can be negative, for a reactant, or positive, for a product. In order to avoid confusion, chemists define a single rate for a reaction that is always positive

and can be determined from any reactant or product. It is based on the stoichiometry of the reaction.

For a typical reaction with reactants A and B and product C, the equation $aA + bB \rightarrow cC$ tells you that a moles of reactant A and b moles of reactant B are consumed to produce c moles of product C. Using the stoichiometric equation, you can determine the reaction rate in terms of any reactant or product:

$$\text{Rate} = \frac{-1}{a} \times \frac{\Delta[A]}{\Delta t} = \frac{-1}{b} \times \frac{\Delta[B]}{\Delta t} = \frac{1}{c} \times \frac{\Delta[C]}{\Delta t}$$

Note that in the equation, each reactant has a factor of -1 to ensure the calculated reaction rate is positive.

Concentration Changes Over Time The purple gas iodine (I_2) reacts with hydrogen gas (H_2) to form the colorless gas hydrogen iodide (HI): $I_2(g) + H_2(g) \rightarrow 2HI(g)$. The graph shows the reaction rate by showing how [HI] and [I_2] change over time.

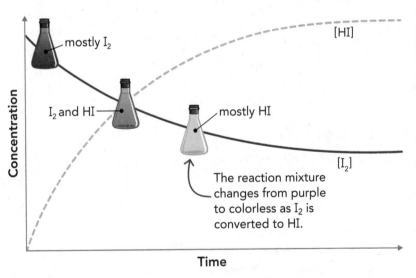

mostly I_2

I_2 and HI

mostly HI

The reaction mixture changes from purple to colorless as I_2 is converted to HI.

[HI]

[I_2]

Concentration

Time

The blue dashed line shows how [HI] changes over time. The line shows that the initial reaction rate is fast ([HI] increases quickly) and then becomes slower over time ([HI] increases slowly).

The purple solid line conveys the same information about reaction rate: the initial rate is fast ([I_2] decreases quickly) and later is slow ([I_2] decreases slowly).

(3) **SEP Construct an Explanation** Why do you think a reaction might start off fast and then slow down as time passes? *Hint:* Recall what you learned about collision theory in previous Investigations.

....

....

....

Calculating Reaction Rates

Hydrogen and iodine gas react to form hydrogen iodide, as shown in the equation $H_2(g) + I_2(g) \rightarrow 2HI(g)$. Suppose you are given a time interval from $t_1 = 10$ seconds to $t_2 = 20$ seconds and a change in H_2 concentration from 0.210 mol/L to 0.185 mol/L. Use the reaction rate equation to calculate the average reaction rate during that time period.

ANALYZE List the knowns and the unknown.

Knowns	Unknown
$[H_2]_1 = 0.210$ mol/L	Reaction rate = ? mol/L·s
$[H_2]_2 = 0.185$ mol/L	
$t_1 = 10$ s	
$t_2 = 20$ s	

CALCULATE Solve for the unknown.

Write the equation for average reaction rate.

$$\text{Reaction rate} = \frac{-1}{1} \times \frac{\Delta[H_2]}{\Delta t} = \frac{[H_2]_2 - [H_2]_1}{t_2 - t_1}$$

Substitute the knowns into the equation and solve.

$$\text{Reaction rate} = -1 \times \frac{0.185 \text{ mol/L} - 0.210 \text{ mol/L}}{20 \text{ s} - 10 \text{ s}}$$

$$= \frac{0.025 \text{ mol/L}}{10 \text{ s}}$$

$$= 0.0025 \text{ mol/L·s}$$

EVALUATE Does the result make sense?

The calculated rate, 0.0025 mol/L·s, is slow. That makes sense because the concentration of hydrogen gas changed very little (only 0.025 mol/L) in 10 seconds.

(4) For the same reaction between hydrogen and iodine, suppose you have a product concentration of 0.180 mol/L at time $t_1 = 15$ s and a concentration of 0.205 mol/L at time $t_2 = 20$ s. Calculate the average reaction rate for the time interval with respect to the product, HI. ✏

GO ONLINE for more practice problems.

Collision Theory—a Review

Collisions between molecules drive chemical reactions. Recall that collision theory is a model that is used to relate the properties of the colliding particles to the rates of chemical reactions. According to **collision theory,** in order for a collision to be effective, reactant particles must possess a sufficient amount of kinetic energy to break the necessary bonds in the reactants. They must also collide with the right orientation to form the bonds that make the products. The probability of bonds breaking in a collision depends on the kinetic energy of the collision being sufficient to break the necessary bond or bonds in the reactants.

Understanding Reactant Collisions
How must reactant particles collide to **react and form products?**

Incorrect Orientation When reactant particles such as NO_3 and CO collide with the wrong orientation, they bounce apart unchanged. The molecules are **not oriented in a way that allows the required new bonds to form.**

Too Little Energy Many collisions with the molecules oriented correctly are **not energetic enough to break the bonds in the reactant molecules.**

Reaction May Occur Some collisions of reactant particles **are energetic enough to break the bonds, and the orientation of molecules allows new bonds to form.**

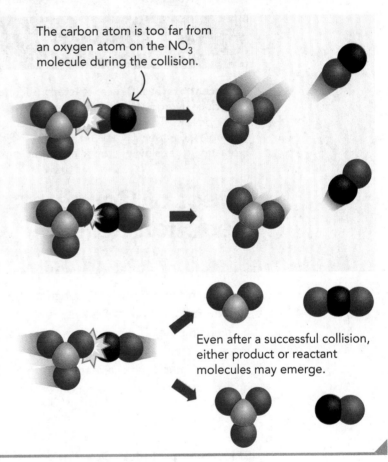

The carbon atom is too far from an oxygen atom on the NO_3 molecule during the collision.

Even after a successful collision, either product or reactant molecules may emerge.

(5) **CCC Patterns** For reacting gases, what effect do you think reducing the reaction vessel's volume has on the probability of reactant particles colliding and forming products? ✏️

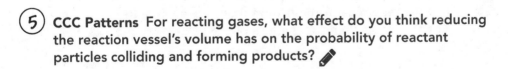

Concentrated vs. Dilute Reactant Sulfuric acid reacts with the metal zinc to produce hydrogen gas. On the left is a test tube with zinc and concentrated sulfuric acid. The reaction quickly produces a large volume of hydrogen gas bubbles. On the right is a test tube with zinc and dilute sulfuric acid. The reaction goes slowly, producing a small amount of hydrogen gas bubbles.

Effect of Concentration on Reaction Rates

From studying collision theory, you know that the rates of many reactions are dependent on reactant concentrations. In such cases, a higher concentration of reactants means a greater number of reactant molecules in a given volume. The result is more collisions per unit of time and, therefore, more collisions that are likely to lead to a reaction. Increasing concentration produces an increase in reaction rate for those cases. For reacting gases, notice you can increase the concentration by decreasing the volume of the reaction vessel.

SEP Develop Models Develop a molecular-level model that demonstrates what generally happens to particle collisions and reaction rates when higher concentrations of reactants are used. Refer to the reaction of zinc and sulfuric acid in the photo as an example. ✏

Effect of Temperature on Reaction Rates

As the temperature of a reaction system increases, the average kinetic energy of the reactant molecules increases. The increased kinetic energy usually means that molecular collisions have a higher probability of breaking bonds and forming new bonds because the molecules are moving faster and collide with greater force. The increased kinetic energy also means the molecules collide more often. Raising the temperature thus usually has a strong effect in increasing a reaction rate. Similarly, a decrease in temperature causes less frequent collisions, each one with lower energy, usually resulting in a decreased reaction rate.

Warm vs. Cool Reaction Conditions The reaction between magnesium and water produces magnesium hydroxide, which is colorless. In order to make the increasing concentration of magnesium hydroxide visible, an indicator that turns purple is added to the test tubes. The two test tubes have the same amounts of all components; the only difference is the temperature of the contents.

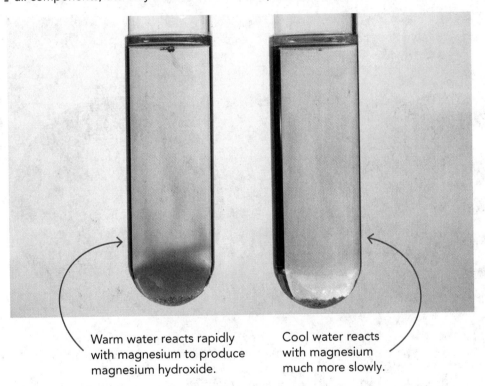

Warm water reacts rapidly with magnesium to produce magnesium hydroxide.

Cool water reacts with magnesium much more slowly.

(7) **CCC Cause and Effect** Food stored in a refrigerator can stay fresh for long periods. However, the same food stored at room temperature quickly spoils. How can you explain the difference in terms of collision theory? ✏

....

....

....

....

Effect of Particle Size on Reaction Rates

You probably know that crushed ice melts faster than ice cubes, or that a spoonful of granulated sugar dissolves more quickly than a sugar cube. Breaking up the ice or the sugar exposes more surface area, and the increase in surface area means that there is more area available for collisions. The increased surface area leads to an increase in the frequency of collisions and therefore speeds up the physical processes of melting and dissolving. The same is true for chemical reactions.

■ **Increasing a reactant's surface area causes an increase in the reaction rate.**

Many chemical manufacturing processes reduce the particle size of the reactants to increase reaction rates. In mining applications, for example, ore is crushed to expose more surface area and optimize the metal extraction process.

Small vs. Large Surface Area When heated in a flame in the presence of oxygen, the iron in steel can combust to form iron oxide. The rate of the reaction differs greatly as a result of the surface area of the metal that is available for collisions with oxygen molecules.

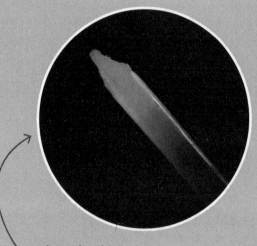

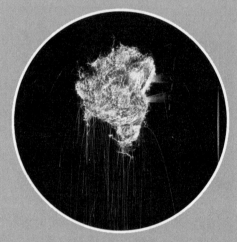

A steel nail, which has a small surface area, glows when it is heated. A tiny amount of iron on the surface of the nail reacts with oxygen to form iron oxide, but there are no sparks.

Steel wool is composed of small strands of steel, which have a large surface area. It reacts with oxygen more readily than the nail, producing a self-sustaining reaction that glows and sparks as the iron combusts.

(8) **CCC Cause and Effect** You may not think of wood as a dangerous material, but sawdust in the air of a woodworking shop can produce an explosion. Explain why sawdust is such a danger. ✏️

....

....

....

INVESTIGATIVE PHENOMENON

GO ONLINE to Elaborate on and Evaluate what you learned about reaction rates by completing the peer review and writing activities.

In the CER worksheet you completed at the beginning of the investigation, you suggested a possible explanation for the formation of limestone caves. With a partner, reevaluate the evidence and the explanation you presented.

9 **CCC Cause and Effect** Suppose changes in climate raised the temperature of the limestone rock in a cave by a small amount. What do you think would be the effect on the reactions that form the cave and the structures within it? Cave formation involves many processes, so you only need to discuss the processes you are sure take place. ✏

....

....

....

....

....

....

The Progress of Chemical Reactions

 GO ONLINE to Explore and Explain what is needed for colliding molecules to undergo a chemical reaction.

Activation Energy

Collision theory helps to explain why changes in conditions, such as temperature, concentration, and particle size can affect reaction rates. Recall that in addition to the correct orientation of the reactants, reactants must have sufficient kinetic energy to break existing bonds. The minimum energy requirement for colliding particles to react is known as the **activation energy.** You can think of the activation energy for a reaction as a barrier that reactants must overcome before products can form.

▮ Increasing the temperature of the reactants is a common way to provide the activation energy needed to start a chemical reaction.

Energy From Friction As the match head moves across the surface, its particles briefly adhere to the surface. Breaking that adhesion makes the particles in the match head vibrate. The energy of vibration supplies the activation energy to ignite the match.

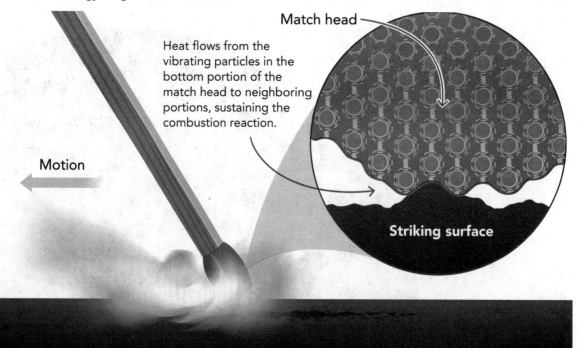

Match head

Heat flows from the vibrating particles in the bottom portion of the match head to neighboring portions, sustaining the combustion reaction.

Motion

Striking surface

Energy Diagrams

The **activated complex** is a transition state that exists for a short period of time in a chemical reaction as the bonds in the reactants are breaking and the bonds in the products are forming. The energy required for reactant particles to form the activated complex is the activation energy.

Understanding Energy Changes in Reactions
What aspects of **reactions are modeled** in energy diagrams?

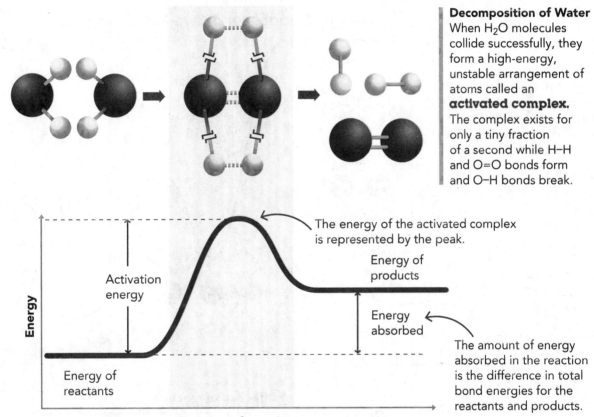

Decomposition of Water
When H_2O molecules collide successfully, they form a high-energy, unstable arrangement of atoms called an **activated complex.** The complex exists for only a tiny fraction of a second while H–H and O=O bonds form and O–H bonds break.

The energy of the activated complex is represented by the peak.

Energy of products

Activation energy

Energy absorbed

Energy

Energy of reactants

The amount of energy absorbed in the reaction is the difference in total bond energies for the reactants and products.

Direction of reaction

Dissecting the Diagram The vertical position of the left side of the curve represents the **energy in the bonds of reactants (2H$_2$O).** The higher position of the right side indicates greater **energy in the bonds of products (2H$_2$ and O$_2$).**

⑩ **CCC Patterns** Why is the activated complex always at a higher energy than the reactants and products? ✏

....

....

One-Step and Multistep Reactions

One-step reactions are reactions in which reactants are converted into products in a single step. Most reactions, however, are multistep reactions. A **reaction intermediate** is a product of one step in a multistep reaction and a reactant in a following step. Intermediates are consumed in the formation of the final products.

For multistep reactions, the slowest reaction is called the rate-determining step, and it affects the overall rate of a reaction. The higher the activation-energy requirement for a step, the slower is the reaction. Similarly, the lower the energy requirement, the faster is the reaction.

Energy Changes for a Two-Step Reaction

Step 1 has a greater activation energy than Step 2, so it is the rate-determining step in this two-step process in which H_2 reacts with ICl to form I_2 and HCl.

Hydrogen iodide (HI), the reaction intermediate, is formed from the reactants and reacts further to provide the final products in the chemical reaction.

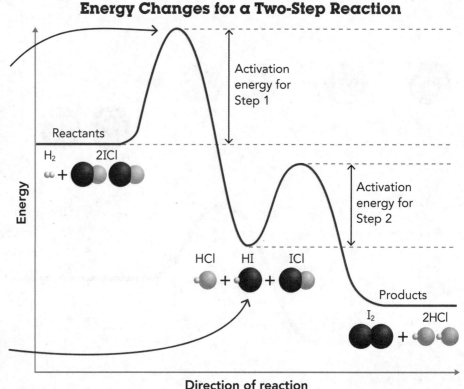

SEP **Construct an Explanation** Describe how the overall reaction rate is controlled by the slowest reaction in the multistep reaction.

....

....

....

....

Lowering Activation Energy

Catalysts Increasing temperature, increasing concentration, or reducing particle size are all ways of increasing reaction rates. Those factors increase reaction rates without affecting the activation energies for the reactions. A **catalyst** is a substance that increases reaction rates by providing a lower energy path for the reaction without being used up during the reaction. The way a catalyst increases a reaction rate is by reducing the activation energy for the reaction. With a lower energy requirement, a greater proportion of the molecules have enough energy to react, and the reaction rate increases.

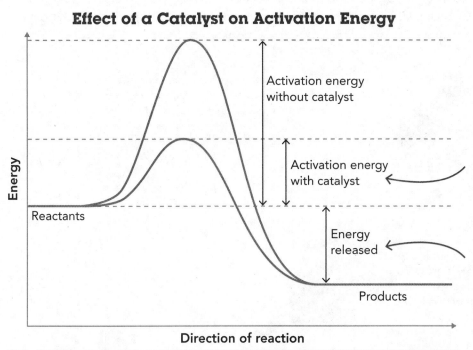

Effect of a Catalyst on Activation Energy

Activation energy without catalyst

Activation energy with catalyst

A catalyst reduces the amount of energy needed to initiate the reaction. Less energy is required to break the bonds in the reactant molecules.

Energy released

Although a catalyst reduces the energy required to initiate the reaction, the overall energy released during the reaction is not affected.

Reactants

Products

Energy

Direction of reaction

12. **SEP Develop a Model** Sketch a graph to show the changes in concentration for the reactants, the product, and the catalyst during this chemical reaction catalyzed by platinum: $2H_2 + O_2 \longrightarrow 2H_2O$. Use the vertical axis of your graph to represent concentration, and the horizontal axis to represent time.

Enzymes There are many important reactions in living systems that would proceed very slowly under normal conditions. The temperature may not be high enough to supply the activation energy to start the reaction. Reactant concentrations may be too low for reactions to occur quickly. Therefore, a biological catalyst called an enzyme is often needed. Enzymes are proteins or other molecules that fold into specific shapes to form indentations called active sites. There, reactant molecules bond with the enzyme. Enzymes help the reactants interact but are not used up in a reaction.

By bonding with the reactants, an enzyme forms an intermediate complex that lowers the activation energy needed to complete the reaction. An enzyme positions the reactants next to each other with the correct orientation for the reaction to proceed. Enzymes are effective in reactions involving small and large molecules. They also speed up decomposition reactions, not just combination reactions.

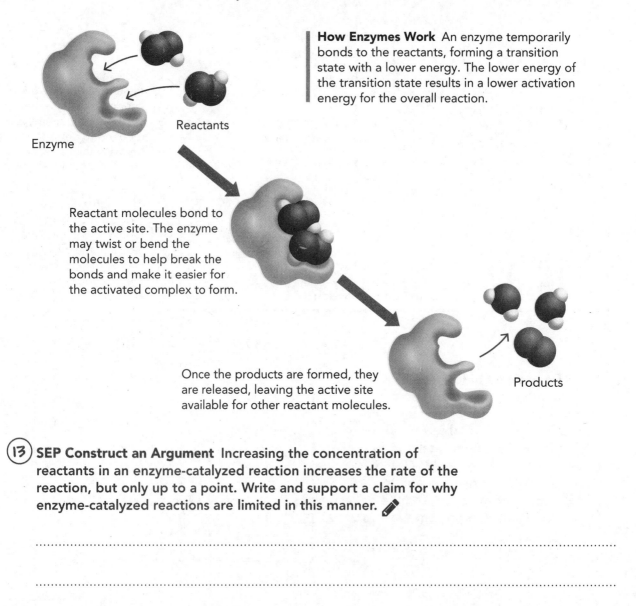

How Enzymes Work An enzyme temporarily bonds to the reactants, forming a transition state with a lower energy. The lower energy of the transition state results in a lower activation energy for the overall reaction.

Enzyme

Reactants

Reactant molecules bond to the active site. The enzyme may twist or bend the molecules to help break the bonds and make it easier for the activated complex to form.

Once the products are formed, they are released, leaving the active site available for other reactant molecules.

Products

(13) **SEP Construct an Argument** Increasing the concentration of reactants in an enzyme-catalyzed reaction increases the rate of the reaction, but only up to a point. Write and support a claim for why enzyme-catalyzed reactions are limited in this manner. ✏

....

....

....

INVESTIGATIVE PHENOMENON

GO ONLINE to Elaborate on and Evaluate what you learned about how reactions occur by completing the class discussion and data analysis activities.

In the CER worksheet you completed at the beginning of the investigation, you suggested a possible explanation for the formation of limestone caves. With a partner, reevaluate the evidence and the explanation you presented.

(14) **SEP Plan an Investigation** In this Experience, you have studied both endothermic reactions (in which products have more energy than reactants) and exothermic reactions (in which products have less energy). Are the chemical processes that form a cave and the structures within it exothermic or endothermic? What experiments could you conduct to find out? ✏️

....

....

....

....

....

Reversible Reactions and Equilibrium

GO ONLINE to Explore and Explain how reversible chemical reactions respond to changing conditions.

Reversible Reactions

When reactants are brought together, a reaction begins, and product concentrations build up. For some reactions, called **reversible reactions,** product molecules under ordinary conditions can react to form the original reactant molecules. Such a reaction can be represented with a double arrow in a chemical equation. The double arrow shows that the reaction proceeds in both directions.

$$2SO_2(g) + O_2(g) \rightleftharpoons 2SO_3(g)$$

In some reversible reactions, the products are favored. Chemists say that the forward reaction, in which the equation is read left to right, predominates, and they represent such a reaction with this arrow symbol: $\rightleftharpoons$. In other reversible reactions, the reactants are favored. Chemists say that the reverse reaction, in which the equation is read right to left, predominates, and they represent such a reaction with this arrow symbol: $\rightleftharpoons$.

Forward and Reverse Reactions The diagram models what happens at the molecular level for the reversible reaction involving SO_2, O_2, and SO_3. Molecules of SO_2 and O_2 react to form SO_3. As the concentration of the product, SO_3, increases, the reverse reaction is able to proceed at the same time as the forward reaction.

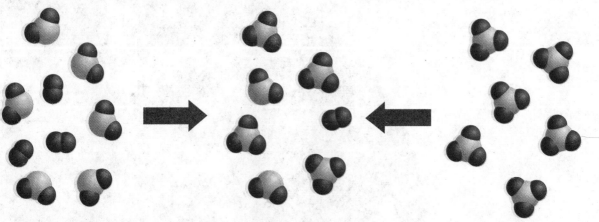

SO_2 and O_2 are reactants for the forward reaction and products for the reverse reaction.

The forward and reverse reactions are both happening, so all reaction species are present at any given time.

SO_3 is the product for the forward reaction and the reactant for the reverse reaction.

Equal Rates When the rate of water entering the bowl and the rate of water exiting the bowl are equal, the water level remains constant. The system is in equilibrium. You can compare the bowl to a reaction system at chemical equilibrium.

Chemical Equilibrium

Reversible reactions eventually reach **chemical equilibrium,** a state of balance in which the rates of the forward and reverse reactions are equal. In other words, the forward and reverse reactions are both happening at the same time and at the same rate.

▶ At equilibrium, the reactant and product concentrations are stable at the macroscopic level, even with constant changes happening at the molecular level.

The relative concentrations of the reactants and products at equilibrium mark the **equilibrium position** of the reaction. Reactions represented using the arrow ⇌ favor the formation of products. In such cases, the equilibrium position is one in which the products are more common. Reactions represented using the arrow ⇌ favor the formation of reactants, and the reactants are more common at equilibrium.

⑮ **CCC Stability and Change** Describe an everyday example of a system that achieves a state of balance. Describe how your example is similar to a reaction system at chemical equilibrium. 🖊

....

....

....

Le Châtelier's Principle

Chemical systems typically progress from states that are not in equilibrium to ones that are. But what happens to a system that has reached equilibrium if the conditions change? **Le Châtelier's principle** states that if a chemical system at equilibrium experiences a disturbance, it changes in a way that counteracts the change as it returns to equilibrium. You can apply Le Châtelier's principle to identify potential changes you can make to a reaction system to increase the amounts of desired reaction species at equilibrium.

Disturbing Equilibrium
How does a system at equilibrium respond to a change?

Equilibrium When docked, a ship bobs up and down in the water but maintains a stable position. **A chemical system at equilibrium is similar—the forward and reverse reactions still happen, but there is no net change.**

Disturbing the Equilibrium Although the ship-and-water system is a physical system, it responds to a change in a way similar to a chemical system at equilibrium.

New Equilibrium The loaded ship reaches a new stable position in the water. **When you change a chemical system at equilibrium, it also shifts to restore the equilibrium.**

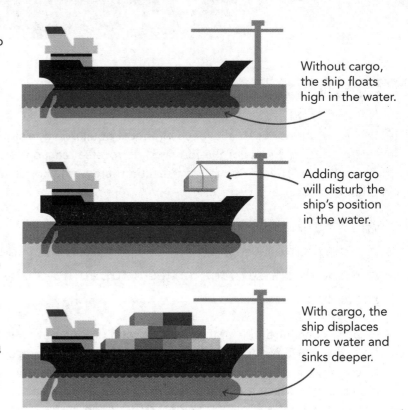

Without cargo, the ship floats high in the water.

Adding cargo will disturb the ship's position in the water.

With cargo, the ship displaces more water and sinks deeper.

---

(16) **CCC Cause and Effect** Use Le Châtelier's principle to predict what will happen if a chemical reaction system is disturbed by removing the product from the system through a precipitation reaction. ✏️

....

....

....

How Concentration Affects Equilibrium

At the molecular level, a disturbance involving a change to one component of a system at equilibrium affects other components. Changing the concentration of one component will change the rate of the forward or reverse reaction—whichever one the changed component is a reactant in—until the forward and reverse reaction rates are equal again. Consider the following reaction:

$$A + B \rightleftharpoons C$$

If a reactant concentration increases, then according to Le Châtelier's principle, the system counteracts the change. The reaction shifts to the right, converting reactants into products and lowering the reactant concentration. If a reactant concentration decreases, the reaction shifts to the left to increase reactant concentrations. Likewise, if product concentrations change, the reaction shifts to the left or the right to offset the change.

Balancing CO_2 and H_2CO_3 Carbon dioxide and carbonic acid in your blood follow this reversible reaction:

$$CO_2(aq) + H_2O(l) \rightleftharpoons H_2CO_3(aq)$$

Le Châtelier's principle explains how the system adjusts to minimize the effects of a disturbance.

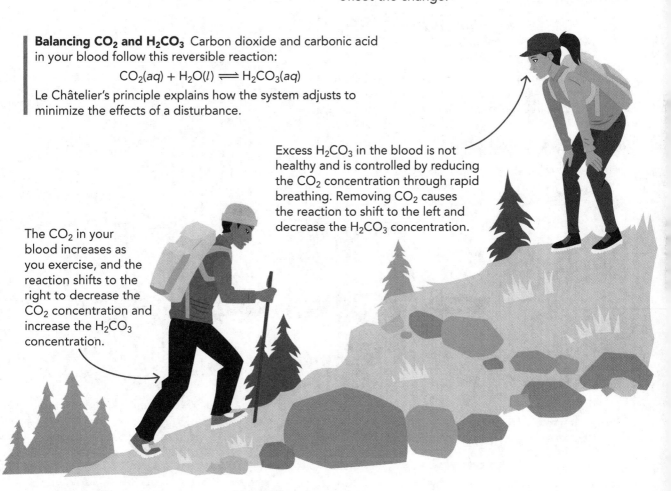

Excess H_2CO_3 in the blood is not healthy and is controlled by reducing the CO_2 concentration through rapid breathing. Removing CO_2 causes the reaction to shift to the left and decrease the H_2CO_3 concentration.

The CO_2 in your blood increases as you exercise, and the reaction shifts to the right to decrease the CO_2 concentration and increase the H_2CO_3 concentration.

(17) **SEP Design a Solution** Consider the following reversible reaction: $2CO(g) + O_2(g) \rightleftharpoons 2CO_2(g)$. Describe a way to increase the CO concentration at equilibrium. Explain your reasoning. ✏️

....

....

....

How Pressure Affects Equilibrium

If the volume of a gas mixture is changed, the pressure of the gases also changes. (You can think of a change in volume as a change in concentration, since the number of particles in a given volume changes.) According to Le Châtelier's principle, a disturbance in the pressure of a reaction mixture of gases at equilibrium shifts the system in a direction that offsets the change in pressure. Consider the reaction for the formation of hydrogen sulfide gas.

$$2H_2(g) + S_2(g) \rightleftharpoons 2H_2S(g)$$

When the system shifts to the right, three moles of gas are converted to two moles of gas. A decrease in the number of moles of gas results in a decrease in pressure. Therefore, a change in volume that results in an increase in pressure shifts the reaction to the right to decrease the number of gas molecules. Likewise, if the volume changes so that the pressure decreases, the reaction shifts to the left in order to produce a greater number of gas molecules.

Effect of Increasing Pressure If you push down on the piston, reducing the volume and increasing the pressure, the system shifts in the direction that has fewer molecules of gas.

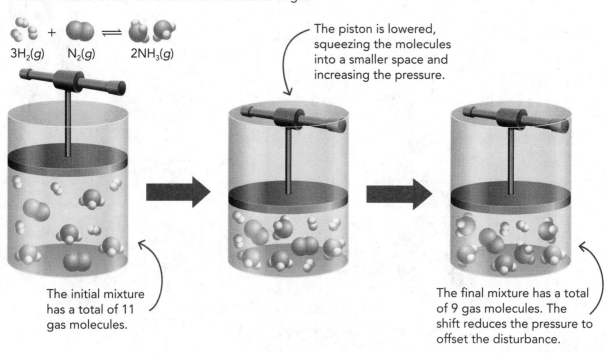

$3H_2(g)$ $N_2(g)$ $\rightleftharpoons$ $2NH_3(g)$

The piston is lowered, squeezing the molecules into a smaller space and increasing the pressure.

The initial mixture has a total of 11 gas molecules.

The final mixture has a total of 9 gas molecules. The shift reduces the pressure to offset the disturbance.

18) **SEP Use Models** Draw what happens to the equilibrium mixture of gases when the pressure increases for the following reaction: $2NO_2(g) \rightleftharpoons 2NO(g) + O_2(g)$. Assume the initial equilibrium mixture has two NO_2, four NO, and two O_2 molecules. ✏️

How Temperature Affects Equilibrium

When a system at equilibrium is disturbed by an increase in temperature, the reaction shifts in the direction that tends to decrease the temperature, meaning that it shifts in the direction that absorbs heat. Consider the following reaction:

$$N_2(g) + 3H_2(g) \rightleftharpoons 2NH_3(g) + \text{heat}$$

When ammonia is produced from nitrogen and hydrogen gas, heat is a product of the exothermic reaction. Raising the temperature of the reaction under equilibrium conditions causes the reaction to shift to the left, so less heat is released and more reactants are formed. The system absorbs heat to minimize an increase in temperature. Conversely, lowering the temperature shifts the reaction to the right, releasing heat and forming more products. The system produces heat to offset a decrease in temperature.

Effects of Heating and Cooling Nitrogen dioxide (NO_2) is a brown-colored gas produced when colorless dinitrogen tetroxide (N_2O_4) decomposes in the endothermic reaction $N_2O_4 + \text{heat} \rightleftharpoons 2NO_2$. The photo shows how the system shifts in response to heating and cooling the reaction mixture.

Warming the equilibrium mixture causes the reaction to shift to the right, absorbing heat. Absorbing heat helps to offset the increase in temperature and results in the formation of more of the brown gas NO_2.

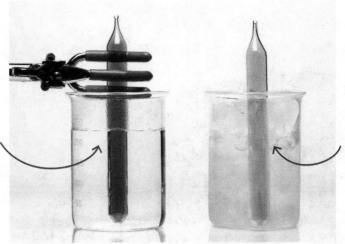

Cooling the equilibrium mixture causes the reaction to shift to the left, releasing heat and increasing the concentration of the colorless gas N_2O_4.

(19) **CCC Stability and Change** When the temperature is lowered for an exothermic reaction at equilibrium, which way does the reaction shift? Explain your reasoning using Le Châtelier's principle. 🖉

....

....

....

INVESTIGATIVE PHENOMENON

GO ONLINE to Elaborate on and Evaluate what you learned about reversible reactions by completing the class discussion and engineering design activities.

In the CER worksheet you completed at the beginning of the investigation, you suggested a possible explanation for the formation of limestone caves. With a partner, reevaluate the evidence and the explanation you presented.

20 **CCC Patterns** Burning coal with a high sulfur content can increase the acidity of precipitation. Using Le Châtelier's principle, explain how the increasing acidity of precipitation affects the processes that form limestone caves. 🖊

....

....

....

....

....

☑ASSESSMENT

GO ONLINE to Evaluate what you learned about reaction rates and equilibrium by using the available assessment resources.

In the Performance-Based Assessment, you explained the results of your investigations for the effects of changing reaction system conditions on equilibrium and reaction rate. Wrap up your explanation by answering the following questions.

21 **SEP Construct an Explanation** In measuring the variation with concentration for the rate of decomposition of hydrogen peroxide, what did you observe? Explain your observation in terms of collision theory. ✏️

....

....

....

....

....

22 **SEP Construct an Explanation** In measuring the variation with temperature for the dissolution of sodium acetate, what did you observe? Explain your observation in terms of collision theory. ✏️

....

....

....

....

....

23 **Revisit the Anchoring Phenomenon** How does what you learned in this investigation help explain the chemistry of ocean acidification? ✏️

....

....

....

▶ **GO ONLINE** to Engage with real-world phenomena by watching a video and to complete a CER interactive worksheet.

How does acid rain impact the environment?

Acid-Base Equilibria

Acid rain damages forests and stone structures and can kill fish, plants, and other organisms living in bodies of water. Government regulations and modern technologies help reduce acid rain. Once you have viewed the Investigative Phenomenon video and used the claim-evidence-reasoning worksheet to draft an explanation for what you observed, answer these reflection questions about acid rain.

1) **SEP Analyze Data** The two maps show acid rain pH levels in the years 1994 and 2017. Summarize what the data show. ✏️

Comparing the pH of Rain in Different U.S. Regions

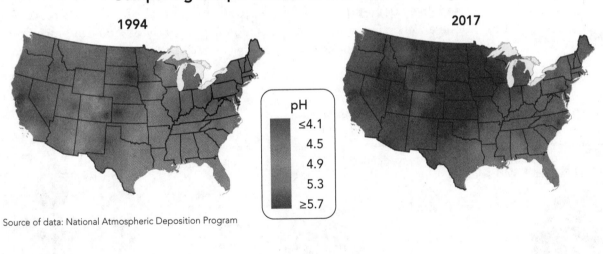

1994

2017

pH
≤4.1
4.5
4.9
5.3
≥5.7

Source of data: National Atmospheric Deposition Program

....

....

2) **SEP Obtain Information** Refer to the online "Lab pH" data for 2008 at the *National Atmospheric Deposition Program—Annual NTN Maps by Year.* Are the data shown by the 2008 map what you would expect to see? Explain. ✏️

....

....

....

Acids, Bases, and Salts

 GO ONLINE to Explore and Explain the properties and strengths of acids and bases and their effects on the pH of solutions.

Properties of Acids, Bases, and Salts

The word *acid* is derived from the Latin word *acidus*, which means "tart" or "sour." The vinegar in salad dressing contains ethanoic acid, CH_3COOH. It is commonly called acetic acid. Your stomach contains hydrochloric acid, HCl, which is used to digest food.

A base has a bitter taste and feels slippery. Various solutions that contain bases are commonly referred to as alkaline solutions. Soaps are often made using the common base sodium hydroxide, $NaOH$.

A salt is an ionic compound that usually consists of positive metal ions and negative nonmetal ions. Salts are produced when acids and bases react with one another. Dissolved salts in solution are electrolytes. You can precipitate a salt from a solution to form a crystalline solid.

Acids, Bases, and Salts in Everyday Life Before eating a meal, most people wash their hands with soap, which is made with basic substances. During the meal, people consume foods containing various acids and salts.

Table salt is used to add more flavor to food.

Ammonia is a base that is used to clean windows.

Citrus fruits (oranges and grapefruits) and vinegar used in salad dressings contain acids.

Defining Acids and Bases

Arrhenius Model of Acids and Bases There is more than one way to explain the behavior of acids and bases. The first explanation was proposed by the Swedish chemist Svante Arrhenius in 1887. In his model, acids are compounds that dissociate and form hydrogen cations, H^+, in an aqueous solution. However, in solution, the H^+ ion does not exist. Instead, a species called the **hydronium ion,** H_3O^+, forms when the dissociated H^+ ion combines with a water molecule, H_2O.

> **Hydrochloric Acid** Hydrochloric acid is actually an aqueous solution of hydrogen chloride. Hydrogen chloride forms hydronium ions, making the compound an acid.

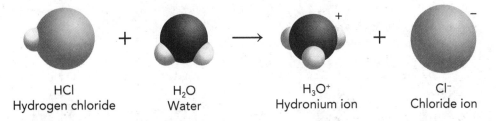

HCl	H₂O	H₃O⁺	Cl⁻
Hydrogen chloride	Water	Hydronium ion	Chloride ion

Arrhenius acids with only one hydrogen that can be ionized, such as hydrochloric acid, HCl, and nitric acid, HNO_3, are classified as monoprotic acids. The prefix *mono-* means "one," and *protic* means "proton," which is another way to describe a hydrogen cation. Carbonic acid, H_2CO_3, and sulfuric acid, H_2SO_4, are diprotic acids, as they contain two hydrogens that can be ionized. Phosphoric acid, H_3PO_4, is a triprotic acid.

An Arrhenius base is an ionic compound that releases a hydroxide ion, OH^-, when it dissociates in aqueous solution. For example, the compounds sodium hydroxide, NaOH, and potassium hydroxide, KOH, dissociate in aqueous solution to produce a metal ion and a hydroxide ion. They are both monoprotic bases. Calcium hydroxide, $Ca(OH)_2$, and magnesium hydroxide, $Mg(OH)_2$, are diprotic bases.

> **Sodium Hydroxide** Sodium hydroxide is an ionic solid that dissociates in water to form hydroxide ions, making this compound a base.

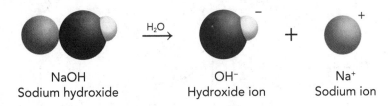

NaOH	OH⁻	Na⁺
Sodium hydroxide	Hydroxide ion	Sodium ion

(3) Apply Concepts Ethanoic acid, CH_3COOH, ionizes to form an ethanoate ion (CH_3COO^-) in aqueous solution. What else does it form? Is it a monoprotic acid?

Brønsted-Lowry Model of Acids and Bases According to the Arrhenius model, ammonia, NH_3, and sodium carbonate, Na_2CO_3, are not classified as bases because they do not contain at least one unit of OH in their chemical formulas. However, when you prepare solutions of NH_3 and Na_2CO_3, they react with water and produce hydroxide ions.

Johannes Brønsted and Thomas Lowry proposed a new way to define acids and bases. In their model, an acid is a hydrogen-ion donor and a base is a hydrogen-ion acceptor. For example, when ammonia and water react, a water molecule donates a hydrogen ion to an ammonia molecule. The reaction produces ammonium ions and hydroxide ions. Note that the Brønsted-Lowry model applies not just to aqueous solutions, but to any medium or phase. For instance, NH_3 and HCl are a base and an acid that can react in the gas phase.

Ammonia in Water Ammonia, NH_3, is a base because it accepts hydrogen ions. Water is an acid in this example because it donates hydrogen ions.

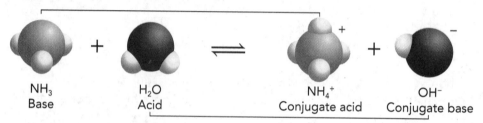

NH_3	H_2O	NH_4^+	OH^-
Base	Acid	Conjugate acid	Conjugate base

In the Brønsted-Lowry model, the products of acid-base reactions are referred to as conjugates. A **conjugate acid** is the ion or molecule formed when a base gains a hydrogen ion. A **conjugate base** is the ion or molecule that remains after an acid donates a hydrogen ion. A **conjugate acid-base pair** consists of two ions or molecules related by the loss or gain of one hydrogen ion.

Conjugate Acid-Base Pairs Conjugate acids are always paired with bases, and conjugate bases are always paired with acids. The table shows several examples, including the ammonium ion, NH_4^+, which is the conjugate acid of the base ammonia, NH_3.

Hydrogen chloride is a Brønsted-Lowry acid. The chloride ion is the conjugate base of the acid HCl.

Water is amphoteric, which means it can act as either an acid (donate H^+) or a base (accept H^+).

Note that OH^- and H_3O^+ are not conjugates of each other because they differ by more than one hydrogen ion.

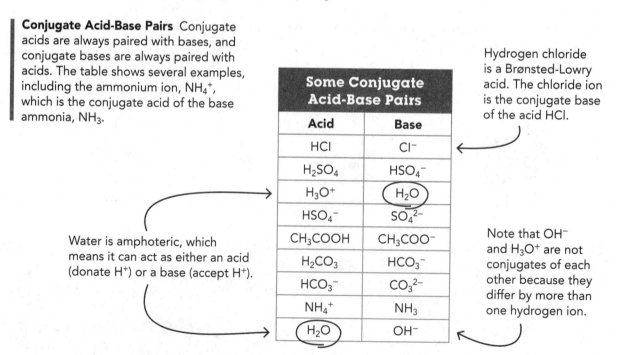

Some Conjugate Acid-Base Pairs	
Acid	**Base**
HCl	Cl^-
H_2SO_4	HSO_4^-
H_3O^+	H_2O
HSO_4^-	SO_4^{2-}
CH_3COOH	CH_3COO^-
H_2CO_3	HCO_3^-
HCO_3^-	CO_3^{2-}
NH_4^+	NH_3
H_2O	OH^-

Lewis Model of Acids and Bases Another model used to classify acids and bases was developed by Gilbert Lewis. Instead of donated or accepted hydrogen ions (as in the Brønsted-Lowry model), the Lewis model uses electron pairs. A **Lewis base** is a substance that donates a pair of electrons to form a covalent bond. A **Lewis acid** is a substance that accepts a pair of electrons to form a covalent bond.

▶ **The Lewis model of acids and bases is the broadest of the three models.**

The Lewis model extends to substances that cannot be classified as acids and bases according to either the Arrhenius or Brønsted-Lowry models.

Electron Donors and Acceptors Lewis bases donate pairs of electrons. Lewis acids accept pairs of electrons.

Electron dot structures make it easy to see that the fluoride ion and the ammonia molecule act as Lewis bases in donating electrons.

(4) **SEP Construct an Explanation** When hydrogen chloride gas is added to water, the products are hydronium ions and chloride ions. Explain why, according to the Brønsted-Lowry and Lewis models, water can be described as a base in the reaction. ✏

....

....

....

(5) **SEP Use Models** Use electron dot structures to model the reaction between NH_3 and BF_3. Use an arrow to show how the electron pair is donated. Identify the Lewis acid, Lewis base, and the electron pair. ✏

Changing Concentrations In pure water, the concentrations of H_3O^+ and OH^- change at the molecular level, but the concentrations at the macroscopic level are equal and constant.

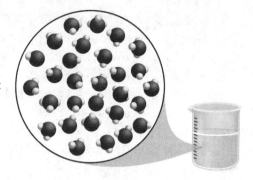

The Self-Ionization of Water

Pure water ionizes to a minimal extent to form hydronium ions (H_3O^+) and hydroxide ions (OH^-). The process happens because water is an amphoteric substance, and two molecules of water can react with each other, one acting as an acid and the other as a base. The process is reversible and is called the self-ionization of water.

$$H_2O(l) + H_2O(l) \rightleftharpoons H_3O^+(aq) + OH^-(aq)$$

Recall that brackets around a species means "concentration of." For example, $[H_3O^+]$ represents the concentration of hydronium ions. In pure water at 25°C, the concentration of H_3O^+ is only $1 \times 10^{-7}M$. The concentration of OH^- is also $1 \times 10^{-7}M$, as the amount of H_3O^+ ions and the amount of OH^- ions are equal in pure water. Any aqueous solution in which $[H_3O^+]$ and $[OH^-]$ are equal is a **neutral solution.**

In water or aqueous solutions at 25°C, the product of the hydronium-ion concentration and the hydroxide-ion concentration, known as the **ion-product constant for water** (K_w), equals 1.0×10^{-14}.

$$K_w = [H_3O^+] \times [OH^-] = 1.0 \times 10^{-14}$$

Reversible Reaction The self-ionization of water is a reversible ionization. The reactants are H_2O molecules, and the products are H_3O^+ and OH^- ions.

According to Le Châtelier's principle, if the system is disturbed, it will adjust to restore equilibrium. When $[H_3O^+]$ increases, $[OH^-]$ decreases. Likewise, when $[H_3O^+]$ decreases, $[OH^-]$ increases.

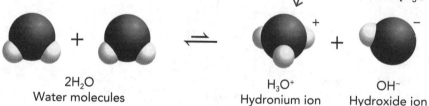

2H₂O
Water molecules

H₃O⁺
Hydronium ion

OH⁻
Hydroxide ion

6 **SEP Use Mathematics** For each given $[H_3O^+]$ or $[OH^-]$, find the corresponding $[OH^-]$ or $[H_3O^+]$ at 25°C. 🖊

$[H_3O^+] = 1.00 \times 10^{-10}M$ $[OH^-] = $ ....

$[OH^-] = 1.00 \times 10^{-4}M$ $[H_3O^+] = $ ....

$[H_3O^+] = 9.90 \times 10^{-6}M$ $[OH^-] = $ ....

Calculating pH

Instead of expressing hydronium ion concentration, $[H_3O^+]$, in molarity, the logarithmic pH scale is used to express $[H_3O^+]$. The pH of a solution is the negative logarithm of the hydronium ion concentration. Thus, every unit decrease in pH corresponds to a tenfold increase in $[H_3O^+]$. The pH is represented using the following equation.

$$pH = -\log[H_3O^+]$$

A solution with a pH of 7.0, such as pure water, is neutral.

$$pH = -\log(1 \times 10^{-7}) = 7.0$$

Summarizing pH Concepts

What are the relationships among $[H_3O^+]$, $[OH^-]$, and pH?

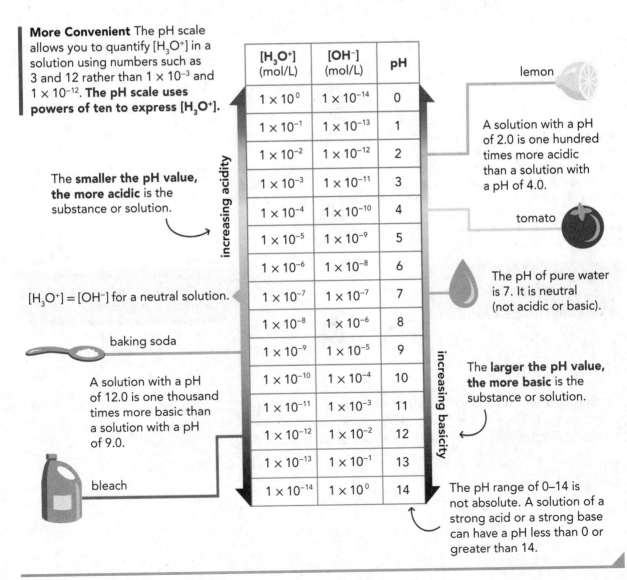

More Convenient The pH scale allows you to quantify $[H_3O^+]$ in a solution using numbers such as 3 and 12 rather than 1×10^{-3} and 1×10^{-12}. **The pH scale uses powers of ten to express $[H_3O^+]$.**

The **smaller the pH value, the more acidic** is the substance or solution.

$[H_3O^+] = [OH^-]$ for a neutral solution.

baking soda

A solution with a pH of 12.0 is one thousand times more basic than a solution with a pH of 9.0.

bleach

increasing acidity

$[H_3O^+]$ (mol/L)	$[OH^-]$ (mol/L)	pH
1×10^{0}	1×10^{-14}	0
1×10^{-1}	1×10^{-13}	1
1×10^{-2}	1×10^{-12}	2
1×10^{-3}	1×10^{-11}	3
1×10^{-4}	1×10^{-10}	4
1×10^{-5}	1×10^{-9}	5
1×10^{-6}	1×10^{-8}	6
1×10^{-7}	1×10^{-7}	7
1×10^{-8}	1×10^{-6}	8
1×10^{-9}	1×10^{-5}	9
1×10^{-10}	1×10^{-4}	10
1×10^{-11}	1×10^{-3}	11
1×10^{-12}	1×10^{-2}	12
1×10^{-13}	1×10^{-1}	13
1×10^{-14}	1×10^{0}	14

increasing basicity

lemon

A solution with a pH of 2.0 is one hundred times more acidic than a solution with a pH of 4.0.

tomato

The pH of pure water is 7. It is neutral (not acidic or basic).

The **larger the pH value, the more basic** is the substance or solution.

The pH range of 0–14 is not absolute. A solution of a strong acid or a strong base can have a pH less than 0 or greater than 14.

Writing $[H_3O^+]$ in scientific notation makes it easier to calculate pH. For example, it is easier to express 0.000010M as $1.0 \times 10^{-5}M$. When the coefficient in front of the power of 10 is 1, the pH is simply the negative of the exponent. The 0.000010M solution has $[H_3O^+] = 1.0 \times 10^{-5}M$ and a pH of 5.0. When the coefficient is a number other than 1, you can use logarithms to calculate the pH. If an acid has $[H_3O^+] = 2.0 \times 10^{-6}M$, you need to find the negative of the logarithm of 2.0×10^{-6}. A calculator will tell you that the negative of the logarithm is 5.7.

Sometimes it is useful to work with $[OH^-]$ instead of $[H_3O^+]$. Then you can use the quantity pOH, which is defined in a way similar to pH.

$$pOH = -\log [OH^-]$$

You can use pH and pOH to rewrite the K_w expression.

$$pH + pOH = 14.$$

Acidic, Neutral, and Basic Solutions A solution is acidic, neutral, or basic depending on whether its hydronium ion concentration is greater than, equal to, or less than its hydroxide ion concentration.

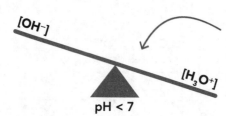

Acidic Solutions that contain more hydronium ions than hydroxide ions are acidic. The pH of those solutions is less than 7. For example, a solution with $[H_3O^+] = 1.0 \times 10^{-2}M$ has a $[OH^-] = 1.0 \times 10^{-12}M$ and has a pH of 2.

Neutral Solutions that contain the same amount of hydronium ions and hydroxide ions are neutral. Such solutions have a pH of 7. The hydronium ion and hydroxide ion concentrations in neutral solutions are the same $(1.0 \times 10^{-7}M)$.

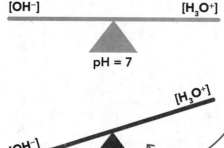

Basic Solutions that contain more hydroxide ions than hydronium ions are basic. The pH of those solutions is greater than 7. For example, a solution with $[H_3O^+] = 1.0 \times 10^{-12}M$ has a $[OH^-] = 1.0 \times 10^{-2}M$ and has a pH of 12.

(7) **SEP Use Mathematics** Three solutions have pH values of 6, 7, and 11. How much more acidic is the pH 6 solution than the pH 7 solution if acidity is defined as $[H_3O^+]$? How much more basic is the pH 11 solution than the pH 7 solution if basicity is defined as $[OH^-]$? ✎

Calculating pH from H_3O^+ Concentration

What is the pH of a solution with a hydronium ion concentration of $4.2 \times 10^{-10}M$?

ANALYZE List the known and the unknown.

Known	Unknown
$[H_3O^+] = 4.2 \times 10^{-10}M$	pH = ?

CALCULATE Solve for the unknown.

Start with the equation for finding pH from $[H_3O^+]$.

$$pH = -\log[H_3O^+]$$

Substitute the known $[H_3O^+]$ and use the log function on your calculator to calculate the pH.

$$pH = -\log (4.2 \times 10^{-10})$$
$$= -(-9.37675)$$
$$= 9.37675$$

Round the pH to two decimal places because the hydronium concentration has two significant figures.

$$= 9.38$$

EVALUATE Does the result make sense?

The value of the hydronium ion concentration is between $1 \times 10^{-9}M$ and $1 \times 10^{-10}M$. So, the calculated pH should be between 9 and 10, which it is.

(8) What are the pH values of the following solutions, based on their H_3O^+ concentrations? 🖊

a. $[H_3O^+] = 1.4 \times 10^{-4}M$

b. $[H_3O^+] = 8.7 \times 10^{-12}M$

GO ONLINE for more practice problems.

Strengths of Acids and Bases

The classification of acids and bases as strong or weak is based on the degree to which they ionize in water. A general way to represent Arrhenius acid reactions in equation form uses "HA" for acids. Ionization of an acid (HA) in water yields H_3O^+ and an anion (A^-).

$$HA(aq) + H_2O(l) \rightleftharpoons H_3O^+(aq) + A^-(aq)$$

A hydroxide salt acts as a base by releasing a hydroxide ion. Other bases do not dissociate but instead remove a hydrogen ion from water. A general equation for a base reaction can be written using "B."

$$B(aq) + H_2O(l) \rightleftharpoons BH^+(aq) + OH^-(aq)$$

Comparing Strong and Weak Acids The bar graphs show the extent of ionization of a strong acid and weak acid. Strong acids, like HCl, ionize completely in aqueous solutions, while weak acids, such as HCOOH, only ionize slightly.

$$HCl(g) + H_2O(l) \longrightarrow H_3O^+(aq) + Cl^-(aq)$$

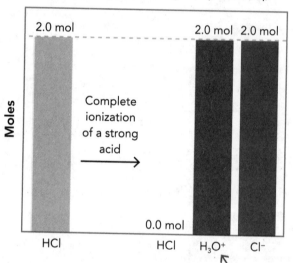

All of the HCl molecules ionize in solution, so $[H_3O^+]$ is high in an aqueous solution of a **strong acid.**

$$HCOOH(aq) + H_2O(l) \rightleftharpoons H_3O^+(aq) + HCOO^-(aq)$$

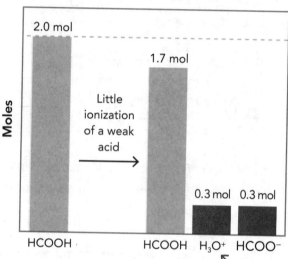

Only a small fraction of the HCOOH molecules ionize in solution, so $[H_3O^+]$ is low in an aqueous solution of a **weak acid.**

9 **Apply Concepts** Suppose four beakers contain 0.01M solutions of monoprotic acids and bases. Solution A has a pH of 10, solution B has a pH of 12, solution C has a pH of 2, and solution D has a pH of 4. Identify each solution as a strong or weak acid or base. Explain. ✏️

....

....

....

Revisit

INVESTIGATIVE PHENOMENON

GO ONLINE to Elaborate on and Evaluate your knowledge of acids, bases, and pH by completing the peer review and writing activities.

In the CER worksheet you completed at the beginning of the investigation, you constructed an explanation for how acid rain can affect a forest. With a partner, reevaluate the evidence you cited in your arguments.

10 **SEP Develop Models** Rain is naturally acidic. Carbon dioxide in the atmosphere dissolves to some extent in water and reacts with it to produce a slightly acidic solution of carbonic acid:

$$CO_2(g) + H_2O(l) \rightarrow H_2CO_3(aq)$$

$$H_2CO_3(aq) + H_2O(l) \rightleftharpoons H_3O^+(aq) + HCO_3^-(aq)$$

The carbonic acid ionizes slightly, leading to rain with a pH around 5.3. Acid rain has pH levels lower than 4.3, as it contains SO_x and NO_x. Complete the equations showing how SO_2 and NO_3 produce sulfuric acid and nitric acid and contribute to rain with lower pH. *Hint:* Use the patterns you observe among the following chemical equations and the provided chemical equations for carbon dioxide. ✏️

SO₂ Reactions

$$SO_3(g) + H_2O(l) \rightarrow \text{..............................}$$

$$H_2SO_4(aq) + H_2O(l)$$
$$\rightarrow \text{..........................} + HSO_4^-(aq)$$

$$\text{..........................} + H_2O(l)$$
$$\rightarrow H_3O^+(aq) + SO_4^{2-}(aq)$$

NO₃ Reactions

$$2NO_2(g) + \text{.....................} \rightarrow HNO_3(aq) + HNO_2(aq)$$

$$2HNO_2(aq) + O_2(g) \rightarrow \text{............................}$$

$$HNO_3(aq) + H_2O(l) \rightarrow H_3O^+(aq) + \text{........................}$$

155

Reactions of Acids and Bases

GO ONLINE to Explore and Explain neutralization reactions and acid-base titrations.

Acid-Base Neutralization Reactions

A reaction in which an acid and a base in an aqueous solution produce a salt and water is called a **neutralization reaction.** Such a reaction can be written with this general form:

$$Acid + Base \rightarrow Salt + Water$$

A neutralization reaction is complete when both reactants are entirely consumed. When a strong acid such as HCl reacts with a strong base such as KOH, a salt solution with a neutral pH results.

$$HCl(aq) + KOH(aq) \rightarrow KCl(aq) + H_2O(l)$$

However, other types of neutralization reactions do not generally result in neutral solutions.

Increasing the pH of a Lake A lake can be made less acidic by adding a base such as lime, $Ca(OH)_2$, to it. The dusty cloud contains lime, which dissolves in the lake, releasing OH^- ions. The OH^- ions react with H_3O^+ ions in the lake to form water and reduce the lake's acidity, moving the pH closer to neutral.

Mole Ratios in Acid-Base Reactions

How do you **determine mole ratios** in neutralization reactions?

Identifying Mole Ratios The ratio between the numbers of moles of substances involved in a reaction is called the mole ratio. **Use the coefficients in the balanced chemical equation to identify the mole ratio of one substance to another.**

Balancing H_3O^+ and OH^- When ionized, a monoprotic acid, such as HCl, forms one H_3O^+ ion in solution. The diprotic acid H_2SO_4 forms two H_3O^+ ions when ionized. In each case, **an equivalent number of OH^- ions are needed to neutralize the H_3O^+ ions.**

The balanced chemical equation shows that it takes one mole of NaOH to neutralize one mole of the monoprotic acid HCl. **The mole ratio is 1:1.**

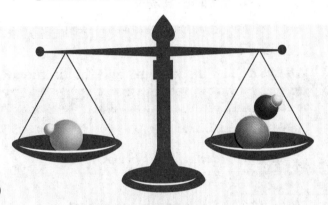

$$1HCl(aq) + 1NaOH(aq) \longrightarrow NaCl(aq) + H_2O(l)$$

The balanced chemical equation shows that it takes two moles of NaOH to neutralize one mole of the diprotic acid H_2SO_4. **The mole ratio is 1:2.**

$$1H_2SO_4(aq) + 2NaOH(aq) \longrightarrow Na_2SO_4(aq) + 2H_2O(l)$$

---

11 **CCC Cause and Effect** Shown here is a balanced equation for the neutralization reaction of hydrochloric acid and calcium hydroxide.

$$2HCl(aq) + Ca(OH)_2(aq) \rightarrow CaCl_2(aq) + 2H_2O(l)$$

Explain what happens if you add 2 moles or 0.5 moles of $Ca(OH)_2$ to a solution containing 2 moles of HCl.

....

....

....

....

Finding the Moles Needed for Neutralization

The term *neutralization* is used to describe both the reaction type and the point at which a neutralization reaction is complete. How many moles of sulfuric acid are required to neutralize 0.50 mol of sodium hydroxide? The chemical equation for the reaction is

$$H_2SO_4(aq) + 2NaOH(aq) \rightarrow Na_2SO_4(aq) + 2H_2O(l)$$

ANALYZE List the knowns and the unknown.

Knowns	Unknown
mol NaOH = 0.50 mol	mol H_2SO_4 = ? mol
1 mol H_2SO_4 reacts with 2 mol NaOH	

CALCULATE Solve for the unknown.

Write the mole ratio of acid to base as a conversion factor.

$$\text{mole ratio} = \frac{1 \text{ mol } H_2SO_4}{2 \text{ mol NaOH}}$$

Multiply the number of moles of NaOH by the conversion factor to determine the number of moles of H_2SO_4.

$$0.50 \text{ mol NaOH} \times \frac{1 \text{ mol } H_2SO_4}{2 \text{ mol NaOH}} = 0.25 \text{ mol } H_2SO_4$$

EVALUATE Does the result make sense?

Because the mole ratio of H_2SO_4 to NaOH is 1:2, the number of moles of H_2SO_4 should be half the number of moles of NaOH.

(12) The neutralization reaction of potassium hydroxide and sulfuric acid is as follows:

$$2KOH(aq) + H_2SO_4(aq) \rightarrow K_2SO_4(aq) + 2H_2O(l)$$

Use the equation to calculate how many moles of KOH are needed to neutralize 0.45 mol of H_2SO_4. ✏️

GO ONLINE for more practice problems.

Salt Solutions and Salt Hydrolysis

Salt Hydrolysis Recall that a salt is one of the products of a neutralization reaction. The acid contributes an anion and the base contributes a cation. **Salt hydrolysis** is a process in which the cations or anions of a dissociated salt accept hydrogen ions from water or donate hydrogen ions to water.

Consider $NaCH_3COO$, the salt of a weak acid and a strong base. In solution, the salt is completely ionized, forming ethanoate ions (CH_3COO^-) and sodium ions (Na^+). The ethanoate ion is a Brønsted-Lowry base, which means it is a hydrogen ion acceptor. At equilibrium, the reactants are favored in the reversible reaction. Therefore a solution of $NaCH_3COO$ is only slightly basic.

$$CH_3COO^-(aq) + H_2O(l) \rightleftharpoons CH_3COOH(aq) + OH^-(aq)$$

Similarly, the salt of a weak base and a strong acid forms an acidic solution, because the conjugate acid donates a hydrogen ion to a water molecule. In contrast, a strong acid or base ionizes completely, and the reverse reaction happens only to a negligible degree. As a result, the conjugate base of a strong acid does not have appreciable basic properties, and the conjugate of a strong base does not have appreciable acidic properties.

(13) **SEP Use Models** Use a chemical equation to explain how the carbonate ions in Mono Lake contribute to its alkalinity. ✏️

....

....

Mono Lake Due to high concentrations of salts that contain carbonates, the lake is alkaline with a pH close to 10. The calcium carbonate formations in the lake are called tufa towers.

Qualitative Determination of pH When they are in solution, the anion and the cation of a salt separate, and each ion acts independently with the water molecules in the solution. Some ions react with water molecules in a way that changes the pH of a solution. For example, the cation NH_4^+ is the conjugate acid of a weak base. It is a Brønsted-Lowry acid that reacts with water to form hydronium ions, making the solution acidic. The anion F^-, the conjugate base of a weak acid, reacts with water to form hydroxide ions, making the solution basic. Such ions are called acidic cations and basic anions, respectively. Other cations (such as Na^+) or anions (such as Cl^-) do not interfere with pH. They are called neutral ions.

■ **The acid-base properties of the ions that make up a salt determine whether a solution of that salt is acidic, neutral, or basic.**

When one or both ions that form a salt are neutral, the prediction is simple. When the cation is acidic and the anion is basic, predicting the pH of a solution requires more information. The pH of such solutions depend on the relative acid-base strengths of the cation and anion.

Neutral cation + **neutral** anion = **neutral** solution
Example: NaCl solution

Acidic cation + **neutral** anion = **acidic** solution
Example: NH_4Cl solution

Neutral cation + **basic** anion = **basic** solution
Example: NaF solution

Acidic cation + **basic** anion = varies
Example: NH_4CN solution

The Effect of Ions on pH		
Ion Type	**How It Affects pH**	**Examples**
Conjugate base of a strong acid or a spectator ion	No effect; results in a **neutral** solution	Cl^-, Br^-, I^-, NO_3^-, Na^+, K^+, Mg^{2+}
Conjugate base of a weak acid	Hydrolyzes; results in a **basic** solution	CH_3COO^-, HCO_3^-, F^-, CN^-
Conjugate acid of a weak base	Hydrolyzes; results in an **acidic** solution	NH_4^+, $C_5H_5NH^+$

(14) **SEP Analyze Data** Use the table to predict whether NH_4Br will form an acidic, neutral, or basic solution. Explain. ✏️

....

....

....

Using the Conjugate-Seesaw Analogy You can think about the relative strengths of the ions that make up a salt and the acid and base that formed the salt as being like objects on seesaws. As with a seesaw, the closer to the ground is one side, the farther from the ground is the other side. When an acid is very strong (at the bottom of the seesaw), the conjugate base is so weak (at the top of the seesaw) that it has no effect on pH. The analogy is appropriate because the strength of an acid and its conjugate base or a base and its conjugate acid are balanced in exactly the same way $[H_3O^+]$ and $[OH^-]$ are balanced with reference to K_w.

How Ions Affect pH

How can you tell whether a salt solution is **acidic, basic, or neutral?**

Consider the Conjugates You can use conjugate seesaws to predict whether a salt solution is acidic, basic, or neutral. **The stronger an acid or base, the weaker is its conjugate. The weaker an acid or base, the stronger is its conjugate.**

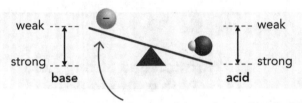

HCl is a **very strong acid, so the conjugate ion Cl⁻ is neutral.** It does not affect pH.

An aqueous solution of the salt NH_4Cl is slightly acidic because NH_4^+ is the only ion involved that affects pH.

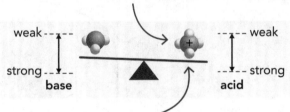

NH_3 is a **weak base, so its conjugate acid NH_4^+ is a weak acid.** A solution with only NH_4^+ would be slightly acidic.

In a solution of NH_4F, both ions affect pH. To determine which ion affects pH more, consider the relative strengths of NH_3 and HF. HF is stronger than NH_3, so F^- is weaker than NH_4^+. Thus, NH_4^+ wins, and the solution is slightly acidic.

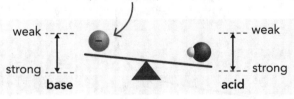

HF is a **weak acid, so its conjugate base F^- is a weak base.** A solution with only F^- would be slightly basic.

(15) **SEP Construct an Explanation** Use the irreversible ionization equation of HCl gas in water and the Brønsted-Lowry model of acids and bases to explain why the Cl^- ion is such a weak base that it can be considered a neutral ion. 🖋

....

....

Acid-Base Titrations

An important method for investigating the interactions of acids and bases is a **titration,** in which a volume of a solution of known concentration is added to a solution of known volume but unknown concentration. The solution of known concentration, called the standard solution, is added in small measured increments until the neutralization reaction is complete. The unknown concentration can then be calculated from the number of moles in the added volume of the standard solution.

Neutralization occurs when the numbers of moles of H_3O^+ and OH^- are equal, and the point in a titration where neutralization occurs is called the **equivalence point.** A simple way to tell when the equivalence point is reached is to add a material that changes color at the equivalence point, called an acid-base indicator.

You can also estimate the equivalence point by following the change in the unknown solution's pH as the standard solution is added. The graph of the unknown solution's pH versus the volume of standard solution added during a titration is called a **titration curve.**

Titration Curve In this titration, the standard solution, 0.10M NaOH, is slowly added to 50.0 mL of an HCl solution. The pH of the solution is measured and recorded periodically.

Beyond the equivalence point (pH > 8), the indicator is blue.

At the equivalence point (pH = 7), the indicator is green. Neutralization occurs when 50.0 mL of NaOH is added to the flask. The titration data allow you to find the concentration of HCl, 0.10M.

Below the equivalence point (pH < 6), the indicator is yellow.

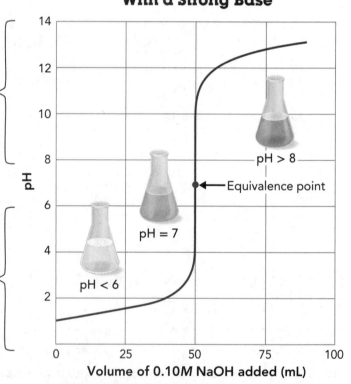

Titration of a Strong Acid With a Strong Base

(16) **SEP Use Mathematics** How many milliliters of 0.450M HCl will neutralize 25.0 mL of 1.00M KOH?

Titrations and pH Curves

The shape of the titration curve not only makes it possible to determine the equivalence point in the titration but also allows you to select a suitable indicator. When NaOH is titrated with HCl, the curve is the mirror image of the strong acid–strong base titration, with pH decreasing throughout the titration. The reaction produces a neutral salt, and the equivalence point is at pH = 7.

When a weak acid such as CH_3COOH is titrated with a strong base such as NaOH, the curve shows pH increasing. The salt produced in the reaction is $NaCH_3COO$. Recall that Na^+ does not affect pH, and CH_3COO^-, the conjugate base of a weak acid, reacts with water molecules to increase the pH. Thus, the equivalence point is at a pH greater than 7, at pH = 9.

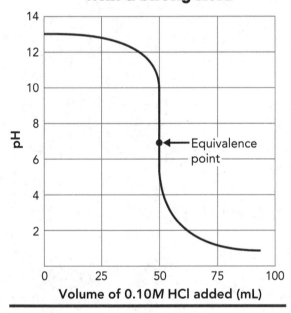

Titration of a Strong Base With a Strong Acid

Equivalence point

Volume of 0.10*M* HCl added (mL)

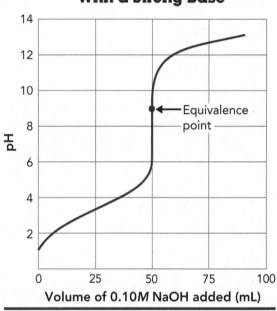

Titration of a Weak Acid With a Strong Base

Equivalence point

Volume of 0.10*M* NaOH added (mL)

(17) **SEP Interpret Data** Use the titration curves and your knowledge of conjugate acid and base behavior to predict whether the titration of a weak base with a strong acid would have an equivalence point greater than or less than 7. Explain your reasoning. ✎

....

....

....

....

Determining the Concentration by Titration

A 25-mL sample of a solution containing an unknown concentration of H_2SO_4 was titrated with a standard solution of $1.0M$ NaOH. If 18 mL of the NaOH solution was required to reach the equivalence point, what was the concentration of H_2SO_4 in the unknown solution? The chemical equation for the reaction is

$$H_2SO_4(aq) + 2NaOH(aq) \rightarrow Na_2SO_4(aq) + 2H_2O(l)$$

ANALYZE List the knowns and the unknown.

Knowns	Unknown
[NaOH] = $1.0M$	$[H_2SO_4]$ = ?M
V_{NaOH} = 18 mL = 0.018 L	
$V_{H_2SO_4}$ = 25 mL = 0.025 L	

CALCULATE Solve for the unknown.

Use the molarity to convert the volume of base to moles of base.

$$0.018 \text{ L NaOH} \times \frac{1.0 \text{ mol NaOH}}{1 \text{ L NaOH}} = 0.018 \text{ mol NaOH}$$

Use the mole ratio to find the moles of acid.

$$0.018 \text{ mol NaOH} \times \frac{1 \text{ mol } H_2SO_4}{2 \text{ mol NaOH}} = 0.0090 \text{ mol } H_2SO_4$$

Calculate the molarity by dividing moles of acid by liters of solution.

$$\text{molarity} = \frac{\text{mol of solute}}{\text{L of solution}} = \frac{0.0090 \text{ mol}}{0.025 \text{ L}} = 0.36M \text{ } H_2SO_4$$

EVALUATE Does the result make sense?

If the acid had the same molarity as the base ($1.0M$), 50 mL of base would neutralize 25 mL of acid. Because the volume of base is much less than 50 mL, the molarity of the acid must be much less than $1.0M$.

(18) **What is the molarity of a solution of H_3PO_4 if 10.2 mL is neutralized by 53.5 mL of $0.20M$ KOH?** ✏️

GO ONLINE for more practice problems.

GO ONLINE to Elaborate on and Evaluate your knowledge of neutralization reactions and acid-base titrations by completing the peer review and data analysis activities.

In the CER worksheet you completed at the beginning of the investigation, you constructed an explanation for how acid rain can affect a forest. With a partner, reevaluate your arguments.

(19) **SEP Construct an Explanation** Some lakes in Illinois are alkaline. The average pH of those lakes is 8 to 9 because the rock formations that surround the lakes contain high levels of calcium carbonate. Use chemical equations to explain how calcium carbonate neutralizes the acidity of rain containing HNO_3 and H_2SO_4. ✏

....

....

....

....

....

....

Buffers and Equilibria

GO ONLINE to Explore and Explain how the components of a buffer system work together to maintain pH.

Example of a Buffer System

A solution in which pH remains relatively constant when small amounts of acid or base are added is called a **buffer.** Because buffers resist pH changes by neutralizing added acids or bases, they are important in biological systems. For example, the pH of human blood needs to be kept close to 7.4 because many of the chemical reactions that take place in cells are sensitive to slight changes in pH. To maintain that pH, blood contains a buffer system consisting of a mixture of carbonic acid and its conjugate base, hydrogen carbonate ion. The system ensures that the pH of the blood remains relatively constant.

When blood pH is less than 7.35, a condition called acidosis occurs. It is often caused by too much CO_2 in the blood, which dissolves in water to produce carbonic acid and increase the amount of H_3O^+. Treatment often includes infusing a solution with hydrogen carbonate ions into the blood. The hydrogen carbonate ion reduces acidity because it is the conjugate base of carbonic acid. As a base, it can react with the additional H_3O^+ in the blood. When blood pH is greater than 7.45, the opposite condition, alkalosis, occurs. It is often caused by too little CO_2 or H_3O^+ in the blood. Treatment may involve breathing in and out of a paper bag.

Balancing Blood pH When a person hyperventilates, the increase in the amount of CO_2 exhaled effectively lowers the amount of carbonic acid in the blood. Removing acid from the blood increases pH. Using a paper bag to re-breathe the exhaled CO_2 helps the body bring blood pH levels back to normal.

Breathing into a paper bag ensures that the exhaled CO_2 is breathed back in.

Buffer Solutions

How Buffers Work Buffer systems consist of either a weak acid and its conjugate base or a weak base and its conjugate acid. They can react with H_3O^+ and OH^- ions. Buffer solution components work together to keep the pH relatively constant no matter which ions (H_3O^+ or OH^-) are added.

> ◼ In general, adding acids or bases to a buffered solution results in only a small change in pH.

One example of a buffer system is a solution of ethanoic acid (weak acid) and the ethanoate ion (conjugate base). The system can be used to show how a buffer works. When you add acid to the buffer solution, the ethanoate ions (CH_3COO^-) act like a H_3O^+ "sponge." When you add a base, the ethanoic acid (CH_3COOH) molecules act like an OH^- "sponge."

Adding acid: $CH_3COO^-(aq) + H_3O^+(aq) \rightleftharpoons CH_3COOH(aq) + H_2O(l)$

Adding base: $CH_3COOH(aq) + OH^-(aq) \rightleftharpoons CH_3COO^-(aq) + H_2O(l)$

In each case, the reverse reaction happens but is minimal, and therefore the change in pH is very slight.

> **Buffer Solutions Explained** In this buffer solution, the acid is HA, and the conjugate base is the anion A^-. The concentration of HA increases when an acid is added to the solution, while the concentration of A^- decreases. The reverse occurs when a base is added to the solution.

When HCl is added to the solution, the anion reacts with the hydronium ion:
$A^-(aq) + H_3O^+(aq) \rightleftharpoons HA(aq) + H_2O(l)$
There is very little change in pH.

When NaOH is added to the solution, the acid reacts with the hydroxide ion:
$HA(aq) + OH^-(aq) \rightleftharpoons A^-(aq) + H_2O(l)$
There is very little change in pH.

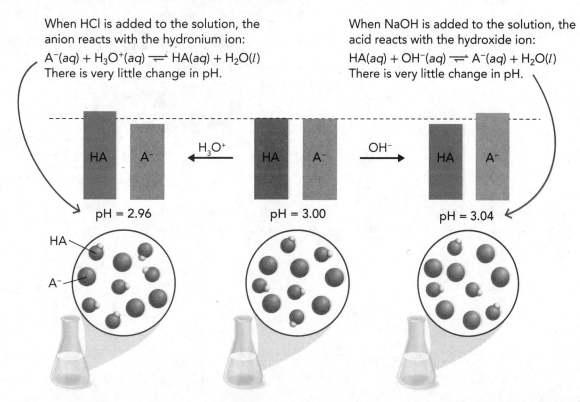

Buffer Solutions and Equilibrium Buffers work by applying Le Châtelier's principle to weak acid equilibrium. Consider the ethanoic acid–ethanoate ion buffer system again. When an acid is added to the buffer, the equilibrium is disturbed by the increase in the concentration of hydronium ions. The disturbance pushes the reaction in the direction of the products and results in a new equilibrium with a lower concentration of hydronium ions and a higher concentration of products.

$$CH_3COO^-(aq) + H_3O^+(aq) \rightleftharpoons CH_3COOH(aq) + H_2O(l)$$

When hydroxide ions are added, the equilibrium is disturbed by the increase in the concentration of hydroxide ions. The disturbance causes the reaction to shift away from hydroxide ion and in the direction of the products.

$$CH_3COOH(aq) + OH^-(aq) \rightleftharpoons CH_3COO^-(aq) + H_2O(l)$$

Again, a new equilibrium is established with a lower concentration of hydroxide ions and a higher concentration of products.

Making an Acidic Buffer When a weak acid, CH_3COOH, and a salt of its conjugate base, such as $NaCH_3COO$, are added to water, the species in the solution are CH_3COOH, H_3O^+, CH_3COO^-, and Na^+.

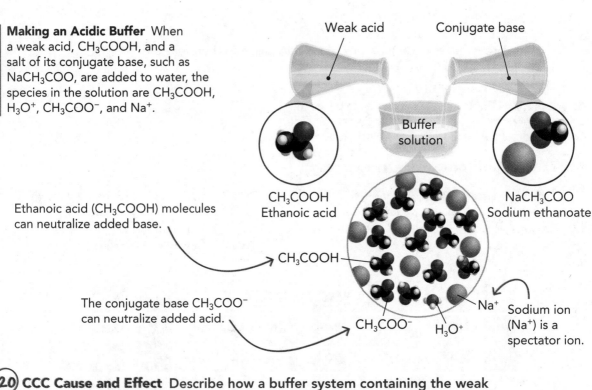

Weak acid

Conjugate base

Buffer solution

CH_3COOH
Ethanoic acid

$NaCH_3COO$
Sodium ethanoate

Ethanoic acid (CH_3COOH) molecules can neutralize added base.

CH_3COOH

The conjugate base CH_3COO^- can neutralize added acid.

CH_3COO^- H_3O^+

Na^+ Sodium ion (Na^+) is a spectator ion.

20 **CCC Cause and Effect** Describe how a buffer system containing the weak base NH_3 and the salt NH_4Cl is affected by the addition of an acid. ✏

....

....

....

Buffer Capacity and Range

For a buffer to be effective, it should be able to neutralize added acids and bases, while keeping the pH relatively constant. However, there are limits to how much acid or base a buffer can neutralize before a drastic change in pH happens. **Buffer capacity** is a measure of the amount of acid or base that may be added to a buffer system before a significant change in pH happens. The effectiveness of a buffer depends on the concentration of the buffer components. **Buffer range** is the overall pH range in which a buffer system is effective at maintaining a relatively constant pH.

Concentration and Buffers
Increasing the concentration of the buffer components increases buffer capacity. A highly concentrated buffer can neutralize more acid or base than a dilute buffer.

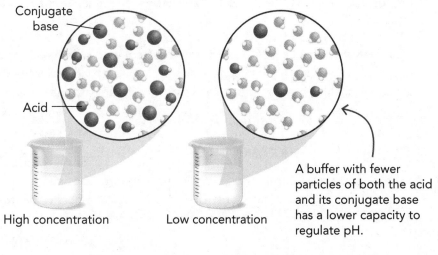

Conjugate base

Acid

High concentration

Low concentration

A buffer with fewer particles of both the acid and its conjugate base has a lower capacity to regulate pH.

Ratio of Acids and Bases
The greatest buffer capacity is achieved when the acid and base concentrations are equal (ratio of 1:1).

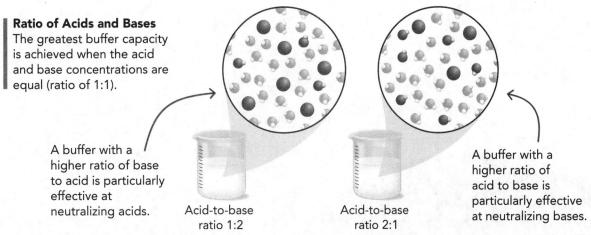

A buffer with a higher ratio of base to acid is particularly effective at neutralizing acids.

Acid-to-base ratio 1:2

Acid-to-base ratio 2:1

A buffer with a higher ratio of acid to base is particularly effective at neutralizing bases.

(21) SEP Design a Solution What are two ways to restore the buffering ability of a solution of ethanoic acid and sodium ethanoate that has neutralized as much acid as it can? (Hint: Think about how a buffer solution follows Le Châtelier's principle.) 🖉

....

....

....

GO ONLINE to Elaborate on and Evaluate your knowledge of buffers by completing the class discussion and writing activities.

In the CER worksheet you completed at the beginning of the investigation, you constructed an explanation for how acid rain can affect a forest. With a partner, reevaluate your arguments.

(22) **SEP Use Models** In waters with underlying calcium carbonate rocks, an important buffer is the carbon dioxide–hydrogen carbonate–carbonate system. 🖊

Complete the equations to show how the system works. At the air-and-water interface, CO_2 from the atmosphere dissolves to form carbonic acid. Carbonic acid reacts with water to produce an acidic hydrogen carbonate solution.

$$CO_2(g) + H_2O(l) \rightleftharpoons H_2CO_3(aq)$$

$$H_2CO_3(aq) + H_2O(l) \rightleftharpoons \text{...}$$

At the rock-and-water interface, calcium carbonate dissolves to produce calcium ions and carbonate ions. The carbonate ion reacts with water to produce a basic hydrogen carbonate solution.

$$CaCO_3(s) + H_2O(l) \rightleftharpoons Ca^{2+}(aq) + CO_3^{2-}(aq) + H_2O(l)$$

$$CO_3^{2-}(aq) + H_2O(l) \rightleftharpoons \text{...}$$

The hydrogen carbonate ion works to neutralize either an acid or a base.

$$HCO_3^-(aq) + H_3O^+(aq) \rightleftharpoons \text{...}$$

$$HCO_3^-(aq) + OH^-(aq) \rightleftharpoons \text{...}$$

GO ONLINE to Evaluate what you learned about acid-base reactions and equilibria by using the available assessment resources.

In the Performance-Based Assessment, you conducted a quantitative analysis of substances involved in acid rain. Wrap up your analysis by answering the following questions.

(23) **SEP Apply Scientific Reasoning** You tested three samples of acids. Which acid is likely to be most damaging to buildings and the biosphere? The least damaging? Explain. ✎

....

....

....

(24) **Connect to Science and Society** In recent decades, efforts have been made to reduce emissions that contribute to acid rain. Based on your measurements, which sort of emissions should be targeted to give the greatest reduction in atmospheric acidity? Is it possible to get rid of all acid-contributing emissions? ✎

....

....

....

....

....

....

(25) **Revisit the Anchoring Phenomenon** Recall the pollution image that introduced Instructional Segment 5. How does what you learned in this investigation relate to that image and help explain how Earth's water resources can become increasingly acidic? ✎

....

....

....

....

....

INVESTIGATIVE PHENOMENON

GO ONLINE to Engage with real-world phenomena by watching a video and to complete a CER interactive worksheet.

What is happening to the world's coral reefs?

Ocean Acidification

Coral reefs need three things to thrive: warm water temperatures, good light levels, and the chemical building blocks of a mineral called aragonite ($CaCO_3$) that can be extracted from seawater and used to build skeletons. Without these three things, the appearance and health of coral reefs change. Once you have viewed the Investigative Phenomenon video and worked on a first draft of a claim-evidence-reasoning exercise to explain what is happening to the world's coral reefs, discuss with a partner the following questions.

(1) **CCC Energy and Matter** Identify at least three ways that you think rising global temperatures could alter the three parameters that coral reefs need to survive. 🖉

....

....

....

....

(2) **CCC Cause and Effect** Corals thrive in clear water that sunlight can penetrate. How might algal blooms affect the clarity of water and thus affect the health of coral ecosystems? 🖉

....

....

....

....

Ocean pH Levels

 GO ONLINE to Explore and Explain ocean pH and acidification.

Carbon Dioxide and Ocean pH

The ocean and atmosphere maintain an equilibrium of their concentrations of carbon dioxide (CO_2). If the system is disrupted, there will be a net flow of carbon between the two reservoirs until equilibrium is restored. Atmospheric CO_2 has been increasing due to the human combustion of fossil fuels, so CO_2 is increasingly being driven into the ocean.

The equilibrium between the atmosphere and ocean has been a helpful counterbalancing feedback that has slowed the rate at which carbon dioxide has increased in the atmosphere. Roughly 30% of the carbon dioxide humans have released has gone into the ocean, lessening the potential greenhouse gas forcing on atmospheric temperature. However, the increased carbon dioxide absorption is dropping ocean pH and making the ocean increasingly acidic.

Correlation between Carbon Dioxide and pH Atmospheric CO_2, oceanic CO_2, and ocean acidity were measured at stations in Hawaii. Atmospheric CO_2 is shown in parts per million (ppm); seawater pCO_2 is the partial pressure of CO_2 gas in solution, expressed in microatmospheres (µatm). As CO_2 concentrations in the atmosphere and ocean have increased, ocean pH has gone down.

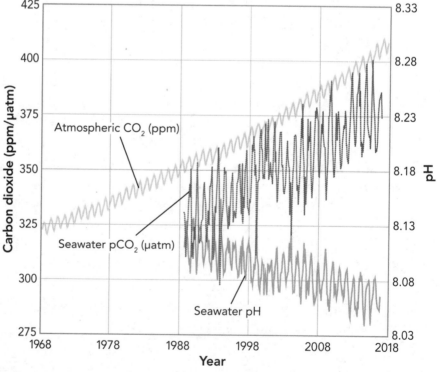

Carbon Dioxide and Acidity in the North Pacific

Atmospheric CO_2 (ppm)

Seawater pCO_2 (µatm)

Seawater pH

A series of chemical reactions in seawater results in a greater number of free hydrogen ions (H⁺), which increases the acidity of the water. First, a carbon dioxide molecule reacts with water to form carbonic acid. Then, the carbonic acid molecule ionizes to form a free H⁺ ion and a hydrogen carbonate ion. The hydrogen carbonate ion then ionizes further, releasing another H⁺ ion and a carbonate ion.

◼ A cause-and-effect relationship exists between carbon dioxide levels and ocean pH. An increase in dissolved carbon dioxide drives a set of chemical reactions that result in increased ocean acidity.

Acid-Forming Reactions in Seawater Adding carbon dioxide to the ocean makes seawater more acidic. One dissolved carbon dioxide molecule may react with water to release two free H⁺ ions.

$$CO_2 \; + \; H_2O \; \longrightarrow \; H_2CO_3 \; \longrightarrow \; H^+ \; + \; HCO_3^-$$

The dissolution of atmospheric carbon dioxide (CO_2) in ocean water **forms carbonic acid** (H_2CO_3).

Carbonic acid ionizes to form hydrogen carbonate (HCO_3^-) and free hydrogen (H^+) ions, **lowering the pH** of the solution.

$$H^+ \; + \; HCO_3^- \; \longrightarrow \; 2H^+ \; + \; CO_3^{2-}$$

Hydrogen carbonate ions ionizes further to form carbonate ions (CO_3^{2-}) and more free hydrogen ions, **further lowering pH.**

$$CO_2 \; + \; H_2O \; \rightleftharpoons \; H_2CO_3 \; \rightleftharpoons \; H^+ \; + \; HCO_3^- \; \rightleftharpoons \; 2H^+ \; + \; CO_3^{2-}$$

In a system of dynamic equilibrium, **the direction of the chemical reaction can shift** depending on the relative concentrations of reactants and products.

The system continually shifts between higher or lower pH depending on the amount of carbon dioxide and carbonate and hydrogen carbonate ions in the seawater.

③ **CCC Stability and Change** Describe what will happen to the flow of these reactions if carbonate ions are continuously removed from the system by marine organisms that use the ions to make calcium carbonate shells. ✏

....

....

....

Geographic Ocean pH Variation

Factors Influencing pH Ocean pH varies significantly around the world. Several factors influence horizontal and vertical variance in pH levels. Latitude and ocean currents affect water temperature and salinity. Warmer water and less saline waters have lower pH. The influx of fresh water near coastal areas and upwelling of deep currents make waters more acidic. Runoff of fertilizers from agriculture can lead to algal blooms, which then decay by bacterial respiration that increases CO_2 and lowers pH.

In general, tropical and temperate oceans, where coral reefs grow, have fairly stable pH levels of about 8.05–8.15, though the mid-Pacific varies greatly with El Niño/La Niña oscillations. In polar regions, pH levels rise in the summertime as massive plankton blooms absorb carbon dioxide and fall in the dark winters when the plankton die off. In general, the Indian Ocean is the most acidic ocean basin.

Global pH Variations Ocean pH levels are not constant. pH values vary laterally, vertically, seasonally, and with time in the same location.

Upwelling water from the deep ocean brings dissolved ions and carbon dioxide to surface waters, lowering the pH.

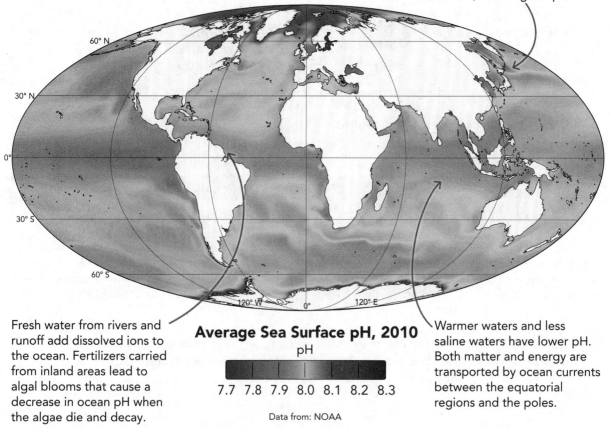

Fresh water from rivers and runoff add dissolved ions to the ocean. Fertilizers carried from inland areas lead to algal blooms that cause a decrease in ocean pH when the algae die and decay.

Average Sea Surface pH, 2010
pH

7.7 7.8 7.9 8.0 8.1 8.2 8.3

Data from: NOAA

Warmer waters and less saline waters have lower pH. Both matter and energy are transported by ocean currents between the equatorial regions and the poles.

Vertical pH Variations As depth increases, water temperature generally decreases and the amount of dissolved carbon dioxide generally increases. More dissolved CO_2 drives the formation of carbonic acid, which means more H^+ ions in solution. As a result, ocean pH generally decreases with depth.

In many coastal regions, surface currents flow parallel to or away from the coastline. Where deep currents encounter seamounts or continental shelves, the acidic deep waters are diverted upward, lowering the pH of surface waters near the coast. While this is a natural process, the significant increase in ocean acidity due to human activities has increased ocean acidity of coastal waters, where most marine life exists, faster than natural processes can buffer the change.

(4) **CCC Patterns** Coastal upwelling brings CO_2-rich, low-pH waters toward the surface. Based on the contours for the partial pressure of CO_2, or pCO_2, and pH, draw on one of the contours what you expect the pattern of ocean flow to be. ✎

pCO_2 with Depth off Point St. George, California, 2007

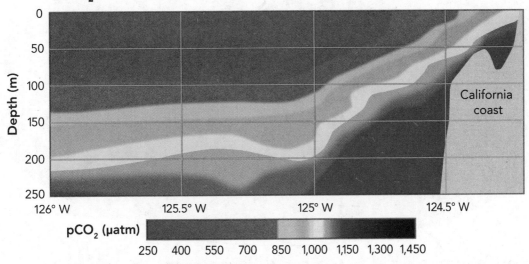

pH with Depth off Point St. George, California, 2007

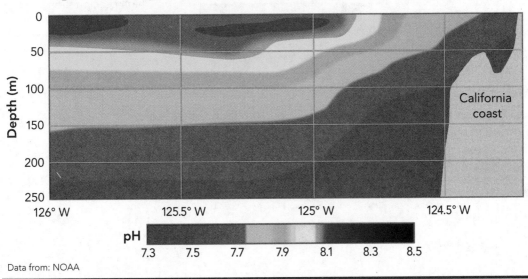

Data from: NOAA

Ocean Salinity

The world's rivers carry salt to the ocean, making seawater saline, or salty. The amount of dissolved salts in water is described as the water's **salinity.** Salt plays critical roles in controlling ocean chemistry and biology. It also controls the pattern of deep ocean currents, because salty water is dense and will sink. In the North Atlantic, water is both cold and salty, making it especially dense. The sinking of this dense water helps to drive the global circulation of deepwater currents.

Ocean Surface Salinity Variations Ocean salinity varies significantly by location. Salinity is affected by air and ocean temperature, evaporation and precipitation rates, and freshwater influx.

The dry latitudes about 30° north and south of the equator have high evaporation rates. Because salts do not leave the ocean with evaporated water, ocean salinity is high in these regions.

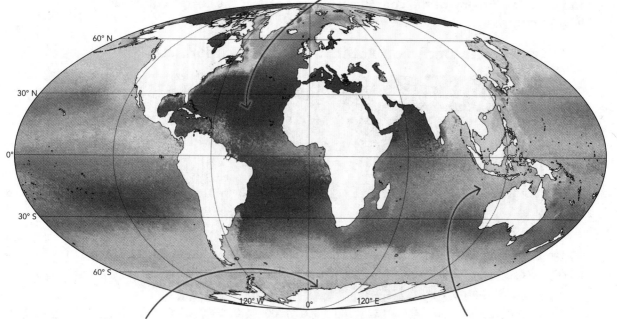

Melting of ice in Antarctica adds fresh water to the ocean, which lowers salinity. Melting of ice in Greenland also lowers salinity.

Sea Surface Salinity, 2005–2017
(practical salinity units, PSU)

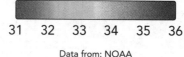

31   32   33   34   35   36

Data from: NOAA

Tropical regions have high evaporation rates but also high precipitation rates, which adds fresh water to the ocean and lowers salinity.

(5) **SEP Construct an Explanation** Rivers carry about 4 billion tons of salt to the ocean each year, and evaporated water does not contain salt. Construct an explanation for why the mean ocean salinity has stayed roughly constant over Earth's history. ✐

....

....

....

Ocean Alkalinity

Total alkalinity (TA) is the sum of excess ions in the water that could absorb H^+ ions. Mostly these ions are hydrogen carbonate (HCO_3^-) and carbonate (CO_3^{2-}). Other ions include hydrogen sulfate (HSO_4^-), hydroxide (OH^-), and phosphates (PO_4^{3-}). These ions all accept extra protons, removing the protons from the seawater. Thus, the alkalinity of the ocean buffers the acidification. The total alkalinity of seawater is not the same thing as the basicity, which is simply a measure of how high the pH is.

Ocean Surface Alkalinity Variations Water with high alkalinity resists acidification by absorbing H^+ ions. The alkalinity itself is not affected by the addition of carbon dioxide.

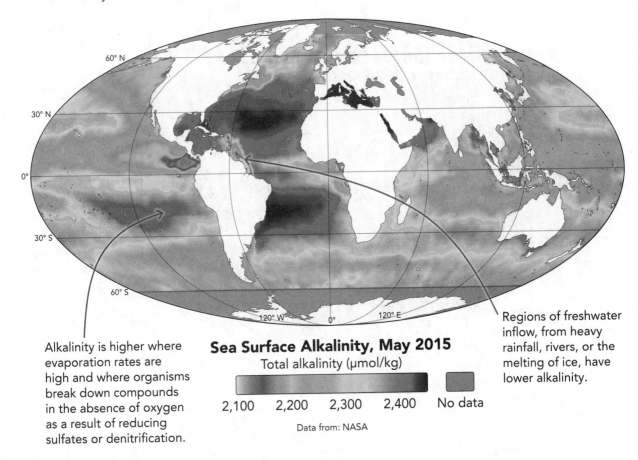

Alkalinity is higher where evaporation rates are high and where organisms break down compounds in the absence of oxygen as a result of reducing sulfates or denitrification.

Regions of freshwater inflow, from heavy rainfall, rivers, or the melting of ice, have lower alkalinity.

Sea Surface Alkalinity, May 2015
Total alkalinity (µmol/kg)

2,100   2,200   2,300   2,400   No data

Data from: NASA

6) **SEP Explain Phenomena** The map shows two regions in the Atlantic Ocean that have very high alkalinity. Construct an explanation for why these two regions have high alkalinity.

....

....

....

Le Châtelier's Principle and Future Ocean pH

The addition of CO_2 to the ocean is disrupting the ocean carbon system, driving the equations for carbon and bicarbonate dissolution toward an increase in carbonate and H^+ ions, increasing acidity. This is an example of Le Châtelier's principle: ocean pH had been fairly stable, but human-released CO_2 is driving that system toward a new equilibrium. Where that equilibrium ends up depends largely on how much CO_2 humans release in the future.

Surface Temperature and pH Projections The Intergovernmental Panel on Climate Change (IPCC) modeled different scenarios of greenhouse gas concentrations called Representative Concentration Pathways (RCPs). In the RCP2.6 model, humans drastically reduce CO_2 emissions in the year 2020. In the RCP8.5 model, humans continue to release CO_2 at high rates.

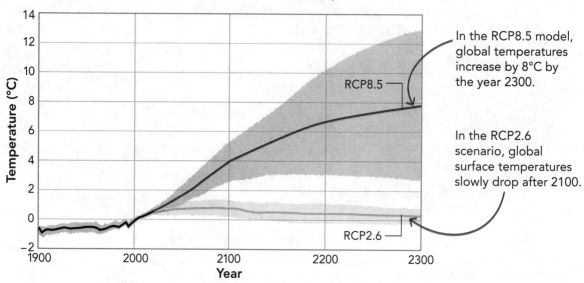

Global Average Surface Temperature Change (Relative to 1986–2005 mean)

In the RCP8.5 model, global temperatures increase by 8°C by the year 2300.

In the RCP2.6 scenario, global surface temperatures slowly drop after 2100.

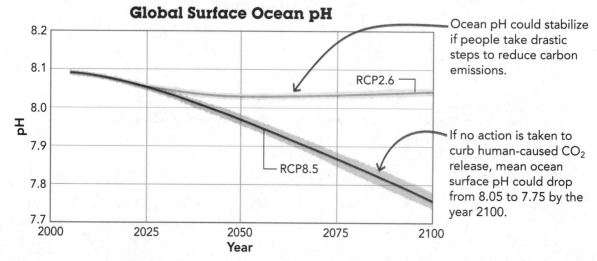

Global Surface Ocean pH

Ocean pH could stabilize if people take drastic steps to reduce carbon emissions.

If no action is taken to curb human-caused CO_2 release, mean ocean surface pH could drop from 8.05 to 7.75 by the year 2100.

Data from: Intergovernmental Panel on Climate Change

7. **CCC Stability and Change** Summarize how Le Châtelier's principle can be applied to describe the dynamic equilibrium between carbon dioxide concentrations in the atmosphere, alkalinity, and ocean pH. ✏️

....

....

....

....

....

INVESTIGATIVE PHENOMENON

GO ONLINE to Elaborate and Evaluate your knowledge of the effects of a changing ocean pH by completing the class discussion and data analysis activities.

In the CER worksheet, you drafted a scientific argument to explain what is happening to the world's coral reefs. With a partner, reevaluate the evidence cited in your arguments.

8. **CCC Cause and Effect** Most corals are adapted to survive in tropical, subtropical, and temperate oceans. Based on patterns of alkalinity and salinity in the oceans, why are corals threatened by changes in ocean pH? ✏️

....

....

....

....

....

The Ocean as a Carbon Sink

GO ONLINE to Explore and Explain how carbon dioxide is exchanged between the ocean and atmosphere.

Ocean–Atmosphere Carbon Dioxide Exchange

Roughly 80 gigatons of carbon—that's 80 billion tons—is exchanged each year between the atmosphere and the ocean surface layer. The increase in atmospheric carbon from preindustrial levels means that more carbon dioxide is exchanged between the ocean surface and atmosphere each year. However, the cycling of carbon between the ocean and atmosphere is more complicated than a simple gas exchange at the ocean surface.

Marine Organisms Are Carbon Reservoirs Carbon in the ocean cycles through both inorganic and organic pathways. **Carbon reservoirs** are components of the Earth system in which carbon is stored. The ocean is sometimes called a carbon sink, or carbon storage area, because of the large amount of carbon stored in ocean carbon reservoirs. Although only about 6 Gt of carbon (GtC) exists within marine life at any given time, due to the short life span of plankton, over eight times that amount cycles through the marine biosphere each year.

Ocean Plankton Most of the carbon in ocean organisms is in the form of calcium carbonate ($CaCO_3$) shells of single-celled plankton, such as coccolithophores. About 50 Gt of carbon is consumed each year by marine life to make their shells and skeletons.

Ocean–Atmosphere Carbon Reservoirs and Rates This image shows the sizes of carbon reservoirs (boxed labels) in gigatons of carbon (GtC) and carbon fluxes and rates (arrows) in gigatons of carbon per year (GtC/yr). The values for human inputs reflect how human activities affect reservoirs and rates.

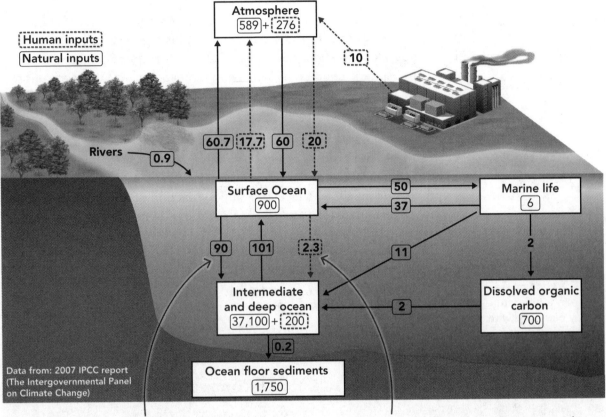

Carbon flows between reservoirs at different rates. Carbon from the surface ocean enters the deep ocean at a natural rate of 90 GtC/yr.

Human activity has increased the amount of carbon in the surface ocean, which increased the rate of flux into the intermediate and deep ocean by 2.3 GtC/yr.

Deep Ocean Carbon Cycling Carbon doesn't stay in the surface ocean layer for long. About one tenth of it sinks down into the intermediate and deeper ocean, where it remains for hundreds or thousands of years. Thus, the deep ocean holds most of the ocean's carbon. Because of the carbon exchange between the ocean and atmosphere, the human contributions to atmospheric carbon are changing the dynamics of the ocean carbon cycle. An additional 2.3 GtC is added to the deeper ocean each year, making the deep ocean increasingly more acidic.

9 **SEP Analyze Data** Most carbon sediment accumulation on the seafloor is in the form of calcium carbonate. These sediments largely become the sedimentary rock limestone. Using the rate of carbon accumulation on the seafloor and the atomic mass of calcium carbonate (100.1 g/mol), compute the mass of new limestone that is generated each year (in tons). 🖉

Temperature, Pressure, and the Carbonate Compensation Depth

The rate of a chemical reaction and its equilibrium point vary as a function of temperature, pressure, and the concentrations of reactants and products. These dependencies affect how ocean CO_2 levels respond to changing global atmospheric conditions. Increasing atmospheric CO_2 concentrations are driving carbon into the ocean, but they also create feedbacks that affect what becomes of that carbon.

Warmer atmospheric temperatures have led to warmer oceans. Near the ocean surface, this process can drive some dissolved carbon dioxide gas out of the ocean and into the atmosphere. However, deeper in the ocean this process drives the chemical dissolution reaction of CO_2 toward an increase in carbonate ions and H^+ ions, lowering the pH and making the ocean more acidic.

Temperature and CO_2 Solubility The solubility of carbon dioxide in water decreases with increasing temperature. An increase in ocean temperature decreases the amount of CO_2 gas that can stay dissolved within the seawater.

Cold water holds carbonation better than warm water does.

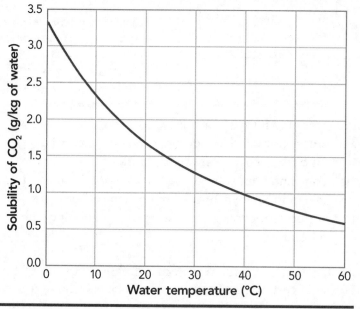

Solubility of CO$_2$ at Different Temperatures

Fizzy carbonated water goes flat as it warms because the solubility of CO_2 decreases as the temperature rises.

The solubility of CO_2 in water is also affected by pressure: higher pressures—found at deeper depths—allow more carbon dioxide to be dissolved within the water. In the ocean, calcium carbonate ($CaCO_3$) becomes increasingly unstable with increasing pressure. Below a certain depth, called the **carbonate compensation depth** or CCD, the $CaCO_3$ shells of organisms dissolve into Ca^{2+} and hydrogen carbonate ions.

Carbonate Compensation Depth
How does $CaCO_3$ solubility change with depth?

Dissolved vs. Deposited Calcareous Sediments Sediments that contain $CaCO_3$ are called calcareous sediments. The relative amount of calcium carbonate that is stored in sediments or dissolved in seawater varies with depth.

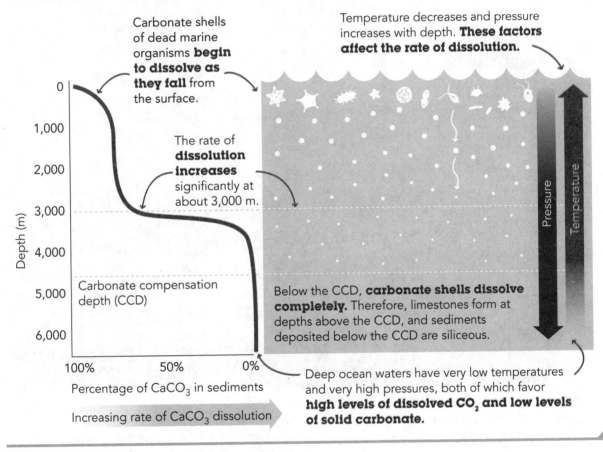

Carbonate shells of dead marine organisms **begin to dissolve as they fall** from the surface.

The rate of **dissolution increases** significantly at about 3,000 m.

Temperature decreases and pressure increases with depth. **These factors affect the rate of dissolution.**

Carbonate compensation depth (CCD)

Below the CCD, **carbonate shells dissolve completely.** Therefore, limestones form at depths above the CCD, and sediments deposited below the CCD are siliceous.

Percentage of $CaCO_3$ in sediments

Increasing rate of $CaCO_3$ dissolution

Deep ocean waters have very low temperatures and very high pressures, both of which favor **high levels of dissolved CO_2 and low levels of solid carbonate.**

(10) **CCC Stability and Change** The solubility of carbon dioxide within liquid magma also increases with pressure. Explain how this could contribute to the explosive nature of some volcanic eruptions. 🖉

....

....

....

Biogenic Carbon

The inorganic and organic chemical reactions involving ocean carbon provide a complex set of cycles. Though they are closely linked, these cycles are often separated out into two parts: a largely inorganic solubility carbon pump and an organic biological carbon pump. The solubility pump takes dissolved surface carbon and brings it into the deep, vast reservoir of dissolved carbon. The biologic pump takes that dissolved carbon and builds organic material from it when currents return it toward the surface.

Solubility Carbon Pump Inorganic chemical reactions begin with the influx of carbon into the ocean in the form of atmospheric CO_2 and the dissolved Ca^+ and CO_3^{2-} ions of weathered continental rock.

Carbon dioxide and water combine to form carbonic acid, which ionizes into hydrogen carbonate and hydrogen ions.

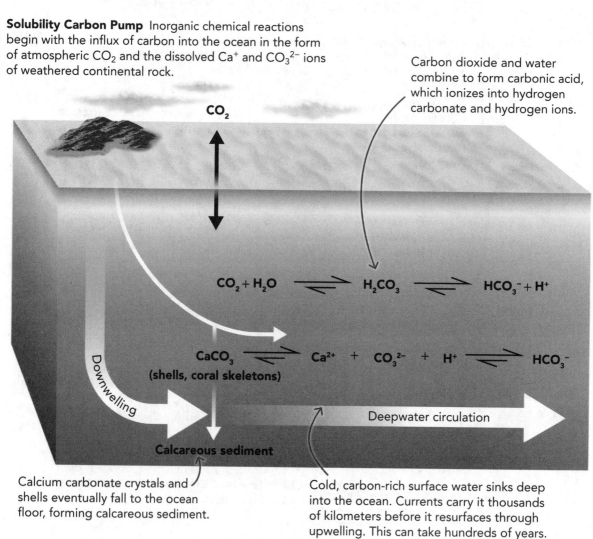

$$CO_2 + H_2O \rightleftharpoons H_2CO_3 \rightleftharpoons HCO_3^- + H^+$$

$$CaCO_3 \rightleftharpoons Ca^{2+} + CO_3^{2-} + H^+ \rightleftharpoons HCO_3^-$$

(shells, coral skeletons)

Downwelling

Deepwater circulation

Calcareous sediment

Calcium carbonate crystals and shells eventually fall to the ocean floor, forming calcareous sediment.

Cold, carbon-rich surface water sinks deep into the ocean. Currents carry it thousands of kilometers before it resurfaces through upwelling. This can take hundreds of years.

Ocean Currents The solubility and biologic carbon pumps are closely connected with the deep ocean currents that move water around Earth's ocean basins. As currents drop below the carbonate compensation depth (CCD), carbonate particles dissolve into hydrogen carbonate ions. These ions are able to form solid carbonate again once the water rises back above the CCD in areas of upwelling.

Carbon in the Marine Biosphere The base of the food web of the marine biosphere is single-celled phytoplankton, which consume CO_2 and water to make organic molecules such as glucose ($C_6H_{12}O_6$). Phytoplankton use the energy from sunlight, so they live in the shallow ocean. All life forms require carbon, but some phytoplankton such as coccolithophores also use carbon to build calcium carbonate shells. The phytoplankton are eaten by zooplankton, which also usually have carbonate shells or skeletons. The plankton are eaten by successively larger organisms, and the carbon moves up the food chain.

Biologic Carbon Pump Organic chemical reactions use CO_2 from the atmosphere and dissolved carbon from weathered land rocks. They also draw heavily upon the upwelling of deep ocean currents, which carry dissolved carbon back toward the surface.

Marine organisms use Ca^{2+} and CO_3^{2-} ions from weathered rock to build their shells. The shells eventually fall toward the ocean floor.

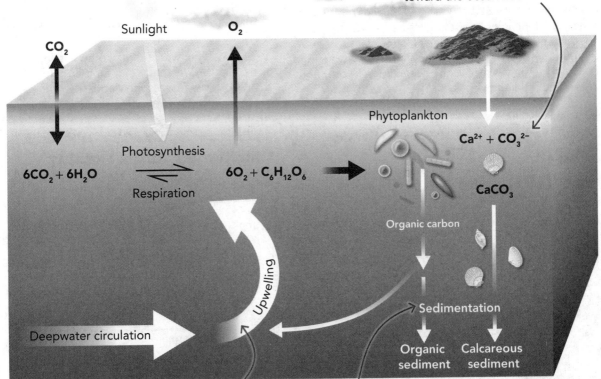

Sunlight
O_2
CO_2
Phytoplankton
$Ca^{2+} + CO_3^{2-}$
Photosynthesis
$6CO_2 + 6H_2O$ ⇌ $6O_2 + C_6H_{12}O_6$
Respiration
$CaCO_3$
Organic carbon
Upwelling
Sedimentation
Deepwater circulation
Organic sediment
Calcareous sediment

Decomposition of dead organisms and dissolution of shells contribute ions and nutrients that are brought to the surface by upwelling and are used by organisms at the surface.

Most of the carbonate sediment from dead organisms becomes part of the dissolved carbon within the deepwater circulation. Above the CCD, these shells form calcareous sediments.

⑪ **SEP Use a Model to Evaluate** What would happen to the annual rates of limestone precipitation in the ocean if the ocean water were to become much warmer and more acidic? (Hint: First describe what will happen to the CCD.) ✎

....

....

....

Methane Hydrates

Methane Gas Deposits Methane (CH_4) gas is formed by bacteria in seafloor sediments. When the methane rises through the seafloor sediments, it reacts with water in the sediments if the conditions are correct. The resulting frozen combinations of methane and water are called **methane hydrates.** These methane ices are stable at temperatures warmer than water ice is usually stable. They are abundant on land within the frozen permafrost of the Arctic tundra and are extremely abundant in shallow marine offshore sediments. Seismic imaging has identified the occurrence of layers of methane hydrates within the top kilometer of ocean sediments all around the globe, and the total global amount of methane within them may be as great as 8 trillion tons.

Methane Hydrate Stability The stability of methane hydrates varies as a function of depth (pressure) and temperature. The frozen hydrates are stable at higher pressures and lower temperatures. Methane hydrates are located by seismic ships that send seismic waves to the ocean floor. Hydrophones detect the reflected waves.

The hydrothermal gradient line shows that water temperature decreases with depth below the ocean surface.

Seismic survey ship

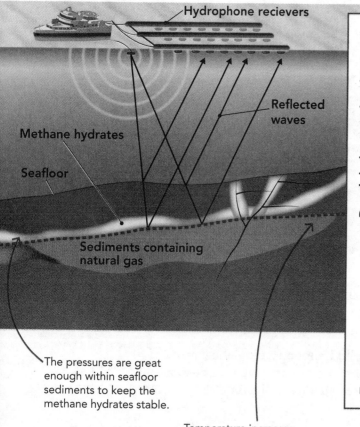

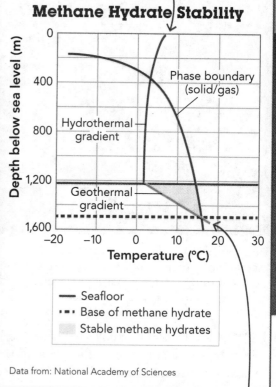

The pressures are great enough within seafloor sediments to keep the methane hydrates stable.

Temperature increases quickly with sediment depth, so the stability zone generally extends only a few hundred meters below the seafloor.

The geothermal gradient line shows that temperature of sediment and rock increases with depth below the seafloor.

Feedbacks with Global Warming Climate change will impact the stability zone of offshore methane gas hydrates. Rising sea levels and the resulting higher pressure favor methane stability. However, warming ocean temperatures are beginning to raise the lower boundary of the frozen methane hydrate, releasing methane gas into the ocean and atmosphere.

◼ **Because methane is a greenhouse gas, a positive feedback loop exists between global warming and the release of methane gas from hydrates.**

(12) **CCC Stability and Change** Would you expect the thickness of the methane hydrate stability zone to be thicker or thinner for deeper ocean locations compared to shallow ocean locations? Explain.

....

....

....

....

Revisit

INVESTIGATIVE PHENOMENON

GO ONLINE to Elaborate on and Evaluate your knowledge of the exchange of carbon between the ocean and atmosphere by completing the peer review and writing activities.

In the CER worksheet, you drafted a scientific argument to explain what is happening to the world's coral reefs. With a partner, reevaluate the evidence cited in your arguments.

(13) **SEP Identify Patterns** Explain two different pathways carbon can take to enter the ocean to become available for marine life.

....

....

....

....

....

The Ocean and Climate Change

🖥️ **GO ONLINE** to Explore and Explain how the ocean influences Earth's climate.

Ocean Surface Currents

Ocean water plays a large role in regional climate patterns. One reason for this is the high specific heat of water, which allows water to store a lot of thermal energy. This energy can be transferred to the atmosphere along the surface of the ocean. **Ocean surface currents** are areas of ocean water that flow steadily in a particular direction close to the ocean's surface. As these currents move water across the globe, they also redistribute thermal energy, affecting regional atmospheric patterns.

Currents within ocean basins largely take the form of rotating spirals called gyres that spin clockwise in the Northern Hemisphere and counterclockwise in the Southern Hemisphere. Gyres often bring warm water toward the poles along the west sides of the ocean basins and return cold water back toward the equator along the east sides of the basins.

Large-scale Surface Ocean Currents This map shows a simplified representation of the main surface ocean currents. The currents are mostly separated among the Pacific, Atlantic, and Indian Ocean basins, and connected only around Antarctica (and by a few narrow straits).

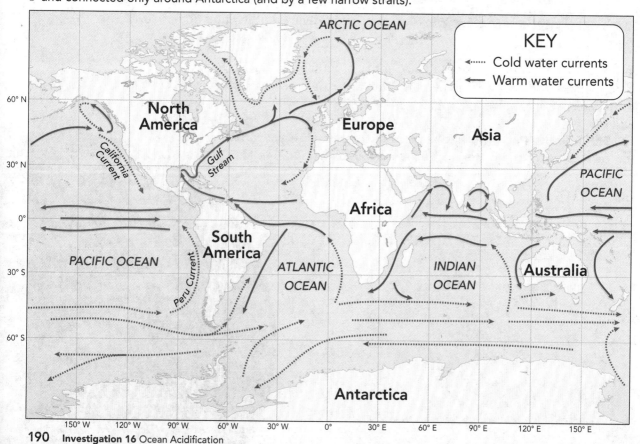

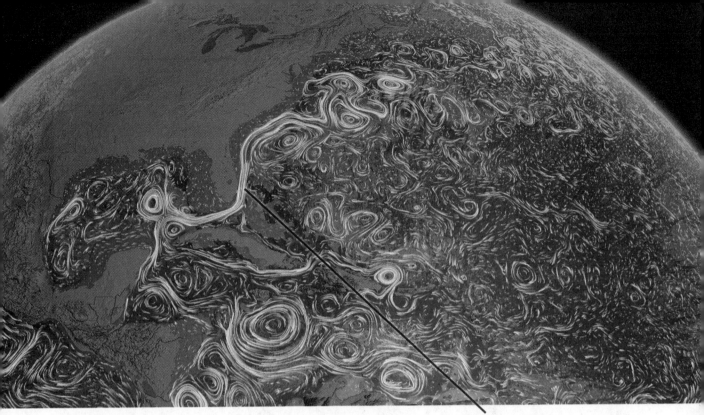

Small-scale Surface Ocean Currents This graphic representation shows the actual pattern of surface ocean currents in the mid-Atlantic in November 2005. Note how currents take the form of many small gyres, within the overall pattern of the large North Atlantic gyre.

The strong narrow current coming out of the Gulf of Mexico and snaking up the eastern U.S. coast is the Gulf Stream.

Surface ocean current patterns are determined by a combination of continental outlines, deep ocean currents, and surface winds. Because winds are always shifting in direction and strength, the exact patterns of surface currents are variable over periods of days, months, years, decades, centuries, and even longer. Surface currents may look very different during ocean storms than during periods of calm winds.

Surface currents can also change over Ice Age cycles. Currently, the Atlantic and Pacific Ocean basins are connected across the Arctic Sea through the Bering Strait (next to Alaska), and the Indian and Pacific Ocean basins are connected through Indonesia. However, during the last Ice Age, when sea levels were about 125 m lower, these shallow straits were all above sea level and the ocean basins were even more cut off from each other.

(14) **CCC Energy and Matter** The coasts of central New Jersey and northern California both share the same latitude, about 40° north. However, if you went swimming in the summer you would likely find the water in New Jersey comfortably warm but the water in northern California uncomfortably cold. Use the ocean surface currents map to explain why this would be so. 🖉

....

....

....

Coriolis Effect

The patterns of clockwise rotation in ocean current gyres in the Northern Hemisphere and counterclockwise rotation in gyres in the Southern Hemisphere are a result of the Coriolis effect. The **Coriolis effect** describes the curved path that an object takes when it moves in a straight line across a rotating object perpendicular to the axis of rotation.

On Earth, the Coriolis effect causes ocean water, air, and even liquid iron in the outer core to move in curved paths as each substance travels north or south. Because ocean water is trapped within ocean basins, the result is a connecting set of rotating gyres.

Coriolis Model Currents traveling toward or away from the equator are redirected by the rotation of Earth.

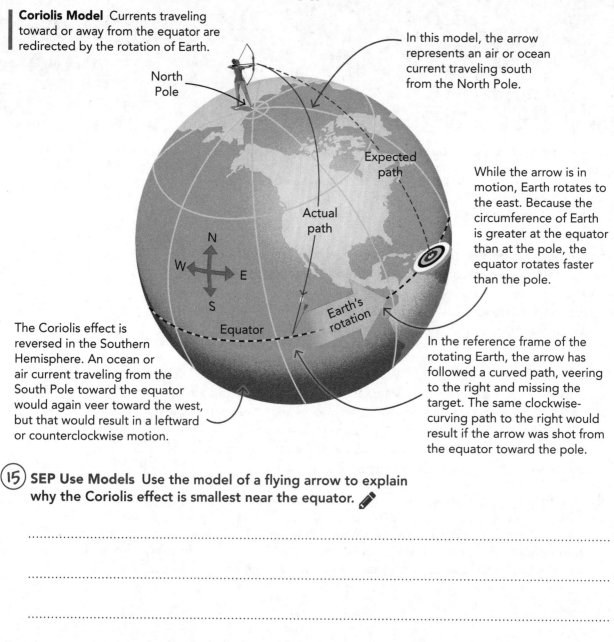

In this model, the arrow represents an air or ocean current traveling south from the North Pole.

North Pole

Expected path

Actual path

While the arrow is in motion, Earth rotates to the east. Because the circumference of Earth is greater at the equator than at the pole, the equator rotates faster than the pole.

N
W   E
S

Equator

Earth's rotation

The Coriolis effect is reversed in the Southern Hemisphere. An ocean or air current traveling from the South Pole toward the equator would again veer toward the west, but that would result in a leftward or counterclockwise motion.

In the reference frame of the rotating Earth, the arrow has followed a curved path, veering to the right and missing the target. The same clockwise-curving path to the right would result if the arrow was shot from the equator toward the pole.

(15) **SEP Use Models** Use the model of a flying arrow to explain why the Coriolis effect is smallest near the equator. ✏️

....

....

....

....

....

Deep Ocean Currents

Connected to surface ocean currents from below is a complex network of deep ocean currents. **Deep ocean currents** are subsurface patterns of ocean circulation that move water within and among the ocean basins. Unlike surface currents, deep currents are driven by differences in density.

The density of water depends on its temperature and salinity. An increase in temperature means a decrease in density, so warmer water resists sinking. An increase in salinity, on the other hand, means an increase in density, so salty water sinks more easily. In general, colder and denser water near the poles sinks while warmer water near the equator rises. Water moves slowly through the system, taking centuries or even millennia before returning to the surface.

Sinking Polar Water This simplified diagram of deep ocean currents shows some of the horizontal and vertical patterns.

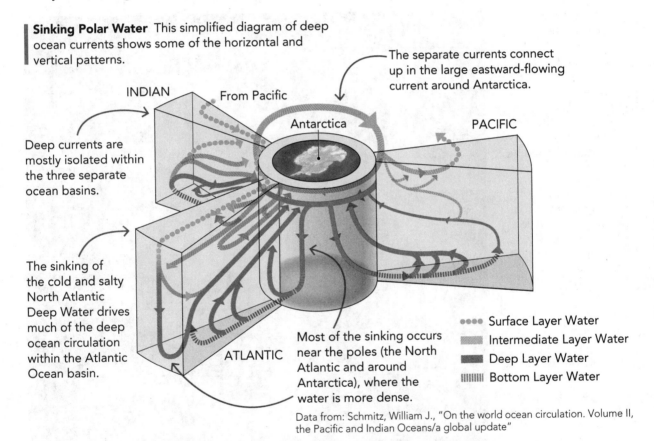

The separate currents connect up in the large eastward-flowing current around Antarctica.

Deep currents are mostly isolated within the three separate ocean basins.

The sinking of the cold and salty North Atlantic Deep Water drives much of the deep ocean circulation within the Atlantic Ocean basin.

Most of the sinking occurs near the poles (the North Atlantic and around Antarctica), where the water is more dense.

INDIAN

From Pacific

Antarctica

PACIFIC

ATLANTIC

●●●● Surface Layer Water
▓▓▓▓ Intermediate Layer Water
■■■■ Deep Layer Water
▥▥▥▥ Bottom Layer Water

Data from: Schmitz, William J., "On the world ocean circulation. Volume II, the Pacific and Indian Oceans/a global update"

16) **CCC Stability and Change** The rate of ice melting in Greenland, located in the northern Atlantic Ocean, is accelerating as global temperatures rise. Predict how this melting could alter the pattern of deep ocean circulation within the Atlantic Ocean basin. (Hint: Ice is fresh water.) 🖉

....

....

....

Ocean Heat Reservoirs

As surface waters are warmed by the atmosphere, deep ocean currents carry the heat below the surface. In this way, the ocean is like a giant battery, storing massive amounts of thermal energy, and ocean currents are like electric currents, carrying energy around the globe to power atmospheric systems.

By storing heat from the atmosphere, the ocean acts as a buffer for global warming and delays climate change. Eventually, currents will carry the warm water to the surface again, raising atmospheric temperatures. Current warming is partly reduced by the upwelling of ancient, colder water that sank into the deep ocean during the Little Ice Age, from 1250–1850 CE.

Warming Ocean The "shells" on these globes represent cross-sections of the upper layer of the Pacific (left) and Atlantic (right) oceans indicating temperature changes at different depths for a succession of decades.

Blue represents cooler temperatures, while red represents warmer temperatures.

Over the past several decades, the surface ocean has warmed and heat has moved deeper into the ocean.

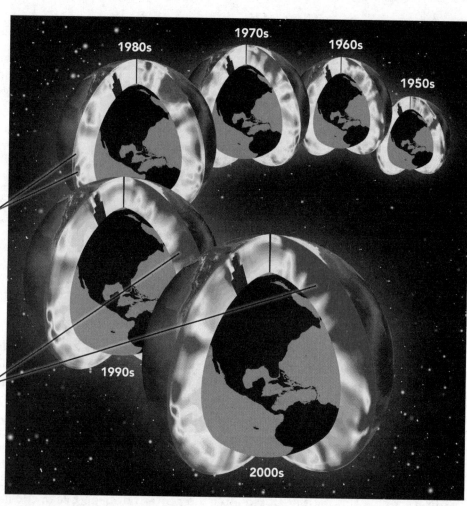

17 **CCC Patterns** Is the overall temperature of the ocean increasing or decreasing? Has the rate at which ocean temperature is changing increased, decreased, or stayed the same? Explain your answer. ✏️

....

....

....

Calculate the Heat Carried by the Gulf Stream

The Gulf Stream carries warm water from the Gulf of Mexico to the Arctic Sea. The current is about 100 km wide and 1 km deep, and flows at a rate of about 1 m/s, resulting in a volumetric flow rate of 1×10^8 m³/s. The water in the Gulf Stream is about 10°C warmer than surrounding water. Assuming a specific heat of seawater of about 4,000 J/m³·°C, calculate how many terawatts of power the Gulf Stream carries. (Note: 1 terawatt (TW) = 10^{12} watts = 10^{12} J/s.)

Analyze List the knowns and unknowns.

Knowns	Unknown
volumetric flow rate = 1×10^8 m³/s	Power = ? TW
$\Delta T = +10°C$	
Specific heat of seawater = 4,000 J/m³·°C	

Calculate Solve for the unknown.

Analyze the units of the given measurements to derive an equation that converts the flow rate (m³/s) into an energy transfer rate (J/s).

Power = flow rate × volumetric heat capacity × ΔT
= (m³/s) × J/m³·°C × °C = J/s

Substitute the knowns into the equation and solve.

Power = 1×10^8 m³/s × 4,000 J/m³·°C × 10°C
= 4×10^{12} J/s × $\dfrac{1 \text{ TW}}{10^{12} \text{ J/s}}$ = 4 TW

Evaluate Does the result make sense?

A huge volume of warm water flows through the Gulf Stream, so it makes sense that it would transport a significant amount of thermal energy.

18. **CCC Scale, Proportion, and Quantity** The Kuroshio Current is a warm-water current that flows northward along the coast of Japan. It flows at a rate of 40,000,000 m³/s, and its temperature difference is the same as the Gulf Stream's. Calculate the power, in TW, of the Kuroshio Current. 🖉

GO ONLINE for more practice problems.

Ocean Thermoclines

The ocean is divided into horizontal temperature layers, with a warm layer near the surface and a cold layer below. A **thermocline** marks the transition zone between the upper and lower water layers. It is steeper in tropical regions and almost non-existent in polar regions.

In many parts of the ocean, the surface layer is home to large populations of photosynthetic phytoplankton that require the sunlight found there. These organisms also rely on the upwelling of ocean currents to bring a steady supply of nutrients up to the surface. However, if the thermocline gets too steep, the warm surface layer becomes very buoyant, suppressing upwelling and ocean convection. Plankton then die off because they don't get the nutrients they need.

Thermocline Variation This graph shows sample thermoclines for polar, temperate, and tropical regions.

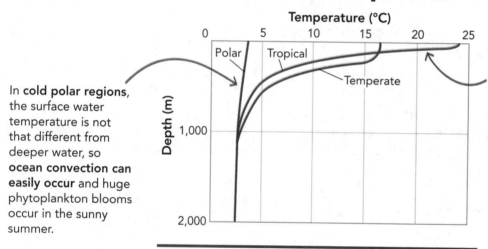

Ocean Thermoclines by Latitude

In **cold polar regions**, the surface water temperature is not that different from deeper water, so **ocean convection can easily occur** and huge phytoplankton blooms occur in the sunny summer.

In **warm tropical regions**, there is no shortage of sunlight, but the surface layer is so **warm that it often prevents upwelling**. As a result, the tropics generally have the lowest phytoplankton activity.

19 **SEP Construct an Explanation** As global atmospheric temperatures continue to rise, scientists are concerned that populations of marine animals that rely on phytoplankton for food might decrease. Construct an explanation for this idea based on what you know about upwelling and the thermocline. ✏

....

....

....

....

....

Ocean Deoxygenation

Another problem associated with global warming is ocean deoxygenation. **Ocean deoxygenation** is the expansion of low-oxygen zones in the ocean as a consequence of rising temperatures. Ocean water loses oxygen when it gets warmer for two main reasons: decreased O_2 solubility and the decline of oxygen-producing phytoplankton populations.

Deoxygenation and Hypoxia

How do **rising ocean temperatures** affect **oxygen dissolution?**

Solubility and Temperature
Solubility of oxygen decreases as water temperature increases. Therefore, warming ocean water holds less dissolved oxygen gas.

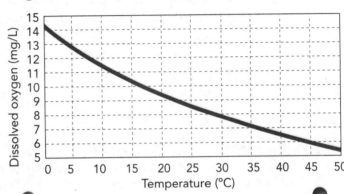

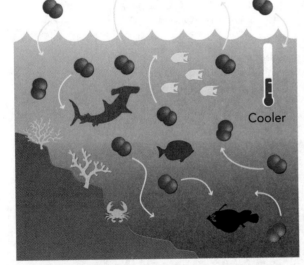

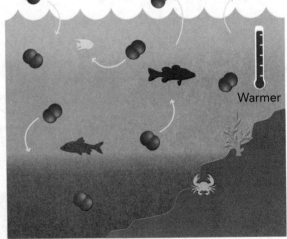

Oxygen (O_2)

Cooler

Warmer

In a cool ocean, natural layers or masses of oxygenated water easily mix. **Mixing transfers oxygen throughout** the water column all the way to the ocean floor.

As ocean water warms, it holds **less dissolved oxygen** gas, and **layers don't mix** as well. This results in hypoxic, or low-oxygen, layers where **organisms struggle** to survive.

20 **SEP Calculate** Suppose that a beaker of water is 15°C and you raise the temperature by 5°C. Use the graph above to calculate the percent decrease in the amount of dissolved O_2 gas. 🖉

El Niño/Southern Oscillation

Ocean currents have a significant effect on regional climates as they redistribute heat around the globe. However, regional climates also change over time as a result of cyclical changes in ocean circulation patterns.

◼️ **The cycling of matter and energy between Earth's ocean and atmosphere creates changes in climate patterns around the globe.**

Perhaps the most significant cyclical ocean circulation pattern in terms of energy redistribution is what is known as ENSO. The **El Niño/Southern Oscillation (ENSO)** is a cyclical circulation pattern in the tropical Pacific that results in periodic variation between below-normal and above-normal sea surface temperatures and dry and wet conditions. The ENSO pattern cycles through three phases: Neutral, El Niño, and La Niña. Neutral indicates that conditions are near their long-term average.

"Neutral" ENSO Walker Circulation ENSO cycles are driven by a pattern of atmospheric flow called the Walker Circulation, with warm moist air rising in the western Pacific (bringing rain) and cold dry air falling in the eastern Pacific. Because the atmospheric systems are all coupled, this Neutral ENSO pattern influences atmospheric flow patterns in the Atlantic and Indian Oceans.

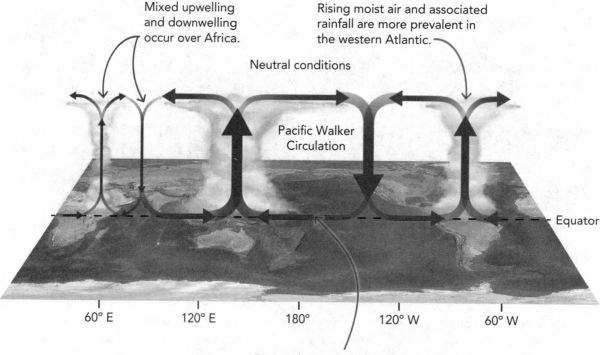

Mixed upwelling and downwelling occur over Africa.

Rising moist air and associated rainfall are more prevalent in the western Atlantic.

Neutral conditions

Pacific Walker Circulation

Equator

60° E   120° E   180°   120° W   60° W

During the neutral phase of ENSO, westward winds above the Pacific Ocean push the ocean currents westward, bringing warm water to the Asian coast.

El Niño is the warm phase of ENSO, as average ocean surface temperatures rise. La Niña is the cool phase, as surface temperatures fall. These two phases shift back and forth irregularly every 2–7 years, triggering predictable disruptions of temperature, air currents, and rainfall that lead to droughts in some places and floods in others. El Niño is usually, but not always, followed by La Niña.

El Niño Walker Circulation During El Niño, there is an increase in rainfall over California and equatorial Africa, but a decrease in rainfall in the Atlantic and western Pacific.

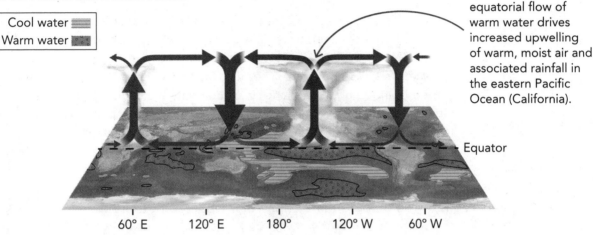

An eastward Pacific equatorial flow of warm water drives increased upwelling of warm, moist air and associated rainfall in the eastern Pacific Ocean (California).

Cool water
Warm water

Equator

60° E   120° E   180°   120° W   60° W

La Niña Walker Circulation La Niña triggers more intense tornadoes in the central U.S. and more hurricanes in the Caribbean and central Atlantic Ocean. It also brings heavy monsoon rains to India, but decreased rainfall over central Africa.

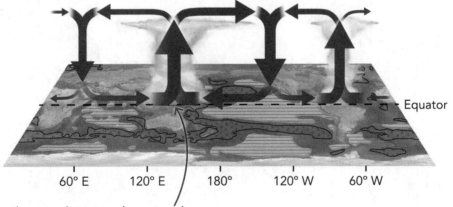

Equator

60° E   120° E   180°   120° W   60° W

A stronger-than-usual westward equatorial Pacific warm-water current drives very strong upwelling and rains in the western Pacific.

21) **CCC Patterns** During a La Niña event, rainfall and hurricanes/cyclones generally increase along the east coasts of both North America and Asia, but they all generally decrease during an El Niño event. Use the diagrams on this page to explain why. 🖉

....

....

....

ENSO Variability and Upwelling

ENSO cycle patterns directly impact global temperatures. During El Niño, Pacific Ocean surface temperatures are warmer than usual and the heat borrowed out of the Pacific Ocean generally causes global temperatures to rise. During La Niña, heat goes back into the Pacific Ocean and global temperatures usually fall. These cycles of heating and cooling impact human societies, sometimes in surprising ways.

Flu Epidemics In 1917–1918, the Spanish flu pandemic killed almost 100 million people worldwide. This pandemic, along with the next three big flu epidemics (1957, 1968, 2009), were each preceded the year before by La Niña. One hypothesis proposes that the La Niña ocean circulation patterns caused changes in atmospheric circulation patterns, which caused changes in bird migration patterns. As a result, large human populations were exposed to new strains of avian flu viruses, which caused the epidemics.

(22) **SEP Analyze Data** Global mean temperatures vary annually. The average temperature for El Niño years (orange circles) is warmer than for La Niña years (blue diamonds). The purple squares show the temperature trend for neutral years. Draw a straight line that goes through most of the orange circles (El Niño years). Then draw a second straight line that goes through most of the blue diamonds (La Niña years).

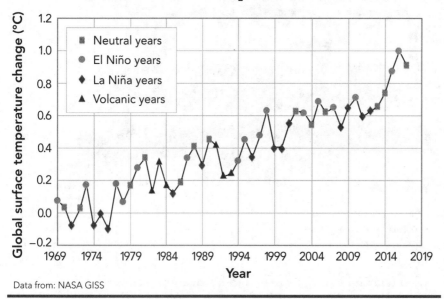

Global Surface Temperature Anomalies

Data from: NASA GISS

(23) **SEP Interpret Data** Describe the difference between the lines you drew.

....

....

....

El Niño and the Thermocline During an El Niño phase, the eastward Pacific current of warm water (black arrows) pushes down the thermocline along the South American coast, limiting upwelling and causing a decrease in marine life there.

La Niña and the Thermocline During a La Niña phase, the westward Pacific current causes the thermocline to lift up along the South American coast, bringing nutrient rich waters that feed booming plankton and fish populations.

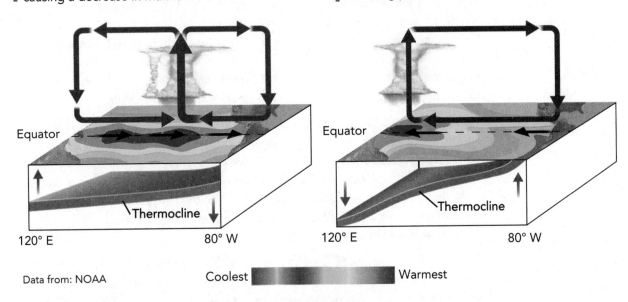

Equator

Thermocline

120° E   80° W

Equator

Thermocline

120° E   80° W

Data from: NOAA   Coolest   Warmest

Economic Effects The ENSO cycle also affects fishing industries. In neutral years, a westward equatorial Pacific current causes upwelling along the coast of South America. This brings nutrients to shallow waters, which supports plankton growth and therefore larger fish and the South American fishing industry.

In addition, a coastal current that travels north along the South American coast veers westward due to the Coriolis effect. This pulls water away from the coast, bringing up more nutrients. This effect is amplified by the stronger currents during a La Niña event, which is usually very good for the fishing industry.

During an El Niño period, warm waters flow east across the Pacific equator and then down the South American coast. The Coriolis effect causes these currents to bend left into the coast and sink, suppressing the upwelling of nutrients. The plankton die and the fishing industry collapses.

24 **SEP Analyze Data** Global temperatures actually decreased slightly in the years 2017 and 2018. Some suggest that this means global warming has stopped. Construct another more plausible explanation for the data. 🖉

....

....

....

....

Other Modes of Ocean Variability

The ENSO cycle of El Niño/La Niña is not the only pattern of oscillating ocean and atmosphere currents. There are many others. For example, the Indian Ocean Dipole (IOD) is an irregular cycle of changing sea-surface temperatures between the east and west sides of the Indian Ocean, with corresponding changes in rainfall. The Antarctic Oscillation (AAO) is a fluctuation in the shape of the ring of winds and waters that circle around Antarctica, changing the locations of heavy winds and storms.

North Atlantic Oscillation (NAO) A significant oscillation in the North Atlantic is the NAO, which is primarily an atmospheric oscillation, closely connected with Arctic air patterns. The NAO oscillates between two modes, referred to as the "positive" and "negative" modes. These modes involve a shifting in the strengths of various high and low pressure zones, and determine which parts of Europe and eastern North America receive warm or cold (and wet or dry) air masses.

Atlantic Multidecadal Oscillation (AMO) Another oscillation in the Atlantic Ocean is the AMO. The AMO involves 20- to 40-year oscillations of long-term sea-surface temperatures in the North Atlantic Ocean. These variations affect air temperatures and rainfall patterns over much of the Northern Hemisphere to the extent that there is a significant correlation between the AMO and mean global temperatures over the past century.

North Atlantic Oscillation: Positive Mode
The polar jet stream follows a relatively straight course from North America to Europe. Eastern North America gets warm air, northern Europe gets wet and warm air, and southern Europe gets cool and dry air.

North Atlantic Oscillation: Negative Mode The polar jet stream meanders up over Greenland. Eastern North America is cold and snowy, northern Europe is cold and dry, and southern Europe is warm and wet.

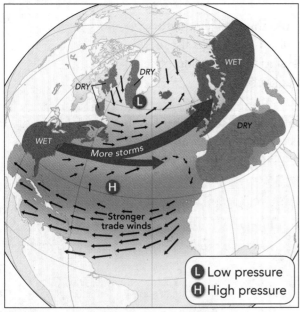

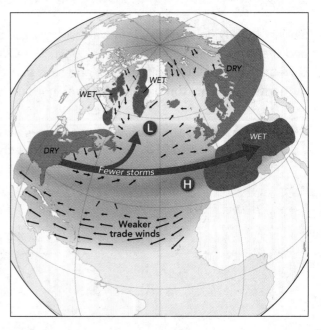

Data from: Yachting World; NAO

25 **CCC Energy and Matter** The histogram below shows the positive and negative phases of the AMO index. The solid and dashed lines show annual variations in the global mean temperature and its 10-year moving average. The correlation between the AMO index and mean global temperature is strong but not perfect. Draw a box around the parts of the two curves where their trends do not correlate.

Global Average Temperature and the AMO

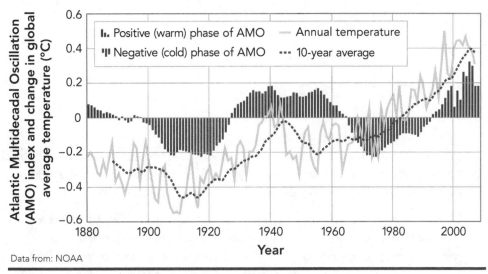

Data from: NOAA

Revisit

INVESTIGATIVE PHENOMENON

GO ONLINE to Elaborate and Evaluate your knowledge of the ocean's influence on Earth's climate by completing the class discussion and data analysis activities.

In the CER worksheet, you drafted a scientific argument to explain what is happening to the world's coral reefs. With a partner, reevaluate the evidence cited in your arguments.

26 **SEP Engage in Argument** Increasing ocean temperatures cause a decrease in ocean oxygen levels. Explain why this is a problem for coral reefs.

....

....

....

....

Consequences of Ocean Acidification

 GO ONLINE to Explore and Explain the effects of ocean acidification.

Calcification

Many marine organisms use carbon from dissolved carbon dioxide to build their shells out of calcium carbonate, $CaCO_3$, in a process called **calcification.** Calcification is a form of biomineralization. The calcium enters the ocean as dissolved ions from the weathering of rocks at or below Earth's surface.

Calcium carbonate has two main crystal forms, or polymorphs, used for making shells and skeletons: calcite and aragonite. These crystals have the same chemical composition, but the calcium, carbon, and oxygen atoms are arranged in different structures. Some organisms prefer one form over the other, and some organisms use both forms to make their shells harder.

Calcification in Acidic Seawater
Marine organisms use calcium ions (Ca^{2+}) and carbonate ions (CO_3^{2-}) in seawater to build their shells of calcite or aragonite.

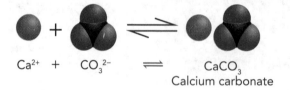

$$Ca^{2+} \; + \; CO_3^{2-} \; \rightleftharpoons \; \underset{\text{Calcium carbonate}}{CaCO_3}$$

Calcium carbonate reacts with carbonic acid to form calcium ions and hydrogen carbonate ions.

Excess hydrogen carbonate can react with free hydrogen ions to form more carbonic acid. This reduces the number of free hydrogen ions in the system and raises the pH of the entire system. However, increased carbonic acid can break down more calcium carbonate shells.

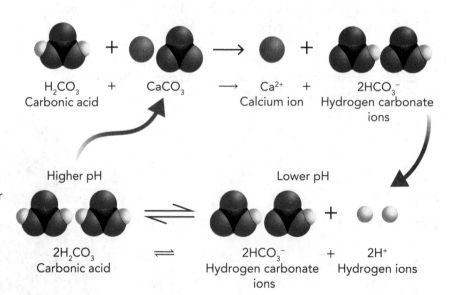

$$\underset{\text{Carbonic acid}}{H_2CO_3} \; + \; CaCO_3 \; \longrightarrow \; \underset{\text{Calcium ion}}{Ca^{2+}} \; + \; \underset{\substack{\text{Hydrogen carbonate} \\ \text{ions}}}{2HCO_3^{-}}$$

Higher pH   Lower pH

$$\underset{\text{Carbonic acid}}{2H_2CO_3} \; \rightleftharpoons \; \underset{\substack{\text{Hydrogen carbonate} \\ \text{ions}}}{2HCO_3^{-}} \; + \; \underset{\text{Hydrogen ions}}{2H^{+}}$$

Buffering the Solution Changing the relative concentrations of reactants and products can shift the pH in either direction. This buffers the solution and slows the rate at which the ocean water's acidity changes.

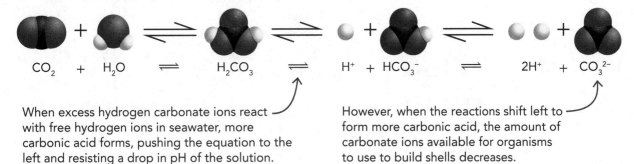

$$CO_2 \quad + \quad H_2O \quad \rightleftharpoons \quad H_2CO_3 \quad \rightleftharpoons \quad H^+ \; + \; HCO_3^- \quad \rightleftharpoons \quad 2H^+ \; + \; CO_3^{2-}$$

When excess hydrogen carbonate ions react with free hydrogen ions in seawater, more carbonic acid forms, pushing the equation to the left and resisting a drop in pH of the solution.

However, when the reactions shift left to form more carbonic acid, the amount of carbonate ions available for organisms to use to build shells decreases.

Dynamic Equilibrium As the ocean becomes more acidic, the relative concentrations of carbonate ions, hydrogen carbonate ions, and carbon dioxide shift to reach a new equilibrium. As pH drops, carbonate concentrations decrease, and hydrogen carbonate and carbon dioxide concentrations increase.

The vertical axis is a logarithmic plot of the reactant concentrations.

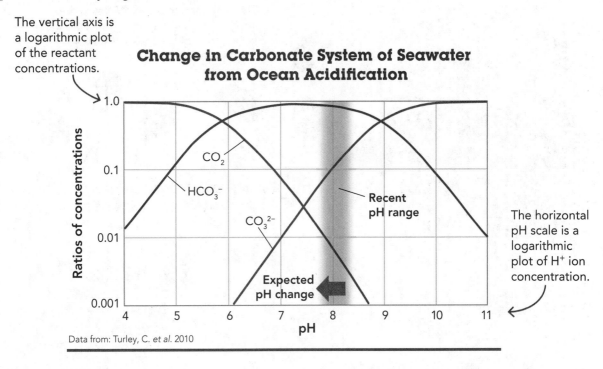

Change in Carbonate System of Seawater from Ocean Acidification

The horizontal pH scale is a logarithmic plot of H^+ ion concentration.

Data from: Turley, C. *et al.* 2010

(27) **SEP Interpret Graphs** Use the vertical logarithmic scale to explain why carbonate ions are mostly converting to hydrogen carbonate ions and not to CO_2 molecules as pH levels fall from the mean ocean surface value of about 8.1. ✎

....

....

....

....

Marine Shell Dissolution

Adding free H^+ ions to the water drives the chemical reactions away from carbonate stability. As the amount of CO_2 in the ocean increases, the amount of CO_3^{2-} decreases, and carbonate ions convert into hydrogen carbonate ions (HCO_3^-), which increases the energy required by organisms to build shells. These changes lower calcification rates and increase dissolution rates.

■ Changes to carbon dioxide levels and ocean pH disrupt the chemical equilibrium that many ocean organisms depend on to make their shells.

Dissolution of Calcium Carbonate Shells

How are **pH** and **CO_2 concentration** related to **carbonate dissolution?**

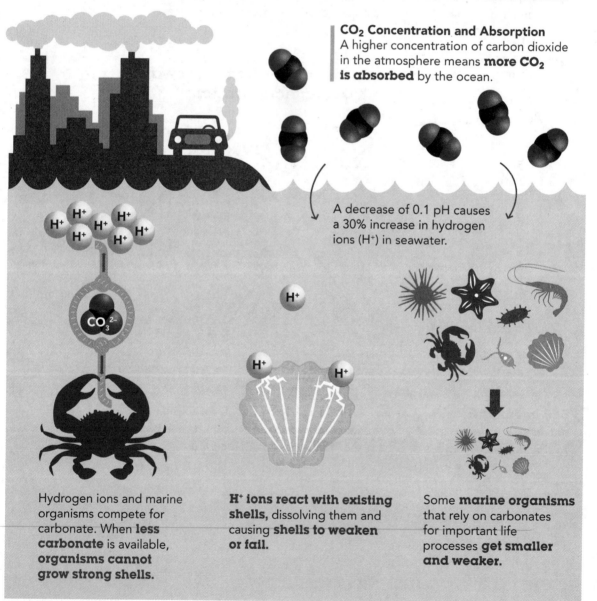

CO_2 Concentration and Absorption
A higher concentration of carbon dioxide in the atmosphere means **more CO_2 is absorbed** by the ocean.

A decrease of 0.1 pH causes a 30% increase in hydrogen ions (H^+) in seawater.

Hydrogen ions and marine organisms compete for carbonate. When **less carbonate** is available, **organisms cannot grow strong shells.**

H^+ ions react with existing shells, dissolving them and causing **shells to weaken or fail.**

Some **marine organisms** that rely on carbonates for important life processes **get smaller and weaker.**

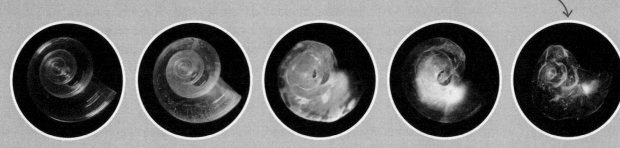

Calcium Carbonate Dissolution in Acid
Increased ocean acidity increases the dissolution rate of calcium carbonate shells once they are built.

Shells become weaker over time and may fail completely. As shells weaken or fail, populations of carbonate-shelled organisms will likely decline over time.

Increasing acidity

Calcite and Aragonite Organisms that use aragonite to build their shells are more at risk than organisms that use only calcite. Aragonite is a harder mineral than calcite, so it adds extra protection from predators, but it is only weakly stable at Earth's surface and is 1.5 times as soluble in seawater than calcite.

Arctic Food Webs Cold, arctic waters absorb atmospheric CO_2 faster than other regions and act as carbon sinks. The Arctic food web is very dependent upon shelled mollusks that have aragonite shells. Damage to the base of the Arctic food web would cause damage all the way up the chain, including damage to fish, seals, and whales.

Larvae Ocean acidification is particularly damaging to marine organisms that have a larval stage, such as plankton, bivalves, and sea urchins. The larvae of marine organisms that grow in high-CO_2 waters tend to be stunted and deformed, making them less able to feed and function properly.

28 **CCC Stability and Change** Suppose there are two closely related species of clam. One makes its shell out of aragonite, the other out of calcite. As the ocean becomes more acidic, predict what will happen to the relative populations of the two species, and what will happen to the population of a predator species that feeds on the aragonite-shelled clams. ✏

....

....

....

....

Disruption of Marine Ecosystems

Increased CO_2 concentrations and ocean acidification are impacting marine organisms and communities in many different ways. Some organisms, such as the jumbo squid, are suffering from reduced metabolic rates. Others, such as the longfin squid, are taking longer to grow and are more frequently small and misshapen. Some species, such as blue mussels, are showing a reduced immune system. Others are showing a decrease in their ability to smell or hear predators.

Some organisms are actually doing better and are thriving in higher-CO_2, lower-pH waters. One study of an ecosystem found that predators such as crabs and lobsters were becoming bigger and stronger, while their prey, such as clams and oysters, were doing worse, disrupting the predator–prey dynamic. In many environments, disruptions and damages to the ecosystem are greater due to the combination of increased temperature, higher acidity, and deoxygenation. These combined effects are much greater than the effects from just one factor.

Jumbo Squid Studies have shown that increased ocean carbon dioxide levels can damage the metabolic rates of marine organisms such as the Humboldt, or jumbo, squid.

Red Tides Blooms of toxic cyanobacteria and algae, commonly called red tides, occur more frequently in warmer and more acidic oceans. When the algae and cyanobacteria die and decay, oxygen is stripped from the water and large "dead zones" form in the ocean. In these hypoxic zones, oxygen levels are so low that fish, turtles, marine mammals, and seabirds cannot survive. Algal blooms often occur near the mouths of large rivers, which carry phosphates and other chemicals from fertilizers that run off farmland into rivers.

Plastics Another ecological hazard comes from human use and disposal of plastics. Plastic floats and degrades slowly and often accumulates within broad ocean gyres, which may hold 100 million tons of plastic. One such gyre had more than 6 times as much plastic in the water as plankton. Synthetic fabrics are one of the largest sources of plastic in the ocean because they release huge numbers of microfibers with each washing. These microfibers pass through filtration plants and into the ocean.

Toxic Red Tides
Warm water and higher carbon dioxide levels favor photosynthesis, which leads to blooms of toxic cyanobacteria and algae such as this bloom off the coast of South Africa.

(29) **SEP Design Your Solution** Propose two different ways that the number of damaging toxic ocean red tides could be reduced. ✏

....

....

....

....

Coral Bleaching

Corals are tiny marine animals that enjoy a symbiotic relationship with photosynthetic algae that live in their tissues and supply them with a source of food. If the corals become stressed, the algae will leave, causing the corals to turn white, a phenomenon known as **coral bleaching.** There are many different causes of coral bleaching, including ocean acidification and water pollution. But the greatest cause is warming ocean temperatures.

Corals' Response to Ocean Changes
How do **temperature** and **pH** affect **corals**?

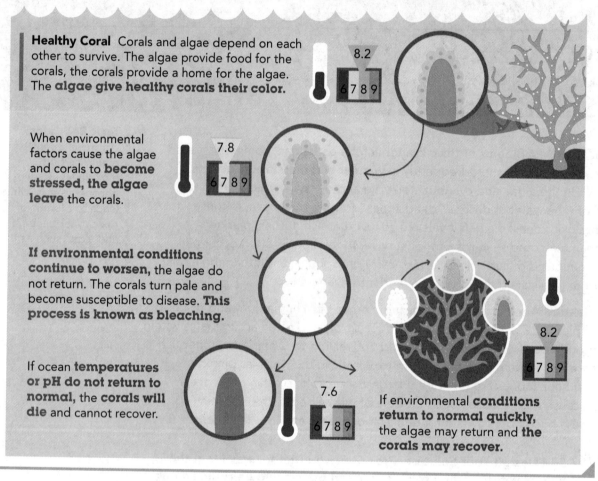

Healthy Coral Corals and algae depend on each other to survive. The algae provide food for the corals, the corals provide a home for the algae. **The algae give healthy corals their color.**

When environmental factors cause the algae and corals to **become stressed, the algae leave** the corals.

If environmental conditions continue to worsen, the algae do not return. The corals turn pale and become susceptible to disease. **This process is known as bleaching.**

If ocean **temperatures or pH do not return to normal, the corals will die** and cannot recover.

If environmental **conditions return to normal quickly,** the algae may return and **the corals may recover.**

---

(30) **CCC Stability and Change** Coral reefs play an important role in many marine ecosystems. Describe what you think would happen to coral reef ecosystems if the corals died. ✏

....

....

....

Analyze Rates of Coral Bleaching Events

Between 2014 and 2017, an ocean heat wave caused 75% of the world's coral reefs to demonstrate bleaching-level heat stress. About 30% of the corals died. Before the 1980s, mass-bleaching events were occurring approximately once every 30 years. As of 2017, these events were happening every 6 years. How many times more frequent are these events occurring now than in the 1980s?

ANALYZE List the knowns and unknowns.

Knowns	Unknown
frequency before 1980s $= \dfrac{1 \text{ event}}{30 \text{ years}}$	multiplicative increase in frequency $= ?$
frequency in 2017 $= \dfrac{1 \text{ event}}{6 \text{ years}}$	

CALCULATE Solve for the unknown.

Express the multiplicative increase in frequency as a ratio.

$$\text{multiplicative increase in frequency} = \frac{\text{new rate}}{\text{old rate}} = \frac{\text{frequency in 2017}}{\text{frequency before 1980s}}$$

Substitute the knowns into the equation and solve.

$$\frac{\text{new rate}}{\text{old rate}} = \frac{\left(\dfrac{1 \text{ event}}{6 \text{ years}}\right)}{\left(\dfrac{1 \text{ event}}{30 \text{ years}}\right)}$$

Rearrange and simplify. Note that the units cancel.

$$= \frac{1 \text{ event}}{6 \text{ years}} \div \frac{1 \text{ event}}{30 \text{ years}} = \frac{1 \text{ event}}{6 \text{ years}} \times \frac{30 \text{ years}}{1 \text{ event}} = 5$$

EVALUATE Does the result make sense?

Mass-bleaching events are happening five times more frequently than before the 1980s. This makes sense because global ocean temperatures have increased significantly since the 1980s.

(31) SEP Use Math Scientists project that the frequency of mass-bleaching events will continue to accelerate at a rate of 4% per year. Compared to 2020, how many times more frequent will mass-bleaching events occur in 2050?
(Hint: multiplicative increase = (rate of change)$^{\text{number of years}}$) ✏️

GO ONLINE for more practice problems.

Calcite and Aragonite Stability Depths

Recall that the carbonate compensation depth (CCD) is the depth below which $CaCO_3$ is not stable and will dissolve according to the equation:

$$CaCO_3 + CO_2 + H_2O \rightleftharpoons Ca^{2+} + 2HCO_3^-$$

However, this reaction is different for the two different mineral forms of $CaCO_3$, calcite and aragonite. Because aragonite is more soluble than calcite, its compensation depth is shallower. Solubility also depends on ocean temperature and CO_2 concentration, so the CCDs for calcite and aragonite vary according to geographic location.

Concentrations of CO_2 are often highest in regions of ocean upwelling, causing shallower CCDs in the northern and eastern Pacific Ocean. Concentrations of CO_2 tend to be lower in sinking waters, such as those in the northern Atlantic Ocean. Calcite stability depths are deeper throughout the oceans because of the higher stability of calcite.

(32) **SEP Develop Models** At the center of the diagram, draw a seamount with a summit that lies 3,500 m below sea level. Then, use Xs to identify the location(s) on the seamount where calcite sediments would be deposited in each scenario (cooler and warmer ocean). Use Os to identify any location(s) where aragonite sediments may collect. ✏️

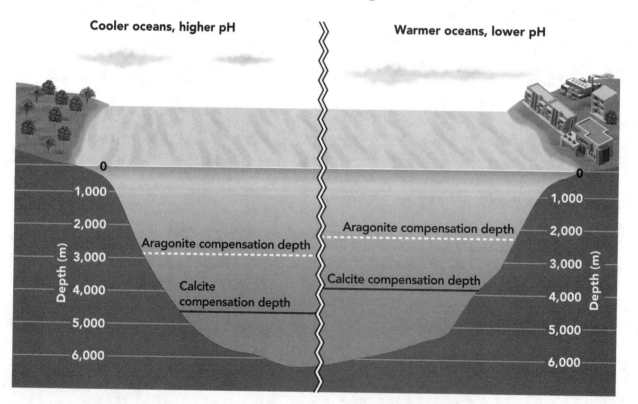

Paleocene-Eocene Thermal Maximum

The fossil record tells us that 55 million years ago, during a time called the Paleocene-Eocene Thermal Maximum (PETM), there was a huge and sudden release of atmospheric carbon, and global temperatures rose 5°C to 8°C. In the ocean, there was a massive die-off of some organisms but an upsurge in others. Fossils show that it took almost 100,000 years for ocean conditions to stabilize. This event gives us some idea of what might occur in the ocean if atmospheric carbon and temperatures continue to rise.

PETM Carbonate Compensation Depths About 55 million years ago, the ocean quickly became very warm and rich in CO_2. The carbonate compensation depth became so shallow that no $CaCO_3$ fossils are found from this time.

These three curves show the weight percentage of $CaCO_3$ in seafloor sediments as a function of time in three different locations at three different depths.

All three curves go to zero at 55 million years ago, but recover at different rates over the next 100,000 years.

Calcium Carbonate Content of Ocean Sediments Across the PETM

Based on report from Science Magazine, 10 June 2005, Vol 308.

(33) **SEP Use Models** How does the fossil record serve as a model to help us understand what impact we are having on the planet today? ✏️

....

....

....

....

GO ONLINE to Elaborate on and Evaluate your knowledge of the effects of ocean acidification by completing the class discussion and engineering design activities.

In the CER worksheet, you drafted a scientific argument to explain what is happening to the world's coral reefs. With a partner, reevaluate the evidence cited in your arguments.

(34) **SEP Construct an Explanation** Corals are made of calcium carbonate, $CaCO_3$. Carbon dioxide is required to make these coral skeletons. Explain why having too much CO_2 makes it harder for these shells to form. ✏️

....

....

....

....

....

....

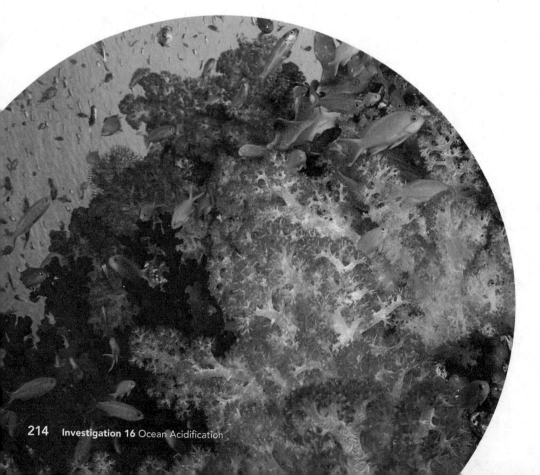

GO ONLINE to Evaluate what you learned about the role of carbon and human influences in ocean acidification.

In the Performance-Based Assessment, you collected evidence for determining the effects of pH on calcium carbonate shells. Wrap up your analysis by answering the following question.

(35) **SEP Refine Your Plan** How might you modify your investigation procedure if you wanted to test how temperature affects the rate of the chemical reaction between carbonic acid and calcium carbonate shells? Describe alterations to your procedure and list any additional materials or equipment you would need to perform the modified test. ✏️

....

....

....

....

....

....

Revisit
ANCHORING PHENOMENON

(36) **SEP Apply Scientific Reasoning** Based on what you learned in this investigation, select an activity you listed in the Anchoring Phenomenon and describe how you would change it and why. ✏️

....

....

....

 GO ONLINE for a **problem-based learning** activity that you can tackle after completing Instructional Segment 5.

End-of-Book Resources

TABLE A.1
PHYSICAL CONSTANTS

Atomic mass unit	$1 \text{ amu} = 1.6605 \times 10^{-24} \text{ g}$
Avogadro's number	$N = 6.02 \times 10^{23} \text{ particles/mol}$
Gas constant	$R = 8.31 \text{ L} \cdot \text{kPa/K} \cdot \text{mol}$
Ideal gas molar volume	$V_m = 22.4 \text{ L/mol}$
Masses of subatomic particles	
Electron (e^-)	$m_e = 0.000549 \text{ amu} = 9.1094 \times 10^{-28} \text{ g}$
Proton (p^+)	$m_p = 1.00728 \text{ amu} = 1.67262 \times 10^{-24} \text{ g}$
Neutron (n^0)	$m_n = 1.00867 \text{ amu} = 1.67493 \times 10^{-24} \text{ g}$
Speed of light in a vacuum	$c = 3.00 \times 10^8 \text{ m/s}$

TABLE A.2
COMMON SYMBOLS AND ABBREVIATIONS

α	alpha rays	GWP	global warming potential	mm	millimeter
β	beta rays	H	enthalpy	mol	mole
γ	gamma rays	ΔH_f	heat of formation	mp	melting point
Δ	change in	h	hour	n^0	neutron
$\delta+, \delta-$	partial ionic charge	h	Planck's constant	n	number of moles
λ	wavelength	Hz	hertz	n	principal quantum number
π	pi bond	J	joule		
σ	sigma bond	K	kelvin	P	pressure
ν	frequency	K_a	acid dissociation constant	p^+	proton
amu	atomic mass unit	K_b	base dissociation constant	Pa	pascal
(aq)	aqueous solution	K_{eq}	equilibrium constant	R	ideal gas constant
atm	atmosphere	K_w	ion product constant for water	S	entropy
bp	boiling point			s	second
°C	degree Celsius	kcal	kilocalorie	(s)	solid
c	speed of light in a vacuum	kg	kilogram	STP	standard temperature and pressure
cm	centimeter	kPa	kilopascal		
E	energy	L	liter	T	temperature
e^-	electron	(l)	liquid	$t_{1/2}$	half-life
EFM	empirical formula mass	M	molarity	V	volume
fp	freezing point	m	meter	v	velocity
G	Gibbs free energy	m	mass	Z_{eff}	effective nuclear charge
g	gram	m	molality		
(g)	gas	mL	milliliter		

TABLE A.3

SOME PROPERTIES OF THE ELEMENTS

Element	Symbol	Atomic number	Atomic mass	Melting point (°C)	Boiling point (°C)	Density (g/cm³) (gases at STP)	Oxidation numbers
Actinium	Ac	89	(227)	1050	3200	10.07	+3
Aluminum	Al	13	26.98154	660.37	2467	2.6989	+3
Americium	Am	95	243	994	2607	13.67	+3, +4, +5, +6
Antimony	Sb	51	121.75	630.74	1587	6.691	−3, +3, +5
Argon	Ar	18	39.948	−189.2	−185.7	0.0017837	
Arsenic	As	33	74.9216	817	613	5.73	−3, +3, +5
Astatine	At	85	(210)	302	337	—	
Barium	Ba	56	137.33	725	1640	3.5	+2
Berkelium	Bk	97	(247)	986	—	14.78	
Beryllium	Be	4	9.01218	1278	2970	1.848	+2
Bismuth	Bi	83	208.9804	271.3	1560	9.747	+3, +5
Bohrium	Bh	107	(264)	—	—	—	
Boron	B	5	10.81	2075	3675	2.34	+3
Bromine	Br	35	79.904	−7.2	58.78	3.12	−1, +1, +5
Cadmium	Cd	48	112.41	320.9	765	8.65	+2
Calcium	Ca	20	40.08	839	1484	1.55	+2
Californium	Cf	98	(251)	900	—	14	
Carbon	C	6	12.011	3550	4827	2.267	−4, +2, +4
Cerium	Ce	58	140.12	799	3426	6.657	+3, +4
Cesium	Cs	55	132.9054	28.40	669.3	1.873	+1
Chlorine	Cl	17	35.453	−100.98	−34.6	0.003214	−1, +1, +5, +7
Chromium	Cr	24	51.996	1907	2672	7.18	+2, +3, +6
Cobalt	Co	27	58.9332	1495	2870	8.9	+2, +3
Copernicium	Cn	112	(277)	—	—	—	
Copper	Cu	29	63.546	1083.4	2567	8.96	+1, +2
Curium	Cm	96	(247)	1340	—	13.51	+3
Darmstadtium	Ds	110	(269)	—	—	—	
Dubnium	Db	105	(262)	—	—	—	
Dysprosium	Dy	66	162.50	1412	2562	8.550	+3
Einsteinium	Es	99	(252)	—	—	—	
Erbium	Er	68	167.26	159	2863	9.066	+3
Europium	Eu	63	151.96	822	1597	5.243	+2, +3
Fermium	Fm	100	(257)	—	—	—	
Flerovium	Fl	114	(289)	—	—	—	
Fluorine	F	9	18.998403	−219.62	−188.54	0.00181	−1
Francium	Fr	87	(223)	27	677	—	+1
Gadolinium	Gd	64	157.25	1313	3266	7.9004	+3
Gallium	Ga	31	69.72	29.78	2204	5.904	+3
Germanium	Ge	32	72.59	937.4	2830	5.323	+2, +4
Gold	Au	79	196.9665	1064.43	2856	19.3	+1, +3
Hafnium	Hf	72	178.49	2227	4602	13.31	+4
Hassium	Hs	108	(265)	—	—	—	
Helium	He	2	4.00260	−272.2	−268.934	0.0001785	
Holmium	Ho	67	164.9304	1474	2695	8.795	+3
Hydrogen	H	1	1.00794	−259.14	−252.87	0.00008988	−1, +1
Indium	In	49	114.82	156.61	2080	7.31	+1, +3
Iodine	I	53	126.9045	113.5	184.35	4.93	−1, +1, +5, +7
Iridium	Ir	77	192.22	2410	4130	22.42	+3, +4
Iron	Fe	26	55.847	1535	2750	7.874	+2, +3
Krypton	Kr	36	83.80	−156.6	−152.30	0.003733	
Lanthanum	La	57	138.9055	921	3457	6.145	+3
Lawrencium	Lr	103	(262)	—	—	—	+3
Lead	Pb	82	207.2	327.502	1740	11.35	+2, +4
Lithium	Li	3	6.941	180.54	1342	0.534	+1
Livermorium	Lv	116	(293)	—	—	—	
Lutetium	Lu	71	174.967	1663	3395	9.840	+3
Magnesium	Mg	12	24.305	648.8	1107	1.738	+2
Manganese	Mn	25	54.9380	1244	1962	7.32	+2, +3, +4, +7

SOME PROPERTIES OF THE ELEMENTS

Element	Symbol	Atomic number	Atomic mass	Melting point (°C)	Boiling point (°C)	Density (g/cm³) (gases at STP)	Oxidation numbers
Meitnerium	Mt	109	(278)	—	—	—	
Mendelevium	Md	101	257	—	—	—	+2, +3
Mercury	Hg	80	200.59	−38.842	356.58	13.55	+1, +2
Molybdenum	Mo	42	95.94	2617	4612	10.22	+6
Moscovium	Mc	115	(289)	—	—	—	
Neodymium	Nd	60	144.24	1021	3068	6.90	+3
Neon	Ne	10	20.179	−248.67	−246.048	0.0008999	
Neptunium	Np	93	(237)	640	3902	20.25	+3, +4, +5, +6
Nickel	Ni	28	58.69	1453	2732	8.902	+2, +3
Nihonium	Nh	113	(286)	—	—	—	
Niobium	Nb	41	92.9064	2468	4742	8.57	+3, +5
Nitrogen	N	7	14.0067	−209.86	−195.8	0.0012506	−3, +3, +5
Nobelium	No	102	(259)	—	—	—	+2, +3
Oganesson	Og	118	(294)	—	—	—	
Osmium	Os	76	190.2	3045	5027	22.57	+3, +4
Oxygen	O	8	15.9994	−218.4	−182.962	0.001429	−2
Palladium	Pd	46	106.42	1554	2970	12.02	+2, +4
Phosphorus	P	15	30.97376	44.1	280	1.82	−3, +3, +5
Platinum	Pt	78	195.08	1772	3627	21.45	+2, +4
Plutonium	Pu	94	(244)	641	3232	19.84	+3, +4, +5, +6
Polonium	Po	84	(209)	254	962	9.32	+2, +4
Potassium	K	19	39.0982	63.25	760	0.862	+1
Praseodymium	Pr	59	140.9077	931	3512	6.64	+3
Promethium	Pm	61	(145)	1168	2460	7.22	+3
Protactinium	Pa	91	231.0359	1560	4027	15.37	+4, +5
Radium	Ra	88	(226)	700	1140	5.5	+2
Radon	Rn	86	(222)	−71	−61.8	0.00973	
Rhenium	Re	75	186.207	3180	5627	21.02	+4, +6, +7
Rhodium	Rh	45	102.9055	1966	3727	12.41	+3
Roentgenium	Rg	111	(272)	—	—	—	
Rubidium	Rb	37	85.4678	38.89	686	1.532	+1
Ruthenium	Ru	44	101.07	2310	3900	12.41	+3
Rutherfordium	Rf	104	(261)	—	—	—	
Samarium	Sm	62	150.36	1077	1791	7.520	+2, +3
Scandium	Sc	21	44.9559	1541	2831	2.989	+3
Seaborgium	Sg	106	(263)	—	—	—	
Selenium	Se	34	78.96	217	684.9	4.79	−2, +4, +6
Silicon	Si	14	28.0855	1410	2355	2.33	−4, +2, +4
Silver	Ag	47	107.8682	961.93	2212	10.50	+1
Sodium	Na	11	22.98977	97.81	882.9	0.971	+1
Strontium	Sr	38	87.62	769	1381	2.63	+2
Sulfur	S	16	32.06	112.8	444.7	2.07	−2, +4, +6
Tantalum	Ta	73	180.9479	2996	5425	16.654	+5
Technetium	Tc	43	(98)	2172	4877	11.50	+4, +6, +7
Tellurium	Te	52	127.60	449.5	989.8	6.24	−2, +4, +6
Tennessine	Ts	117	(294)	—	—	—	
Terbium	Tb	65	158.9254	1356	3123	8.229	+3
Thallium	Tl	81	204.383	303.5	1457	11.85	+1, +3
Thorium	Th	90	232.0381	1750	4790	11.72	+4
Thulium	Tm	69	168.9342	1545	1947	9.321	+3
Tin	Sn	50	118.69	231.968	2270	7.31	+2, +4
Titanium	Ti	22	47.88	1660	3287	4.54	+2, +3, +4
Tungsten	W	74	183.85	3410	5660	19.3	+6
Uranium	U	92	238.0289	1132.3	3818	18.95	+3, +4, +5, +6
Vanadium	V	23	50.9415	1890	3380	6.11	+2, +3, +4, +5
Xenon	Xe	54	131.29	−111.9	−107.1	0.005887	
Ytterbium	Yb	70	173.04	819	1194	6.965	+2, +3
Yttrium	Y	39	88.9059	1522	3338	4.469	+3
Zinc	Zn	30	65.38	419.58	907	7.133	+2
Zirconium	Zr	40	91.22	1852	4377	6.506	+4

TABLE A.4

ELECTRON CONFIGURATION OF THE ELEMENTS

	Element	Sublevels																		
		1s	2s	2p	3s	3p	3d	4s	4p	4d	4f	5s	5p	5d	5f	6s	6p	6d	7s	7p
1	Hydrogen	1																		
2	Helium	2																		
3	Lithium	2	1																	
4	Beryllium	2	2																	
5	Boron	2	2	1																
6	Carbon	2	2	2																
7	Nitrogen	2	2	3																
8	Oxygen	2	2	4																
9	Fluorine	2	2	5																
10	Neon	2	2	6																
11	Sodium	2	2	6	1															
12	Magnesium	2	2	6	2															
13	Aluminum	2	2	6	2	1														
14	Silicon	2	2	6	2	2														
15	Phosphorus	2	2	6	2	3														
16	Sulfur	2	2	6	2	4														
17	Chlorine	2	2	6	2	5														
18	Argon	2	2	6	2	6														
19	Potassium	2	2	6	2	6		1												
20	Calcium	2	2	6	2	6		2												
21	Scandium	2	2	6	2	6	1	2												
22	Titanium	2	2	6	2	6	2	2												
23	Vanadium	2	2	6	2	6	3	2												
24	Chromium	2	2	6	2	6	5	1												
25	Manganese	2	2	6	2	6	5	2												
26	Iron	2	2	6	2	6	6	2												
27	Cobalt	2	2	6	2	6	7	2												
28	Nickel	2	2	6	2	6	8	2												
29	Copper	2	2	6	2	6	10	1												
30	Zinc	2	2	6	2	6	10	2												
31	Gallium	2	2	6	2	6	10	2	1											
32	Germanium	2	2	6	2	6	10	2	2											
33	Arsenic	2	2	6	2	6	10	2	3											
34	Selenium	2	2	6	2	6	10	2	4											
35	Bromine	2	2	6	2	6	10	2	5											
36	Krypton	2	2	6	2	6	10	2	6											
37	Rubidium	2	2	6	2	6	10	2	6			1								
38	Strontium	2	2	6	2	6	10	2	6			2								
39	Yttrium	2	2	6	2	6	10	2	6	1		2								
40	Zirconium	2	2	6	2	6	10	2	6	2		2								
41	Niobium	2	2	6	2	6	10	2	6	4		1								
42	Molybdenum	2	2	6	2	6	10	2	6	5		1								
43	Technetium	2	2	6	2	6	10	2	6	5		2								
44	Ruthenium	2	2	6	2	6	10	2	6	7		1								
45	Rhodium	2	2	6	2	6	10	2	6	8		1								
46	Palladium	2	2	6	2	6	10	2	6	10										
47	Silver	2	2	6	2	6	10	2	6	10		1								
48	Cadmium	2	2	6	2	6	10	2	6	10		2								
49	Indium	2	2	6	2	6	10	2	6	10		2	1							
50	Tin	2	2	6	2	6	10	2	6	10		2	2							
51	Antimony	2	2	6	2	6	10	2	6	10		2	3							
52	Tellurium	2	2	6	2	6	10	2	6	10		2	4							
53	Iodine	2	2	6	2	6	10	2	6	10		2	5							
54	Xenon	2	2	6	2	6	10	2	6	10		2	6							
55	Cesium	2	2	6	2	6	10	2	6	10		2	6			1				
56	Barium	2	2	6	2	6	10	2	6	10		2	6			2				
57	Lanthanum	2	2	6	2	6	10	2	6	10		2	6	1		2				
58	Cerium	2	2	6	2	6	10	2	6	10	1	2	6	1		2				
59	Praseodymium	2	2	6	2	6	10	2	6	10	3	2	6			2				

ELECTRON CONFIGURATION OF THE ELEMENTS

	Element	1s	2s	2p	3s	3p	3d	4s	4p	4d	4f	5s	5p	5d	5f	6s	6p	6d	7s	7p
60	Neodymium	2	2	6	2	6	10	2	6	10	4	2	6			2				
61	Promethium	2	2	6	2	6	10	2	6	10	5	2	6			2				
62	Samarium	2	2	6	2	6	10	2	6	10	6	2	6			2				
63	Europium	2	2	6	2	6	10	2	6	10	7	2	6			2				
64	Gadolinium	2	2	6	2	6	10	2	6	10	7	2	6	1		2				
65	Terbium	2	2	6	2	6	10	2	6	10	9	2	6			2				
66	Dysprosium	2	2	6	2	6	10	2	6	10	10	2	6			2				
67	Holmium	2	2	6	2	6	10	2	6	10	11	2	6			2				
68	Erbium	2	2	6	2	6	10	2	6	10	12	2	6			2				
69	Thulium	2	2	6	2	6	10	2	6	10	13	2	6			2				
70	Ytterbium	2	2	6	2	6	10	2	6	10	14	2	6			2				
71	Lutetium	2	2	6	2	6	10	2	6	10	14	2	6	1		2				
72	Hafnium	2	2	6	2	6	10	2	6	10	14	2	6	2		2				
73	Tantalum	2	2	6	2	6	10	2	6	10	14	2	6	3		2				
74	Tungsten	2	2	6	2	6	10	2	6	10	14	2	6	4		2				
75	Rhenium	2	2	6	2	6	10	2	6	10	14	2	6	5		2				
76	Osmium	2	2	6	2	6	10	2	6	10	14	2	6	6		2				
77	Iridium	2	2	6	2	6	10	2	6	10	14	2	6	7		2				
78	Platinum	2	2	6	2	6	10	2	6	10	14	2	6	9		1				
79	Gold	2	2	6	2	6	10	2	6	10	14	2	6	10		1				
80	Mercury	2	2	6	2	6	10	2	6	10	14	2	6	10		2				
81	Thallium	2	2	6	2	6	10	2	6	10	14	2	6	10		2	1			
82	Lead	2	2	6	2	6	10	2	6	10	14	2	6	10		2	2			
83	Bismuth	2	2	6	2	6	10	2	6	10	14	2	6	10		2	3			
84	Polonium	2	2	6	2	6	10	2	6	10	14	2	6	10		2	4			
85	Astatine	2	2	6	2	6	10	2	6	10	14	2	6	10		2	5			
86	Radon	2	2	6	2	6	10	2	6	10	14	2	6	10		2	6			
87	Francium	2	2	6	2	6	10	2	6	10	14	2	6	10		2	6		1	
88	Radium	2	2	6	2	6	10	2	6	10	14	2	6	10		2	6		2	
89	Actinium	2	2	6	2	6	10	2	6	10	14	2	6	10		2	6	1	2	
90	Thorium	2	2	6	2	6	10	2	6	10	14	2	6	10		2	6	2	2	
91	Protactinium	2	2	6	2	6	10	2	6	10	14	2	6	10	2	2	6	1	2	
92	Uranium	2	2	6	2	6	10	2	6	10	14	2	6	10	3	2	6	1	2	
93	Neptunium	2	2	6	2	6	10	2	6	10	14	2	6	10	4	2	6	1	2	
94	Plutonium	2	2	6	2	6	10	2	6	10	14	2	6	10	6	2	6		2	
95	Americium	2	2	6	2	6	10	2	6	10	14	2	6	10	7	2	6		2	
96	Curium	2	2	6	2	6	10	2	6	10	14	2	6	10	7	2	6	1	2	
97	Berkelium	2	2	6	2	6	10	2	6	10	14	2	6	10	9	2	6		2	
98	Californium	2	2	6	2	6	10	2	6	10	14	2	6	10	10	2	6		2	
99	Einsteinium	2	2	6	2	6	10	2	6	10	14	2	6	10	11	2	6		2	
100	Fermium	2	2	6	2	6	10	2	6	10	14	2	6	10	12	2	6		2	
101	Mendelevium	2	2	6	2	6	10	2	6	10	14	2	6	10	13	2	6		2	
102	Nobelium	2	2	6	2	6	10	2	6	10	14	2	6	10	14	2	6		2	
103	Lawrencium	2	2	6	2	6	10	2	6	10	14	2	6	10	14	2	6	1	2	
104	Rutherfordium	2	2	6	2	6	10	2	6	10	14	2	6	10	14	2	6	2	2	
105	Dubnium	2	2	6	2	6	10	2	6	10	14	2	6	10	14	2	6	3	2	
106	Seaborgium	2	2	6	2	6	10	2	6	10	14	2	6	10	14	2	6	4	2	
107	Bohrium	2	2	6	2	6	10	2	6	10	14	2	6	10	14	2	6	5	2	
108	Hassium	2	2	6	2	6	10	2	6	10	14	2	6	10	14	2	6	6	2	
109	Meitnerium	2	2	6	2	6	10	2	6	10	14	2	6	10	14	2	6	7	2	
110	Darmstadium	2	2	6	2	6	10	2	6	10	14	2	6	10	14	2	6	9	1	
111	Roentgenium	2	2	6	2	6	10	2	6	10	14	2	6	10	14	2	6	10	1	
112	Copernicium	2	2	6	2	6	10	2	6	10	14	2	6	10	14	2	6	10	2	
113	Nihonium	2	2	6	2	6	10	2	6	10	14	2	6	10	14	2	6	10	2	1
114	Flerovium	2	2	6	2	6	10	2	6	10	14	2	6	10	14	2	6	10	2	2
115	Moscovium	2	2	6	2	6	10	2	6	10	14	2	6	10	14	2	6	10	2	3
116	Livermorium	2	2	6	2	6	10	2	6	10	14	2	6	10	14	2	6	10	2	4
117	Tennessine	2	2	6	2	6	10	2	6	10	14	2	6	10	14	2	6	10	2	5
118	Oganesson	2	2	6	2	6	10	2	6	10	14	2	6	10	14	2	6	10	2	6

TABLE A.5
COMMON POLYATOMIC IONS

Charge	Name	Formula	Charge	Name	Formula
1−	Chlorate	ClO_3^-	2−	Carbonate	CO_3^{2-}
	Chlorite	ClO_2^-		Chromate	CrO_4^{2-}
	Cyanide	CN^-		Dichromate	$Cr_2O_7^{2-}$
	Dihydrogen phosphate	$H_2PO_4^-$		Oxalate	$C_2O_4^{2-}$
	Ethanoate	CH_3COO^-		Peroxide	O_2^{2-}
	Hydroxide	OH^-		Silicate	SiO_3^{2-}
	Hydrogen carbonate	HCO_3^-		Sulfate	SO_4^{2-}
	Hydrogen sulfate	HSO_4^-		Sulfite	SO_3^{2-}
	Hydrogen sulfite	HSO_3^-		Thiosulfate	$S_2O_3^{2-}$
	Hypochlorite	ClO^-			
	Nitrate	NO_3^-	3−	Phosphate	PO_4^{3-}
	Nitrite	NO_2^-		Phosphite	PO_3^{3-}
	Perchlorate	ClO_4^-			
	Permanganate	MnO_4^-	1+	Ammonium	NH_4^+
	Thiocyanate	SCN^-			

TABLE A.6
SOLUBILITIES OF COMPOUNDS AT 25°C

	ethanoate	bromide	carbonate	chlorate	chloride	hydroxide	iodide	nitrate	oxide	perchlorate	phosphate	sulfate	sulfide
aluminum	S	S	X	S	S	I	S	S	I	S	I	S	d
ammonium	S	S	S	S	S	X	S	S	X	S	S	S	S
barium	S	S	I	S	S	S	S	S	sS	S	I	I	d
calcium	S	S	I	S	S	S	S	S	sS	S	I	sS	I
copper(II)	S	S	X	S	S	I	S	S	I	S	I	S	I
iron(II)	S	S	I	S	S	I	S	S	I	S	I	S	I
iron(III)	S	S	X	S	S	I	S	S	I	S	I	sS	d
lithium	S	S	sS	S	S	S	S	S	S	S	sS	S	S
magnesium	S	S	I	S	S	I	S	S	I	S	I	S	d
potassium	S	S	S	S	S	S	S	S	S	S	S	S	S
silver	sS	I	I	S	I	X	I	S	I	S	I	sS	I
sodium	S	S	S	S	S	S	S	S	S	S	S	S	S
strontium	S	S	I	S	S	S	S	S	S	S	I	I	I
zinc	S	S	I	S	S	I	S	S	I	S	I	S	I

Key: S = soluble   d = decomposes in water
      sS = slightly soluble   X = no such compound
      I = insoluble

TABLE A.7

SI UNITS AND EQUIVALENTS

Quantity	SI unit	Common equivalents		
Length	meter (m)	1 meter	=	1.0936 yards
		1 centimeter	=	0.39370 inch
		1 inch	=	2.54 centimeters
		1 mile	=	5280 feet
			=	1.6093 kilometers
Volume	cubic meter (m^3)	1 liter	=	10^{-3} m^3
			=	1.0567 quarts
		1 gallon	=	4 quarts
			=	8 pints
			=	3.7854 liters
		1 quart	=	32 fluid ounces
			=	0.94635 liter
Temperature	kelvin (K)	1 kelvin	=	1 degree Celsius
		°C	=	$\frac{5}{9}$ (F − 32)
		K	=	°C + 273.15
Mass	kilogram (kg)	1 kilogram	=	1000 grams
			=	mass weighing 2.2046 pounds
		1 amu	=	1.6605×10^{-27} kilograms
Time	second (s)	1 hour	=	60 minutes
		1 hour	=	3600 seconds
Energy	joule (J)	1 joule	=	1 kg•m^2/s^2 (exact)
		1 joule	=	0.2390 calorie
		1 calorie	=	4.184 joules
Pressure	pascal (Pa)	1 atmosphere	=	101.3 kilopascals
			=	760 mm Hg (Torr)
			=	14.70 pounds per square inch

The experiments in this program have been carefully designed to minimize the risk of injury. However, safety is also your responsibility. The following rules are essential for keeping you safe in the laboratory. The rules address pre-lab preparation, proper laboratory practices, and post-lab procedures.

Pre-Lab Preparation

1. Read the entire procedure before you begin. Listen to all of your teacher's instructions. When in doubt about a procedure, ask your teacher.

2. Do only the assigned experiments. Only do experiments when your teacher is present and has given you permission to work.

3. Know the location and operation of the following safety equipment: fire extinguisher, fire blanket, emergency shower, and eye wash station.

4. Know the location of emergency exits and escape routes. To make it easy to exit quickly, do not block walkways with furniture. Keep your work area orderly and free of personal belongings, such as coats and backpacks.

5. Protect your clothing and hair from chemicals and sources of heat. Tie back long hair and roll up loose sleeves when working in the laboratory. Avoid wearing bulky or loose-fitting clothing. Remove dangling jewelry. Wear closed-toe shoes at all times in the laboratory.

Proper Laboratory Practices

6. Even with well-designed and tested laboratory procedures, an accident may occur while you are working in the lab. Report any accident, no matter how minor, to your teacher.

7. Wear chemical splash goggles at all times when working in the laboratory. These goggles are designed to protect your eyes from injury. While working in the lab, do not rub your eyes, because chemicals are easily transferred from your hands to your eyes.

⚠ If, despite these precautions, a chemical gets in your eye, remove any contact lenses and immediately wash your eye with a continuous stream of lukewarm water for at least 15 minutes.

8. Always use the minimal amounts of chemicals specified for an experiment to reduce danger, waste, and cleanup.

9. Never taste any chemical used in the laboratory, including food products that are the subject of an investigation. Treat all items as though they are contaminated with unknown chemicals that may be toxic. Keep all food and drink that is not part of an experiment out of the laboratory. Do not eat, drink, or chew gum in the laboratory.

⚠ If you accidentally ingest a substance, notify your teacher immediately.

10. Don't use chipped or cracked glassware. Don't handle broken glass. If glassware breaks, tell your teacher and nearby classmates. Discard broken glass as instructed by your teacher.

⚠ If, despite these precautions, you receive a minor cut, allow it to bleed for a short time. Wash the injured area under cold, running water and notify your teacher. More serious cuts or puncture wounds require immediate medical attention.

11. Do not handle hot glassware or equipment. You can prevent burns by being aware that hot and cold equipment can look exactly the same.

⚠ If you are burned, immediately run cold water over the burned area for several minutes until the pain is reduced. Cooling helps the burn heal. Ask a classmate to notify your teacher.

12. Recognize that the danger of an electrical shock is greater in the presence of water. Keep electrical appliances away from sinks and faucets to minimize the risk of electrical shock. Be careful not to spill water or other liquids in the vicinity of an electrical appliance.

⚠ If, despite these precautions, you spill water near an electrical appliance, stand back, notify your teacher, and warn other students in the area.

13. Report any chemical spills immediately to your teacher. Follow your teacher's instructions for cleaning up spills. Warn other students about the identity and location of spilled chemicals.

⚠ If, despite these precautions, a corrosive chemical gets on your skin or clothing, notify your teacher. Then wash the affected area with cold running water for several minutes.

Post-Lab Procedures

14. Dispose of chemicals in a way that protects you, your classmates, and the environment. Always follow your teacher's directions for cleanup and disposal. Clean your small-scale reaction surface by draining the contents onto a paper towel. Then wipe the surface with a damp paper towel and dry the surface completely. Dispose of the paper towels in the waste bin.

15. Wash your hands thoroughly with soap and water before leaving the laboratory.

A Materials Safety Data Sheet (MSDS) for a chemical describes any safety issues. A diagram summarizes risks related to flammability, health, and reactivity. A number scale indicates the level of risk.

0 Low
1 Slight
2 Moderate
3 High
4 Extreme

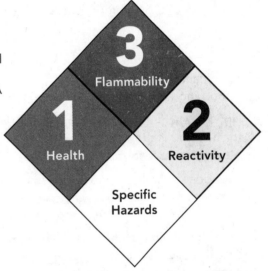

Safety Procedures

 Eye Safety Wear safety goggles.

 Clothing Protection Wear a lab coat or apron when using corrosive chemicals or chemicals that can stain clothing.

 Skin Protection Wear plastic gloves when using chemicals that can irritate or stain your skin.

 Broken Glass Do not use chipped or cracked glassware. Do not heat the bottom of a test tube.

 Open Flame Tie back hair and loose clothing. Never reach across a lit burner.

 Flammable Substance Do not have a flame near flammable materials.

 Corrosive Substance Wear safety goggles, an apron, and gloves when working with corrosive chemicals.

Take appropriate precautions when any of the following safety symbols appears in an experiment.

 Poison Don't chew gum, drink, or eat in the laboratory. Never taste a chemical in the laboratory.

 Fume Avoid inhaling substances that can irritate your respiratory system. Use a fume hood whenever possible.

 Thermal Burn Do not touch hot glassware or equipment.

 Electrical Equipment Keep electrical equipment away from water or other liquids.

 Sharp Object To avoid a puncture wound, use scissors or other sharp objects only as intended.

 Disposal Dispose of chemicals only as directed.

 Hand Washing Wash your hands thoroughly with soap and water.

INVESTIGATION 12

1. What are the two sources of energy for Earth's geological systems?

2. What energy source primarily drives the water cycle? Explain how the force of gravity and this energy source work together to drive the water cycle.

3. Do the following processes store or release carbon in the carbon cycle? What source of energy ultimately drives each process?
   a. Photosynthesis
   b. Rock formation
   c. Volcanic eruption
   d. Burning fossil fuels

4. How do each of the three types of rock form? What is the effect of melting glaciers on rock formation?

5. How does reinforcing and counterbalancing feedback work to keep a system in equilibrium? What is an example of each?

6. What is non-linear feedback? Describe how the collapse of an ice shelf is an example of non-linear feedback.

7. Describe how atmospheric composition is affected by geologic processes and how human activity affects atmospheric composition.

8. How does solar radiation influence each of the following?
   a. Evaporation
   b. Atmospheric convection
   c. Atmospheric pressure and wind

9. What is albedo and what role does it play in arctic sea ice feedbacks?

10. Are the following feedback cycles reinforcing or counterbalancing in regard to global warming? Why?
    a. Ocean and carbon dioxide feedbacks
    b. Biomass feedbacks
    c. Methane hydrate feedbacks
    d. Surface radiation feedbacks

11. What has been the trend with solar output over the history of Earth?

12. How does each of the following impact atmospheric CO_2 long-term? What is the effect on temperature?
    a. Life
    b. Erosion
    c. Volcanic activity

13. What is currently happening in Earth's long-term, intermediate-term, and short-term climate, and for how long has it been happening?

14. What are the three orbital parameters, and how do they affect Earth's climate?

15. How do volcanic eruptions affect climate in the short-term?

16. How do changes in solar radiation affect intermediate-term climate?

17. What are the effects of short-term ocean circulation changes like ENSO on the atmosphere?

INVESTIGATION 13

1. Imagine a world where the initial atmospheric concentration of CO_2 is 420.00 ppm and the initial average global temperature is 4.00°C. If CO_2 concentration, in ppm, annually increases 0.7% and average temperature, in °C, annually increases 0.1%, what are the expected CO_2 concentration, in ppm, and average global temperature, in °C, in
   a. 1 year?
   b. 5 years?
   c. 25 years?
   d. 100 years?

2. What is the greenhouse effect in terms of energy absorption and radiation? Why are greenhouse gases called greenhouse gases?

3. What modes of oscillation do the following have? How does this affect energy absorption?
   a. H_2O
   b. CO_2

4. What was sea level like and how did it affect human settlements
   a. 22,000 years ago?
   b. 8,000 years ago?
   c. in 2017?

5. Explain how each of the following types of geologic data is used to track changes in Earth's past climate?
   a. Ice cores
   b. Tree rings
   c. Varves

6. What is the effect of warmer global temperatures on sea level? How would this affect human settlements?

7. Refer to page 79. What is the difference between the 1917 NASA temperature series and the 2017 temperature series for the following places? What could be a reason for the difference?
   a. Atlantic Ocean near Greenland
   b. Eastern South America
   c. Western North America
   d. Northern Europe

8. What is the effect of increased CO_2 on the temperature of the Arctic compared to other regions of Earth? Why?

9. Since 1960, global GDP per capita has increased from ~$500 to ~$10,500 in 2015, while the average global temperature has increased from ~−0.1°C to ~0.8°C. Explain how these factors are related.

10. How do climate scientists use the ratio of carbon-12 to carbon-13? What does it mean if carbon-13 is lower than expected?

11. Describe how weather models and climate models are similar.

12. Describe how weather models and climate models are different.

13. The Intergovernmental Panel on Climate Change uses several models to predict climate change. How would average global temperatures be likely to respond to the following changes in greenhouse gas emissions?
    a. Greenhouse gas emissions continue to rise indefinitely.
    b. Greenhouse gas emissions continue until 2080, then decrease.
    c. Greenhouse gas emissions peak in 2020, then decrease significantly.

14. What would humanity have to do to achieve the following gas emissions changes?
    a. Greenhouse gas continues to rise indefinitely.
    b. Greenhouse gas emissions continue to rise until 2080, then decrease.
    c. Greenhouse gas emissions peak in 2020, then decrease significantly.

15. Alpine and tidewater glaciers cover 730,000 km^2 of land and are on average 2.0 kilometers thick.
    a. How much water do they hold?
    b. If the glaciers completely melted, how many meters would the level of the oceans rise if they covered 361,900,000 km^2?
    c. What would be the expected effects on people if alpine and tidewater glaciers melted?

16. Solar panels that are 1 m^2 in size produce 260 kWh per year. The average person uses 10,932 kWh per year, but only 2% of that comes from solar. How many more square meters of solar panels are needed per person for 100% solar power?

17. Are each the following methods of addressing climate change more feasible now, in the near future, or far future? Explain why you chose "Now", "Future", or "Far Future."
    a. Changing building codes to require building carbon-neutral buildings
    b. Injecting aerosols into the atmosphere
    c. Promoting electric vehicles and building infrastructure to support them
    d. Capturing and storing carbon dioxide and other carbon compounds

18. One option to address climate change is carbon sequestration. What are the potential concerns for using this method?

INVESTIGATION 14

1. For the reaction
$2NO_2(g) \rightarrow 2NO(g) + O_2(g)$, determine the rate of disappearance of NO_2 if its concentration is 0.0055 mol/L at 150 seconds and drops to 0.0048 mol/L at 200 seconds.

2. Explain what is meant when a reaction rate is determined to be a negative value for a chemical during a reaction.

3. Explain how an increase in temperature can affect the rate of a chemical reaction.

4. The following reaction, $A + 2B \rightarrow C$, is run twice. If the concentration of A is cut in half for the second trial, predict what will happen to the rate of the reaction compared to the first trial.

5. Will the addition of a catalyst to a reaction increase, decrease, or have no effect on the rate of the reaction?

6. In your lab, you are asked to react antacid tablets with water to produce carbon dioxide gas, but you are short on time. How could you change the tablet to increase the reaction rate? Why does that work?

7. If the rate of reaction has been calculated to be 2.6×10^{-3} mol/L·s, how long will it take the concentration of a species to drop from 1.68×10^{-3} mol/L to 2.5×10^{-4} mol/L?

8. How does activation energy affect a chemical reaction?

9. Give an "everyday example" of activation energy being overcome.

10. Sketch an energy diagram for an endothermic reaction.

11. Explain what is meant by a one-step and a multi-step reaction.

12. Explain how the addition of a catalyst to a reaction does not violate the law of conservation of mass.

13. Given the following reaction diagram, determine which step in the multi-step reaction is the rate-determining step.

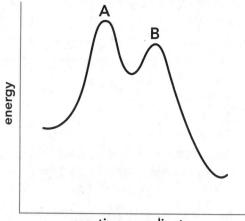

reaction coordinate

14. What is occurring in a system that has reached equilibrium?

15. Briefly describe the concepts involved in Le Châtelier's principle.

16. For the equilibrium reaction,
$2SO_2(g) + O_2(g) \rightleftharpoons 2SO_3(g)$, use Le Châtelier's principle to predict what will happen to the remaining two species for each change made.
   a. remove some SO_2
   b. add O_2
   c. remove SO_3

17. Given that the reaction in #16 is endothermic, what will happen to each chemical if the temperature is raised after it reaches equilibrium?

18. For the reaction in #16, what will happen to each substance if the pressure is decreased on the system?

INVESTIGATION 15

1. Acids and bases have distinct properties that distinguish them from one another. Label each description as being a property of a base or a property of an acid.
   a. tastes tart or sour
   b. pH above 7.0
   c. makes skin feel slippery or soapy
   d. pH below 7.0

2. Determine the pH of each solution described.
   a. $[H^+] = 0.0015M$
   b. $[H^+] = 3.8 \times 10^{-5}M$
   c. $[H^+] = 4.13 \times 10^{-9}M$

3. Determine the hydrogen ion concentration in each solution from its given pH.
   a. pH = 2.89
   b. pH = 11.50
   c. pH = 7.0

4. Identify whether each species acts as a Brønsted–Lowry acid or base.
   a. NH_3
   b. $C_2O_4^{2-}$
   c. H_2O
   d. $HC_2H_3O_2$

5. Identify whether each substance is a Lewis acid or Lewis base.
   a. NH_3
   b. PBr_3
   c. BCl_3

6. What is the maximum number of hydrogen ions a molecule of citric acid ($H_3C_6H_5O_7$) can form when in an aqueous solution? Explain your answer.

7. Briefly describe the steps to determine the unknown concentration of an acid if you are given a sample of base with a known concentration.

8. How many milliliters of 0.35M NaOH are needed to neutralize 25.0 mL of 0.40M H_2SO_4?

9. What is the concentration of a sodium hydroxide solution if 85.50 mL is required to neutralize 75.25 mL of 0.500M hydrochloric acid?

10. Will the equivalence point for a strong acid titrating a weak base be in the acidic region, at the neutral point, or in the basic region? Explain your reasoning.

11. Name the salt that is formed in a neutralization reaction between the following acids and bases.
    a. hydrochloric acid, HCl, and calcium hydroxide, Ca(OH)$_2$
    b. sulfuric acid, H_2SO_4, and potassium hydroxide, KOH

c. nitric acid, HNO_3, and lithium hydroxide, LiOH
d. phosphoric acid, H_3PO_4, and sodium hydroxide, NaOH

12. Describe what happens with respect to the pH of the solution as a small amount of a strong acid is slowly added to a buffered solution.

13. Write equations that show what happens when the following situations occur in a buffer solution.
    a. acid is added to a sulfate (SO_4^{2-}) buffer
    b. base is added to a hydrogen carbonate (HCO_3^-) buffer

14. Describe the types of compounds needed to prepare a buffer solution.

INVESTIGATION 16

1. Many marine organisms are dependent on the production of calcium carbonate ($CaCO_3$) to form their skeletons. Describe how increased atmospheric carbon dioxide levels in Earth's atmosphere are affecting these organisms. Use the chemical equations to formulate your answer.

$$CO_2 + H_2O \rightleftharpoons H_2CO_3$$
$$H_2CO_3 \rightleftharpoons H_2O + CO_2$$
$$H_2CO_3 \rightleftharpoons H^+ + HCO_3^-$$

2. Which of the following is true for pH values in the deeper parts of oceans, in general?
   a. In deep parts of the ocean, the temperature is warm, and the solubility of carbon dioxide is high.
   b. In deep parts of the ocean, the temperature is cold, and the solubility of carbon dioxide is high.
   c. In deep parts of the ocean, the temperature is cold, and there are many hydrogen ions.
   d. In deep parts of the ocean, the temperature is warm, and there are few hydrogen ions.

3. How does climate change impact the salinity of ocean water?

4. What factors are methane hydrate stability dependent on? How might global warming impact the stability zone of offshore methane gas hydrates?

5. According to the Scripps Institution of Oceanography, nearly 9.3 billion tons of carbon were released per year during 2002–2011. Of this, an estimated 26% was absorbed by the ocean. How many tons of carbon dioxide were absorbed into the ocean during this time?

6. How will increased temperatures affect the amount of dissolved oxygen in the ocean? What effect will this have on marine life?

7. Global warming causes an increase in temperatures around the world. How does the ocean contribute to equilibration of the rising temperatures from global warming?

8. Explain why algal blooms have such a negative impact on other ocean life. How are these blooms linked to increased CO_2?

9. What are some of the potential impacts of increased concentration of CO_2 on the dynamics of the marine ecosystem's food web?

A

activated complex: an unstable cluster of atoms that exists during the transition from reactants to products (131)

activation energy: the minimum energy colliding particles must have in order to react (130)

albedo: the proportion of incoming sunlight that reflects off an object's surface (29)

Anthropocene: the current geologic time period, characterized by the impact of human activities on Earth's biomes (100)

anthropogenic: caused or produced by humans (82)

B

buffer: a solution in which the pH remains relatively constant when small amounts of acid or base are added; can be either a solution of a weak acid and the salt of a weak acid (conjugate base) or a solution of a weak base and the salt of a weak base (conjugate acid) (166)

buffer capacity: a measure of the amount of acid or base that may be added to a buffer system before a significant change in pH occurs (169)

buffer range: a measure of the overall pH range in which a buffer system is effective at maintaining a relatively constant pH (169)

C

calcification: the use of carbon from dissolved carbon dioxide to build the shells of marine organisms out of calcium carbonate (204)

carbon compensation depth: the depth at which calcium carbonate shells of organisms dissolve into calcium ions and bicarbonate ions (185)

carbon reservoirs: components of the Earth system that store carbon (182)

catalyst: a substance that increases reaction rates by providing a lower energy path for the reaction without being used up during the reaction (133)

chemical equilibrium: a state of balance in which the rates of the forward and reverse reactions are equal (137)

climate forcings: factors driving climate; includes an increase in incoming sunlight (due to changes in the sun's activity), a decrease in how much sunlight gets reflected from the surface back out into space, and an increase in how much of that energy is kept by greenhouse gases (28)

collision theory: a theory that states that bonds are broken when molecules collide with enough energy to break bonds in reactants and with the correct orientation to form bonds that make products (125)

Community Earth System Model (CESM): a powerful Earth System Model that issues predictions based on data provided by climate scientists from all over the world (87)

conjugate acid: the particle formed when a base gains a hydrogen ion (148)

conjugate acid-base pair: two substances that are related by the loss or gain of a single hydrogen ion (148)

conjugate base: the particle that remains when an acid has donated a hydrogen ion (148)

coral bleaching: a phenomenon that occurs when stressed coral loses its photosynthetic algae, removing the coral's food source and color (210)

Coriolis effect: the apparent curved path that an object takes when it moves in a straight line across a rotating object perpendicular to the axis of rotation (192)

counterbalancing feedback: feedback that resists or reduces a change; also called a "negative" feedback (13)

D

deep ocean currents: masses of ocean water below the ocean surface that flow steadily in a particular direction (193)

E

Earth System Model (ESM): a computer model that uses a set of equations to calculate interactions between various parameters (such as pressure, temperature, mass, water vapor amount, and momentum) in specific geographic locations (86)

El Niño/Southern Oscillation (ENSO): the cyclical circulation pattern in the tropical Pacific that results in periodic variation between below-normal and above-normal sea surface temperatures and dry and wet conditions (198)

energy budget: describes where energy at Earth's surface comes from and where it goes; driven by incoming solar radiation (17)

equilibrium position: the relative concentrations of the reactants and products at equilibrium (137)

equivalence point: the point in a titration where the number of moles of hydrogen ions equals the number of moles of hydroxide ions (162)

evapotranspiration: the combination of evaporation from bodies of water and transpiration from the leaves of plants (20)

F

feedback: when an affected system responds to and applies a change back on another system (13)

G

glacier ice: yearly snows that slowly become compacted, building up a record of climate that extends across time (69)

global warming potential (GWP): a measure of the heat-trapping capacity of a greenhouse gas over a given period of time, compared to that of a similar amount of CO_2 (63)

greenhouse effect: the cycle of energy absorbed by Earth's surface being reradiated upward as infrared energy, some of which is absorbed by gases in the atmosphere and then reradiated back toward the surface (17)

greenhouse gas: a gas that absorbs infrared radiation (63)

H

hydronium ion: H_3O^+; the positive ion formed when a water molecule gains a hydrogen ion (147)

I

Intergovernmental Panel on Climate Change (IPCC): a scientific body dedicated to assessing the science of climate change (87)

ion-product constant for water (K_w): the product of the hydrogen-ion concentration and the hydroxide-ion concentration in water or aqueous solutions; equal to 1×10^{-14} at 25°C (150)

L

Le Châtelier's principle: when a chemical system at equilibrium experiences a stress, it changes in a way that relieves the stress (138)

Lewis acid: any substance that can accept a pair of electrons to form a covalent bond (149)

Lewis base: any substance that can donate a pair of electrons to form a covalent bond (149)

Little Ice Age: a period that lasted about 500 years and had several periods of colder temperatures that correlate with periods of decreased solar activity and sunlight (76)

M

metamorphism: primarily a chemical process in which increasing temperature and pressure alter the shape and composition of minerals (12)

methane hydrates: frozen combinations of methane and water (188)

N

neutral solution: an aqueous solution in which the concentrations of hydrogen ions and hydroxide ions are equal; solution with a pH of 7.0 (150)

neutralization reaction: a reaction in which an acid and a base react in an aqueous solution to produce a salt and water (156)

O

ocean deoxygenation: the expansion of low-oxygen zones in the ocean as a consequence of rising temperatures (197)

ocean surface currents: areas of ocean water that flow steadily in a particular direction close to the ocean's surface (190)

P

precipitation: the product of condensation of water vapor that falls toward Earth's surface due to gravity (25)

R

rate: the ratio between two related quantities expressed in different units (122)

reaction intermediate: a product of one step in a multistep reaction and a reactant in the next step (132)

reaction rate: the rate of a chemical reaction; the speed at which reactants become products (123)

reinforcing feedback: feedback that amplifies a change; also called a "positive" feedback (13)

relative humidity: a measure of the percentage of water vapor in the air compared to the maximum amount the air can hold at that particular temperature (24)

reversible reactions: reactions in which the product molecules can react to form the original reactant molecules (136)

rock cycle: the process that describes the changes and cycling of geologic material through Earth's systems; describes the processes that form the three main types of rock: igneous, metamorphic, and sedimentary (11)

S

salinity: the amount of dissolved salts in a solution like water (178)

salt hydrolysis: a process in which the cations or anions of a dissociated salt accept hydrogen ions from water or donate ions to water (159)

T

thermocline: the transition zone between the warm upper and cold lower layers of the ocean; thicker in tropical regions and almost non-existent in polar regions (196)

tipping point: the moment when an old equilibrium of a system cannot be restored by the usual feedback mechanisms (14)

titration: the process used to determine the concentration of a solution (often an acid or base) in which small increments of a measured amount of a solution of known concentration are added to a solution with known volume but unknown concentration until an indicator signals the end point (162)

titration curve: a graph of solution pH versus the volume of standard solution added during a titration; used to determine the equivalence point for a titration (162)

total alkalinity: the sum of excess ions in water that could absorb hydrogen ions (179)

tropical cyclones: large, rapidly rotating storm systems with high winds, a low-pressure center ("eye"), and spiraling arms of thunderstorms (26)

V

varves: annual layers of sedimentation, observed in lakes, that are characterized by larger particles deposited by spring storms, separated by finer particles that accumulate during the rest of the year (73)

The page on which a term is defined is indicated in **boldface** type. Page numbers for appendices begin with *R*.

A

Acceleration, Vol 1: 15
Acid rain, Vol 2: 145
Acidification, Vol 2: 172, 174–175, 184, 204–209
Acidosis, Vol 2: 166
Acids, Vol 2: 146–162
  acid-base indicator, Vol 2: 162
  acidic and basic solutions, Vol 2: 151–152
  Arrhenius model of, Vol 2: 147
  Brønsted-Lowry model of, Vol 2: 148
  buffers, Vol 2: 166–169
  conjugate, Vol 2: 148
  diprotic, Vol 2: 147
  Lewis model of, Vol 2: 149
  mole ratios, Vol 2: 157–158
  neutralization reactions, Vol 2: 156–158
  pH, Vol 2: 151–153, 160–163
  properties of, Vol 2: 146
  and salt solutions, Vol 2: 159–161
  strong and weak, Vol 2: 154, 160–161
  titrations, Vol 2: 162–164
Activated complex, Vol 1: **370;** Vol 2: 131
Activation energy, Vol 1: **19,** 375; Vol 2: 130–132
Activity series, Vol 1: **320**
Actual yield, Vol 1: **363**
Aerosols, sulphate, Vol 2: 53–54
Agriculture, low-carbon, Vol 2: 114
Albedo, Vol 2: **29,** 36
Alkali metals, Vol 1: 138
Alkaline earth metals, Vol 1: 138
Alkalinity, Vol 2: 179
Alkalosis, Vol 2: 166
Allotropes, Vol 1: **227**
Alloys, Vol 1: 235
Altitude, Vol 1: 218–219; Vol 2: 38
Ammonia, Vol 1: 239, 342, 345, 350; Vol 2: 148

Amorphous solids, Vol 1: **210**
Anchoring Phenomena
  How can we produce better foods?, Vol 1: 196–197
  How do our everyday activities impact Earth?, Vol 2: 118–119
  How does this fire keep burning?, Vol 1: 2–3
  What distinguishes the minerals in this mountain?, Vol 1: 96–97
  Why are we seeing more extreme weather?, Vol 2: 2–3
Anions, Vol 1: **146,** 150, 157, 185; Vol 2: 160
Antarctic Oscillation (AAO), Vol 2: 202
Anthropocene, Vol 2: **100**
Anthropogenic carbon emissions, Vol 2: 77–84, 89
Aqueous solutions, Vol 1: **242**–244, 329–335
Aragonite, Vol 2: 207, 212
Arctic food webs, Vol 2: 207
Arctic sea ice feedbacks, Vol 2: 36
Arrhenius, Svante, Vol 2: 147
Arrhenius model of acids and bases, Vol 2: 147
Assessment, Performance-Based, Vol 1: 33, 63, 95, 129, 153, 195, 259, 301, 337, 367, 395; Vol 2: 59, 117, 143, 171, 215
Asthenosphere, Vol 1: 69
Atlantic Multidecadal Oscillation (AMO), Vol 2: 202–203
Atlantic ocean currents, Vol 1: 45
Atmosphere, Earth's, Vol 2: 17–27, 62–68
  carbon dioxide in, Vol 2: 41–42, 78, 81–83, 174
  changing composition of, Vol 2: 41
  convection in, Vol 2: 21
  currents in, Vol 2: 50
  global circulation, Vol 2: 23
  greenhouse effect, Vol 2: 17, 62–63, 77
  human impacts on, Vol 2: 16

layers and properties of, Vol 2: 19
methane in, Vol 2: 33
ocean-atmosphere carbon dioxide exchange, Vol 2: 182–183
and ocean pH, Vol 2: 174
oscillations in, Vol 2: 202
planetary, Vol 2: 34
and radiation absorption, Vol 2: 64–68
temperature and pressure in, Vol 1: 203; Vol 2: 19, 22
winds in, Vol 2: 22
Atmospheric cells, Vol 2: 23
Atmospheric pressure, Vol 1: 203; Vol 2: 19, 22
Atmospheric system feedbacks, Vol 2: 28
Atomic emission spectrum, Vol 1: **110**–111, 113
Atomic mass, Vol 1: **106**–109, 266
  calculating, Vol 1: 105, 107–108, 284–285
  of elements, Vol 1: 106–107
  mole-mass relationship, Vol 1: 267, 272–274
  particles, Vol 1: 25
  percent composition, Vol 1: 280–285
  See also Atoms; Moles
Atomic mass unit, Vol 1: 105
Atomic number, Vol 1: **101**–103, 134
Atomic orbitals, Vol 1: **116,** 118–119, 121–123, 169
Atomic radius, Vol 1: **144**–145, 215, 392
Atomic weight, Vol 1: 267
Atoms, Vol 1: **100**–128
  Bohr atomic model, Vol 1: 112–114
  counting, Vol 1: 264
  effective nuclear charge, Vol 1: 141–142, 144
  electrical forces, Vol 1: 16–17
  and elements, Vol 1: 101
  energy levels in, Vol 1: 112, 114
  isotopes, Vol 1: 25, 104
  kinetic energy of, Vol 1: 37
  mass and properties of, Vol 1: 25, 106–109

Combustion
  complete/incomplete,
    Vol 1: 28
  conservation of mass during,
    Vol 1: 28
  and work, Vol 1: 29–30
  See also Energy; Heat
Combustion reactions, Vol 1:
    315, **324**–325, 327
Common gases, Vol 1: 201
Community Earth System
    Model (CESM), Vol 2: **87**–88
Complete ionic equations,
    Vol 1: **330**–331
Compounds. *See* Molecular
    compounds
Concentrated solutions,
    Vol 1: **291**
Concentration (of reactant), Vol
    2: 123, 126, 139
Concentration (of solution), Vol
    1: **291**–294; Vol 2: 164, 169
Condensation, Vol 1: **214,**
    216–217, 390; Vol 2: 24
Conduction, Vol 1: 39, **42**–43,
    53, 70
  electrolyte, Vol 1: 244–245
  electrons, Vol 1: 39, 44
  ionic compounds, Vol 1: 163
  in lithosphere, Vol 1: 76–77
  in metals, Vol 1: 44, 231
  thermal, Vol 1: 42–43
Conjugate acid-base pair,
    Vol 2: **148**
Conjugate acids, Vol 2: **148**
Conjugate bases, Vol 2: **148**
Conservation of energy, law of,
    Vol 1: 11, 311, 371
Conservation of mass, law of,
    Vol 1: 25–26, 308, 344
Constant composition, law of,
    Vol 1: 282
Continents, Vol 1: 84
  continental collisions, Vol 1:
    81, 89
  continental distribution,
    Vol 2: 45
  continental rifting, Vol 1: 86
  ocean-continent subduction,
    Vol 1: 90
  ocean-ocean subduction, Vol
    1: 91
Convection, Vol 1: 41, **45**–50,
    53, 70–72
  in atmosphere, Vol 2: 21

  in Earth's core, Vol 1: 71
  in Earth's mantle, Vol 1: 49,
    72, 74–75
  in liquids and solids, Vol 1:
    45–46
  Rayleigh number, Vol 1: 48
  thermal, Vol 1: 47
  thermal boundary layers,
    Vol 1: 50
Convective zone of sun, Vol 2:
    39
Copper sulfate, Vol 1: 246
Coral bleaching, Vol 2: **210**–211
Corals, fossil, Vol 2: 73
Core, Earth's, Vol 1: 69–70
Core convection, Vol 1: 71
Core electrons, Vol 1: 126, 138,
    141
Core of sun, Vol 2: 39
Coriolis effect, Vol 2: **192,** 201
Coulomb's Law, Vol 1: 140, 147,
    161
Counterbalancing feedbacks,
    Vol 2: **13,** 34
Covalent bonds, Vol 1: **169**–
    173, 182–183
  atomic orbitals in, Vol 1: 169
  bonding/lone pairs, Vol 1:
    170–171
  electron dot structures, Vol
    1: 171
  electron sharing in, Vol 1:
    170–172, 229
  and electronegativity, Vol 1:
    175
  polar/nonpolar, Vol 1: 175
  types of, Vol 1: 172
Covalent network solids, Vol 1:
    208–**209,** 227
Crosscutting Concepts
  Cause and Effect: Mechanism
    and Explanation, Vol 1: 85,
    159, 176, 232; Vol 2: 19, 21,
    22, 44, 45, 63, 101, 103,
    108, 112, 121, 128, 129,
    138, 157, 168, 173, 181
  Energy and Matter: Flows,
    Cycles, and Conservation,
    Vol 1: 5, 13, 14, 15, 19, 20,
    30, 32, 35, 36, 48, 50, 52,
    65, 77, 99, 113, 161, 183,
    303, 343, 344, 369, 372,
    378, 395; Vol 2: 8, 25, 61,
    65, 67, 80, 81, 111, 173,
    191, 203

  Patterns, Vol 1: 17, 25, 59, 83,
    84, 114, 124, 127, 131, 133,
    137, 147, 150, 151, 155,
    157, 170, 174, 181, 186,
    192, 201, 250, 342, 392; Vol
    2: 10, 20, 24, 61, 96, 125,
    131, 142, 177, 189, 194,
    199
  Scale, Proportion, and
    Quantity, Vol 1: 12, 22, 75,
    79, 93, 100, 101, 241, 261,
    267, 268, 346; Vol 2: 195
  Stability and Change, Vol 1:
    221; Vol 2: 5, 37, 39, 72, 89,
    92, 98, 121, 137, 141, 175,
    181, 185, 189, 193, 207,
    210
  Structure and Function, Vol 1:
    69, 166, 167, 199, 211, 243,
    286, 339; Vol 2: 110
  Systems and System Models,
    Vol 1: 6, 41, 47, 57, 58, 247,
    252, 367; Vol 2: 7, 86, 87, 99
Crust, Earth's, Vol 1: 69
Crystal lattices, Vol 1: **160**–162,
    210–211
Crystalline packing structures,
    Vol 1: 232
Crystalline solids, Vol 1: 209–
    211, 232
Crystals, Vol 1: **210**–211
Cubic systems, Vol 1: 211
Current, Vol 1: **39**

D

Decomposition reactions, Vol 1:
    306, 315, **317**–318, 326
Deep ocean currents, Vol 2: **193**
Definite proportions, law of, Vol
    1: 280
Deforestation, Vol 2: 28
Density, Vol 1: 45, **67**
  and mass, Vol 1: 278–279
  and ocean currents, Vol 2: 193
  and temperature, Vol 2: 193
  of water, Vol 1: 240
Deposition, Vol 1: **214**
Desiccants, Vol 1: 247
Desiccator, Vol 1: 247
Diamond, Vol 1: 17, 227
Diatomic molecules, Vol 1: 177
Digital Learning. *see* Go Online
Dilute solutions, Vol 1: **291**
Dipole interactions, Vol 1:
    180, 207

Diprotic acids and bases, Vol 2: 147

Diseases, infectious, Vol 2: 102

Dislocations, Vol 1: 233–**234**

Dispersed medium, Vol 1: 256

Dispersed phase, Vol 1: 256

Dispersion forces, Vol 1: **179,** 207

Dissolution rate, Vol 1: **249**

Dobereiner, J. W., Vol 1: 132–133

Double covalent bond, Vol 1: **172**

Double-displacement reactions, Vol 1: 322

Double-replacement reactions, Vol 1: 315, **322**–323, 326

Downwelling, mantle, Vol 1: 74

Droughts, Vol 2: 95

Dry ice, Vol 1: 221

Ductility, Vol 1: **230**

E

Earth, Vol 1: 64–79
  conduction, Vol 1: 70
  continents and supercontinents, Vol 1: 84, 86, 89–90
  convection, Vol 1: 70–72
  core of, Vol 1: 69–70
  crust of, Vol 1: 69
  density of materials, Vol 1: 67
  elements of, Vol 1: 67
  energy budget, Vol 2: 17–18
  geotherm, Vol 1: 76
  heat flow within, Vol 1: 66–79; Vol 2: 6
  heat loss, Vol 1: 76–77; Vol 2: 6
  layers of, Vol 1: 68–69
  lithosphere conduction, Vol 1: 76–77
  magnetic field, Vol 1: 71, 82
  mantle convection, Vol 1: 49, 72, 74–75
  mantle of, Vol 1: 69–70, 72–75
  orbital parameters, Vol 2: 48
  physical properties, Vol 1: 68–69
  radiation emission, Vol 1: 70, 78; Vol 2: 34–35, 68
  seismic waves, Vol 1: 66, 73
  surface temperature of, Vol 2: 35, 47, 52–53, 79, 180, 200
  tectonic plates, Vol 1: 80
  water reservoirs, Vol 2: 7

  See also Atmosphere, Earth's; Climate; Earth system; Plate tectonics

Earth system, Vol 2: 7
  carbon in, Vol 2: 10, 32, 41–42
  climate forcings, Vol 2: 28
  couplers, Vol 2: 85
  energy budget, Vol 2: 17–18
  energy flow in, Vol 2: 6
  human impacts on, Vol 2: 15–16
  tipping point, Vol 2: 14
  water in, Vol 2: 7
  See also Earth; Feedbacks

Earth System Models (ESMs), Vol 2: **86**–88

Earthquakes, Vol 1: 66

Effective nuclear charge, Vol 1: **141**–142, 144

Efflorescence, Vol 1: **246**

El Niño/Southern Oscillation (ENSO), Vol 2: 47, 50, 101, **198**–201

Elastic energy, Vol 1: 6

Electrical conductivity, Vol 1: **231**

Electrical forces, Vol 1: 16–17

Electricity, Vol 1: 7, 20, 22, 30, **39**

Electrolytes, Vol 1: **244**–245

Electromagnetic radiation, Vol 1: 7, 78; Vol 2: 6, 28, 34, 64

Electron affinity, Vol 1: **149**

Electron cloud, Vol 1: 100, 116

Electron configurations, Vol 1: **121**–126
  energy and stability, Vol 1:122–123
  noble gas, Vol 1: 126
  patterns in, Vol 1: 124
  and periodic table, Vol 1: 138–140
  shielding effect, Vol 1: 141
  writing, Vol 1: 122, 125–126

Electron dot structures, Vol 1: **127,** 159, 171, 173

Electronegativity, Vol 1: **174**–175

Electrons, Vol 1: **100**–101
  conduction, Vol 1: 39, 44
  core, Vol 1: 126, 138, 141
  delocalized, Vol 1: 229
  energy levels of, Vol 1: 112, 117
  mass, Vol 1: 25, 105
  shell model, Vol 1: 117
  spin of, Vol 1: 122
  subshells, Vol 1: 119

valence, Vol 1: 126–127, 138, 141, 156
  See also Atoms; Chemical bonding; Electron configurations

Elements, Vol 1: **101**–102
  atomic emission spectra, Vol 1: 110–111
  atomic mass of, Vol 1: 106–107
  discovery of, Vol 1: 132–133
  main group elements (periodic table), Vol 1: 136
  molar masses of, Vol 1: 268
  percent composition of, Vol 1: 280–285
  properties of, Vol 1: 151
  See also Periodic table

Empirical formulas, Vol 1: **286**–287

Endothermic reaction, Vol 1: **18**–19, 312

Energy, Vol 1: 6–23
  and carbon cycle, Vol 2: 9–10
  of chemical reactions, Vol 1: 311–312, 370; Vol 2: 130–132
  defined, Vol 1: **7**
  electricity, Vol 1: 7, 20, 22, 30, 39
  electron configurations, Vol 1: 122
  flow, Vol 1: 10, 18, 371; Vol 2: 6
  and forces, Vol 1: 15
  human needs, Vol 1: 20, 22
  internal, Vol 1: 38, 372
  ionization, Vol 1: 147–148
  law of conservation of, Vol 1: 11, 311, 371
  and mass, Vol 1: 30
  modeling, Vol 1: 14–22
  and phase changes, Vol 1: 213–214
  potential, Vol 1: 7, 9–10, 14
  quantum, Vol 1: 112
  transformations, Vol 1: 6, 9–10, 20–21
  units of, Vol 1: 8
  See also Heat; Kinetic energy; Light

Energy budget, Vol 2: **17**–18

Energy levels, atomic, Vol 1: **112,** 114

Energy sources, Vol 2: 107–108

Enthalpy, Vol 1: 372–393
  bond, Vol 1: 373–374

Methane hydrate feedbacks, Vol 2: 33, 189

Methane hydrates, Vol 2: **188**–189

Migration, Vol 2: 103–104

Milankovitch cycles, Vol 2: 48–49

Milk, Vol 1: 257

Mineral resources, Vol 1: 92

Mixtures, Vol 1: 256

See also Solutions

Molar enthalpy of condensation, Vol 1: **390**

Molar enthalpy of fusion, Vol 1: **388**–389

Molar enthalpy of solidification, Vol 1: **388**

Molar enthalpy of solution, Vol 1: **384**–385

Molar enthalpy of vaporization, Vol 1: **390**–392

Molar mass, Vol 1: **266**–269, 278, 350, 356

Molar volume, Vol 1: **275**–277

Molarity, Vol 1: **292**–299

 calculating, Vol 1: 293–294

 diluting solutions, Vol 1: 295–297

 percent solutions, Vol 1: 298–299

Mole-mole flowcharts, Vol 1: 348

Mole-mole graphs, Vol 1: 347

Mole ratios, Vol 1: **347**–348, 350; Vol 2: 157–158

Mole roadmap, Vol 1: 271–272

Molecular compounds, Vol 1: 169, 192, 224–227

 covalent network solids, Vol 1: 208–209, 227

 empirical formulas of, Vol 1: 286–287

 identifying, Vol 1: 193

 melting point, Vol 1: 183, 220

 molar mass of, Vol 1: 268–269

 molecular formulas of, Vol 1: 288–289

 names of, Vol 1: 191

 percent composition of, Vol 1: 280–285

 in periodic table, Vol 1: 225

 properties of, Vol 1: 226

Molecular formulas, Vol 1: **288**–289

Molecular solids, Vol 1: 208–**209**

Molecules, Vol 1: **169**

diatomic, Vol 1: 177

dipole interactions, Vol 1: 180, 207

dispersion forces, Vol 1: 179, 207

electron dot structures, Vol 1: 171–173

hydrogen bonds, Vol 1: 181, 207

intermolecular forces, Vol 1: 206–207, 209, 213

nonpolar, Vol 1: 178–179

octet rule in, Vol 1: 170–171

polar, Vol 1: 176–177, 179, 236

properties of, Vol 1: 182–183

Moles, Vol 1: 147, **264**–278

 converting atoms to moles, Vol 1: 265

 converting mass to moles, Vol 1: 273, 350

 converting moles to mass, Vol 1: 273, 350

 counting with, Vol 1: 264

 and density, Vol 1: 278

 molar mass, Vol 1: 266–269, 278, 350, 356

 molar volume of gases, Vol 1: 275–277

 mole-mass relationship, Vol 1: 267, 272–274

 mole-mole calculations, Vol 1: 347–349

 mole roadmap, Vol 1: 271–272, 354

 mole-volume relationship, Vol 1: 276–277, 352

 and representative particles, Vol 1: 264, 266

 volume and mass of, Vol 1: 266

 See also Atomic mass; Molarity

Momentum, Vol 1: **36**

Monoatomic ions, Vol 1: **185**

Monoprotic acids and bases, Vol 2: 147

Motion of particles, Vol 1: 36, 205, 208

Multi-step chemical reactions, Vol 2: 132

N

Natural gas, Vol 2: 82

Net ionic equations, Vol 1: **330**–331, 335

Neutral solutions, Vol 2: **150**–152

Neutralization reactions, Vol 2: **156**–158

Neutrons, Vol 1: 25, **100,** 103–104

Newlands, John, Vol 1: 132–133

Nile river floods, Vol 2: 56

Nitrous Oxide, Vol 2: 78

Noble gases

 electron configurations, Vol 1: 126, 156–157

 ionization energies, Vol 1: 148

Nonelectrolytes, Vol 1: **244**–245

Nonmetallic character, Vol 1: 150–151

Nonmetals, Vol 1: **135**

 anions in, Vol 1: 146, 150, 157, 185

 electron sharing in, Vol 1: 170–171, 229

 ionization energies, Vol 1: 148

Nonpolar compounds, Vol 1: 243

Nonpolar covalent bonds, Vol 1: **175**

Nonpolar molecules, Vol 1: 178–179

North Atlantic Oscillation (NAO), Vol 2: 202

Nuclear energy, Vol 1: 7; Vol 2: 108

Nuclear reactions, Vol 1: 30

Nucleus, Vol 1: 100, **123,** 141–142

O

Ocean-continent subduction, Vol 1: 90

Ocean deoxygenation, Vol 2: **197**

Ocean-ocean subduction, Vol 1: 91

Ocean surface currents, Vol 2: **190**–191

Oceanic lithosphere, Vol 1: 74, 80, 83

Ocean, Vol 2: 172–213

 acidification, Vol 2: 172, 174–175, 184, 204–209

 alkalinity of, Vol 2: 179

 average sea surface pH, Vol 2: 176, 180

 biologic and solubility carbon pumps, Vol 2: 186–187

 calcification in, Vol 2: 204–205

Power, Vol 1: **10,** 39
Precession of Earth, Vol 2: 48
Precipitates, Vol 1: 322, 330, 333–334
Precipitation, Vol 2: **25,** 91, 93, 95–97
Pressure
in atmosphere, Vol 1: 203; Vol 2: 19, 22
and boiling points, Vol 1: 218–219
and chemical equilibrium, Vol 2: 140
within Earth, Vol 1: 68
and solubility, Vol 1: 254; Vol 2: 185
units of, Vol 1: 203–204
Products (of chemical reactions), Vol 1: **304**
Protons, Vol 1: 25, **100,** 104
atomic number, Vol 1: 101
mass number, Vol 1: 103
Proxy data, Vol 2: 40
psi (pounds per square inch), Vol 1: 203

Q

Quantum mechanical model, Vol 1: **116**–117
Quantum (of energy), Vol 1:**112**

R

Radiation, Vol 1: 41, 53, 70
absorption and reradiation, Vol 2: 64–68
black-body, Vol 1: 52; Vol 2: 35
electromagnetic, Vol 1: 7, 78; Vol 2: 6, 28, 34–35, 64
infrared, Vol 1: 51; Vol 2: 63, 65–68
solar, Vol 2: 6, 17, 51
and temperature, Vol 1: 51, 78
Radiative zone of sun, Vol 2: 39
Radioactive isotopes, Vol 1: 72
Rainfall, Vol 2: 25, 91, 93, 95–97
Rate (of change), Vol 2: **122**
Rayleigh number, Vol 1: 48
Reactants, Vol 1: **304**
See also Chemical reactions
Reaction intermediates, Vol 2: **132**
Reaction rates, Vol 1: **313;** Vol 2: 123–128

calculating, Vol 2: 123–124
and catalysts, Vol 2: 133–134
and collision theory, Vol 2: 125
and concentration, Vol 2: 123, 126
and enzymes, Vol 2: 134
and equilibrium, Vol 2: 121
expressing, Vol 2: 122
and particle size, Vol 2: 128
rate-determining step, Vol 2: 132
and temperature, Vol 1: 313; Vol 2: 127, 130
See also Chemical reactions
Red tides, Vol 2: 209
Regional climate change, Vol 2: 79, 91
Reinforcing feedbacks, Vol 2: **13**
Relative humidity, Vol 2: **24**
Renewable energies, Vol 2: 107–108
Representative Concentration Pathways (RCPs), Vol 2: 89
Representative particles, Vol 1: **264,** 266
Repulsion, Vol 1: 16
Residence time, Vol 2: 7
Resistance (to current flow), Vol 1: **39**
Respiration, Vol 2: 20
Reversible reactions, Vol 2: **136**–137
Rift valleys, Vol 1: 86
Rock cycle, Vol 2: **11**–12
Rockets, Vol 1: 29
Rodinia, Vol 1: 84
Rotation, Vol 1: **205**

S

Salinity, Vol 2: **178,** 193
Salt hydrolysis, Vol 2: **159**
Salt solutions, Vol 2: 159–161
Salts
and acid-base reactions, Vol 2: 156
properties of, Vol 2: 146
San Andreas Fault, Vol 1: 88
Saturated solutions, Vol 1: **250**
Schrödinger, Erwin, Vol 1: 116
Science and Engineering Practices
Analyze Data, Vol 1: 76, 81, 106, 111, 129, 214, 220,

228, 240, 276, 313, 359, 366, 375; Vol 2: 29, 33, 36, 40, 42, 50, 56, 70, 71, 73, 74, 75, 88, 90, 91, 93, 97, 102, 145, 160, 183, 200, 201
Apply Concepts, Vol 1: 123, 126; Vol 2: 147, 154
Apply Mathematical Concepts, Vol 1: 341, 349, 351, 353, 355, 360, 361, 364, 365
Apply Scientific Reasoning, Vol 2: 171, 215
Argue from Evidence, Vol 1: 80, 205, 275, 303, 324, 329; Vol 2: 64, 106, 109
Ask Questions, Vol 1: 217
Calculate, Vol 1: 10; Vol 2: 115, 124, 153, 158, 164, 197
Carry Out Investigations, Vol 1: 37, 38, 91, 234, 292; Vol 2: 16
Communicate Information, Vol 1: 46, 104, 306, 376; Vol 2: 9
Compare, Vol 1: 107
Compare and Contrast, Vol 1: 109, 178
Compare Models, Vol 1: 165
Connect to Society, Vol 2: 117, 171
Construct Explanations, Vol 1: 23, 32, 61, 71, 72, 99, 115, 128, 129, 131, 134, 135, 155, 160, 164, 168, 188, 202, 209, 223, 226, 236, 238, 239, 257, 270, 309, 312, 328, 332, 334, 339, 363, 382, 393, 394; Vol 2: 14, 34, 41, 43, 54, 79, 123, 127, 132, 143, 149, 161, 165, 178, 196, 214
Construct Models, Vol 2: 31
Define Problems, Vol 1: 33, 63, 235, 259, 291, 336, 362; Vol 2: 117
Design Experiments, Vol 1: 337
Design Solutions, Vol 1: 26, 235, 248, 258, 279, 297, 299, 385; Vol 2: 30, 32, 114, 139, 169, 209

CREDITS

PHOTOGRAPHY

Photo locators denoted as follows: Top (T), Center (C), Bottom (B), Left (L), Right (R), Background (Bkgd)

Cover: Sebastian Janicki/Shutterstock; Bkgd: Sylverarts Vectors/Shutterstock

FRONT MATTER

ii: Sebastian Janicki/Shutterstock; iii (TC): Up Late Creative; (B): Kai Kiefer; iv: Tanya Katovich; vi (A): Igor Sasin/AFP/Getty Images; (B): Paolo Lo Pinto/RealyEasyStar/Alamy Stock Photo; (C): Mint Images RF/Getty Images; (D): Eddtoro/Shutterstock; (E): Hendrik Holler/Look-foto/Getty Images

INSTRUCTIONAL SEGMENTS

2: Eddtoro/Shutterstock; 3 (TL): Justin Sullivan/Getty Images; (TR): Tom Radford/Alamy Stock Photo; 118: Hendrik Holler/Look-foto/Getty Images; 119 (TL): Joe Ravi/Shutterstock; (TC): Westend61 GmbH/Heinz Linke/Alamy Stock Photo; (TR): David Fleetham/Alamy Stock Photo

INVESTIGATION 12

4: Justin Sullivan/Getty Images; 11: Barcroft Media/Getty Images; 16: Justin Sullivan/Getty Images; 17: Dennis Hallinan/Alamy Stock Photo; 20: Uladzimir Navumenka/Shutterstock; 26: National Oceanic and Atmospheric Administration; 27: Justin Sullivan/Getty Images; 28: Mattias Klum/National Geographic Image Collection/Getty Images; 33: DOE Photo/Alamy Stock Photo; 34 (T): Pailin Pinrarainon/123RF; (C): Timothy Hodgkinson/Alamy Stock Photo; (B): Tristan3D/Alamy Stock Photo; 37 (T): Roy Langstaff/Alamy Stock Photo; (B): Justin Sullivan/Getty Images; 46: Justin Sullivan/Getty Images; 51: Goddard Space Flight Center/SDO/AIA/HMI/NASA; 53: Design Pics Inc/Alamy Stock Photo; 58: Justin Sullivan/Getty Images

INVESTIGATION 13

60: Tom Radford/Alamy Stock Photo; 67: MODTRAN® is a registered trademark owned by the United States Government as represented by the Secretary of the Air Force. Chart provided courtesy of Spectral Sciences, Inc. 68: Tom Radford/Alamy Stock Photo; 69: Ragnar Th Sigurdsson/Arctic Images/Alamy Stock Photo; 73: Matthijs Wetterauw/Shutterstock; 76: Tom Radford/Alamy Stock Photo; 79: NASA; 80: Thomas La Mela/Shutterstock; 84: Tom Radford/Alamy Stock Photo; 87: Gary Strand/UCAR-NCAR; 88: Figure 10.1 from and Figure 10.1 (b) Adapted from Bindoff, N.L., P.A. Stott, K.M. AchutaRao, M.R. Allen, N. Gillett, D. Gutzler, K. Hansingo, G. Hegerl, Y. Hu, S. Jain, I.I. Mokhov, J. Overland, J. Perlwitz, R. Sebbari and X. Zhang, 2013: Detection and Attribution of Climate Change: from Global to Regional. In: *Climate Change 2013: The Physical Science Basis. Contribution of Working Group I to the Fifth Assessment Report of the Intergovernmental Panel on Climate Change* [Stocker, T.F., D. Qin, G.-K. Plattner, M. Tignor, S.K. Allen, J. Boschung, A. Nauels, Y. Xia, V. Bex and P.M. Midgley (eds.)]. Cambridge University Press, Cambridge, United Kingdom and New York, NY, USA.; 89: Figure TS.19 from Stocker, T.F., D. Qin, G.-K. Plattner, L.V. Alexander, S.K. Allen, N.L. Bindoff, F.-M. Bréon, J.A. Church, U. Cubasch, S. Emori, P. Forster, P. Friedlingstein, N. Gillett, J.M. Gregory, D.L. Hartmann, E. Jansen, B. Kirtman, R. Knutti, K. Krishna Kumar, P. Lemke, J. Marotzke, V. Masson-Delmotte, G.A. Meehl, I.I. Mokhov, S. Piao, V. Ramaswamy, D. Randall, M. Rhein, M. Rojas, C. Sabine, D. Shindell, L.D. Talley, D.G. Vaughan and S.-P. Xie, 2013: Technical Summary. In: *Climate Change 2013: The Physical Science Basis. Contribution of Working Group I to the Fifth Assessment Report of the Intergovernmental Panel on Climate Change* [Stocker, T.F., D. Qin, G.-K. Plattner, M. Tignor, S.K. Allen, J. Boschung, A. Nauels, Y. Xia, V. Bex and P.M. Midgley (eds.)]. Cambridge University Press, Cambridge, United Kingdom and New York, NY, USA.; 91: Box 2.2, Figure 1 from IPCC, 2014: *Climate Change 2014: Synthesis Report. Contribution of Working Groups I, II and III to the Fifth Assessment Report of the Intergovernmental Panel on Climate Change* [Core Writing Team, Pachauri, R.K. and Meyer, L.A. (eds.)]. IPCC, Geneva, Switzerland.; 92: Figure 13.27 from Church, J.A., P.U. Clark, A. Cazenave, J.M. Gregory, S. Jevrejeva, A. Levermann, M.A. Merrifield, G.A. Milne, R.S. Nerem, P.D. Nunn, W.J. Payne, W.T. Pfeffer, D. Stammer and A.S. Unnikrishnan, 2013: Sea Level Change. In: *Climate Change 2013: The Physical Science Basis. Contribution of Working Group I to the Fifth Assessment Report of the Intergovernmental Panel on Climate Change* [Stocker, T.F., D. Qin, G.-K. Plattner, M. Tignor, S.K. Allen, J. Boschung, A. Nauels, Y. Xia, V. Bex and P.M. Midgley (eds.)]. Cambridge University Press, Cambridge, United Kingdom and New York, NY, USA. 93: Figure 12.26 (b) and (c) from Collins, M., R. Knutti, J. Arblaster, J.-L. Dufresne, T. Fichefet, P. Friedlingstein, X. Gao, W.J. Gutowski, T. Johns, G. Krinner, M. Shongwe, C. Tebaldi, A.J. Weaver and M. Wehner, 2013: Long-term Climate Change: Projections, Commitments and Irreversibility. In: *Climate Change 2013: The Physical Science Basis. Contribution of Working Group I to the Fifth Assessment Report of the Intergovernmental Panel on Climate Change* [Stocker, T.F., D. Qin, G.-K. Plattner, M. Tignor, S.K. Allen, J. Boschung, A. Nauels, Y. Xia, V. Bex and P.M. Midgley (eds.)]. Cambridge University Press, Cambridge, United Kingdom and New York, NY, USA.; 94: Tom Radford/Alamy Stock Photo; 95: Scott London/Alamy Stock Photo; 98: USGS/Science Source; 102: Steven Ellingson/Shutterstock; 104: Tom Radford/Alamy Stock Photo; 109: You Touch Pix of EuToch/Shutterstock; 110: Ivan Smuk/123RF; 112: Arnd Wiegmann/Reuters; 114: Bill Barksdale/Design Pics Inc/Alamy Stock Photo; 116: Tom Radford/Alamy Stock Photo; 117: Eddtoro/Shutterstock

INVESTIGATION 14

120: Joe Ravi/Shutterstock; 122: Aleksandr Belugin/Alamy Stock Photo; 126: Andrew Lambert Photography/Science Source; 127: Andrew Lambert Photography/Science Source; 128 (L): IU Liquid and water photo/Shutterstock; (R): SPL/Science Source; 129: Joe Ravi/Shutterstock; 135: Joe Ravi/Shutterstock; 137: Martin Castrogiovanni/Shutterstock; 141: Turtle Rock Scientific/Science Source; 142: Joe Ravi/Shutterstock

INVESTIGATION 15

144: Westend61 GmbH/Heinz Linke/Alamy Stock Photo; 155: Westend61 GmbH/Heinz Linke/Alamy Stock Photo; 156: Universal Images Group Editorial/Getty Images; 159: Mariusz S. Jurgielewicz/Shutterstock; 165: Westend61 GmbH/Heinz Linke/Alamy Stock Photo; 166: Adriaticfoto/Shutterstock; 170: Westend61 GmbH/Heinz Linke/Alamy Stock Photo

INVESTIGATION 16

172: David Fleetham/Alamy Stock Photo; (Inset): Helmut Corneli/Alamy Stock Photo; 179: Rana A. Fine/Debra Willey/Charles Thompson/Marit Jentoft-Nilsen/JPL/NASA; 181: David Fleetham/Alamy Stock Photo; 182: The Natural History Museum/Alamy Stock Photo; 184: Gresei/Shutterstock; 189: David Fleetham/Alamy Stock Photo; 191: Goddard Space Flight Center Scientific Visualization Studio/NASA; 194: Timo Bremer/Lawrence Livermore National Laboratory; 203: David Fleetham/Alamy Stock Photo; 207: David Liittschwager/National Geographic Creative; 208: Carrie Vonderhaar/Ocean Futures Society/National Geographic Image Collection/Getty Images; 209: Merten Snijders/Lonely Planet Images/Getty Images; 214: David Fleetham/Alamy Stock Photo; 215: Hendrik Holler/Look-foto/Getty Images.

TEXT ACKNOWLEDGEMENTS

96: Data from: Karl, T. R., J. T. Melillo, and T. C. Peterson, Eds., 2009: "Global Climate Change Impacts in the United States." 186: Data based on report from *Science* magazine.org, 10 June 2005, Vol 308; 187: Data from: Knevolden (1988); 212: Data from *Science*, 2004.

Notes

Notes

Notes

Notes

Notes

Notes

Notes

Notes

Notes

Notes

Notes

Notes

Notes

Notes

Notes

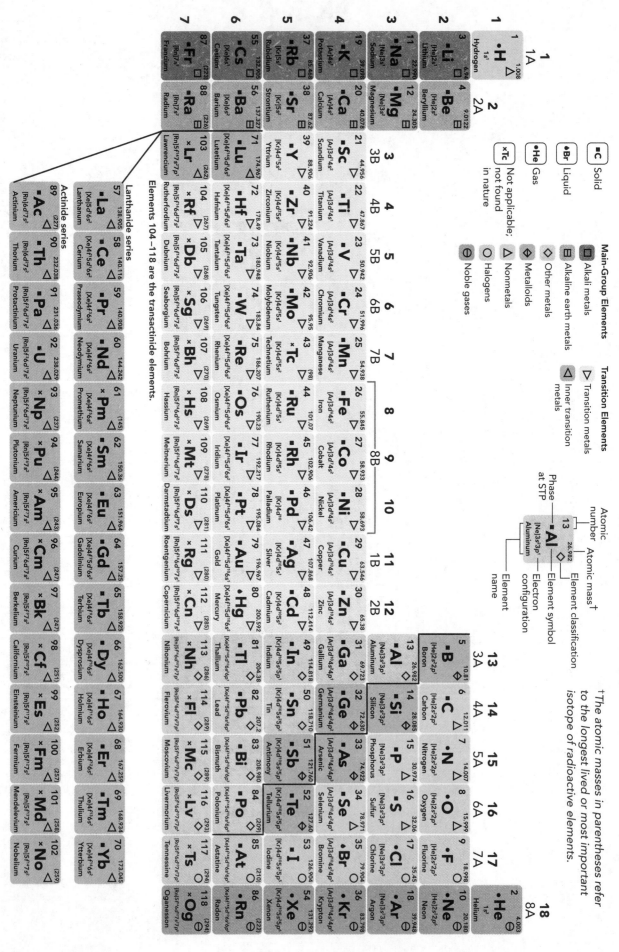

Periodic Table